An Introduction to Robotics

An Introduction to Robotics

Harprit Sandhu

Nexus Special Interests

Nexus Special Interests Ltd.
Nexus House
Boundary Way
Hemel Hempstead
Hertfordshire HP2 7ST
England

First published 1997

ISBN 1-85486-153-0

Typeset by Kate Williams, London
Printed and bound in Great Britain by Biddles Ltd., Guildford & King's Lynn

Contents

CHAPTER ONE

Introduction

This is a serious introduction to robotics for the tinkerer, hobbyist and armchair engineer. It explains how robots actually work in everyday English and includes detailed instructions and plans on how to build and program a biped walking robot.

Computers are changing the way machines work and the way we think about them. This book is about what is happening and how it will affect us. It is about what you need to know to understand this revolution and to participate in it. In particular, it is about robots, about how robots work and how they are controlled in lay terms. The key is software.

There seems to be no doubt that this new discipline will change the way we work and live and that it will be a sea change. Already the richest man in the world is a relatively young man (in his 40s, born 1955) whose company arranges zeros and ones in exquisitely useful ways. We call his company's work, service and products software. His name is William Henry Gates and the firm he and his friend Paul Allen started in 1975 is known to us as the Microsoft Corporation. In 1997 this very young company had $9,000,000,000 (about £5,600,000,000) in cash in the bank. It is possible that this fortune (and more importantly, this work) will have a greater effect on the world than that of men like Bessemer, Carnegie, Ford and Rockefeller.

The work they do at Microsoft is both simple and complex. After all ...

- How complicated can arranging zeros and ones possibly be?
- How valuable can a plastic or aluminium disk with a little bit of iron oxide deposited and oriented on it be?
- How important can it be to manipulate information?

As it turns out the work is quite complicated, very valuable and extremely important. The world would not be the same without Microsoft, because it is everywhere and today no important work can be done without using their products. The way you work has been affected if you are an assembly line worker, if you are a technician, if you are an engineer or if you are a scientist. It has been affected if you are a farmer and it has been affected if you are a politician. No-one will be immune to this change. We are in the information age, the age in which what our machines do depends upon the information we put into them.

In this book I will address the small segment of the revolution that is generally referred to as robotics. I will discuss what robots are and how they work and I will show you how to make and program a small, inexpensive mobile robot that walks on two feet not unlike most bipeds.

The appearance of robots on the workplace floor means we need to understand how robots work so that we can be comfortable with them and prepare ourselves for the changes that they will bring to our lives. No matter what you do and where you do it, computer-controlled machines will be part of your life. No-one will be unaffected because the automation of work means that the work environment itself will change. This change could (hopefully) be for the better or, of course, it could be for the worse. The fact that we will continue to automate work will mean that we will continue to have more time on our hands. A shorter work week can now safely be predicted. 'Eight to five' is already 'nine to four thirty' for many of us. The key to what happens will depend on what we do with this new-found time. Having a rudimentary understanding of robotics and automation will help make you more comfortable with these changes.

I do not intend to use any complicated terms, formulae or diagrams. This is an introduction for the armchair engineer who has an interest in things mechanical, electrical and electronic. The emphasis of the discussion will be on how the machines work rather than how to actually make them work. By this I mean that I will explain, discuss and show you how a computer controls a motor with precision but I will not show you how to actually control a motor with a computer with such precision. The actual techniques for that are beyond the scope of this book but an explanation of how it is done is well within the grasp of everyone interested in these things.

The availability of microprocessors and software is changing the way that machines are designed and used – you will no doubt have noticed that the following once common machines have disappeared, or will soon have disappeared, from our work environment:

- Typewriters, both mechanical and electric
- Mechanical movie cameras and home projectors
- Mechanical adding machines
- Alcohol-based duplicators
- The linotype and other mechanical typesetters
- Wind-up watches and clocks
- Vacuum tube based electronics
- Manually operated machine tools
- Analogue meters (even though they are better for some applications)

In addition, library card catalogues are disappearing, analogue instrument panels on cars are on their way out and printed encyclopedias are threatened.

All this has happened in the last few years, well within the memory of most adults in 1997, all of it due to the invention of the transistor and then the multi-purpose microprocessor.

Soon we can expect that:

- Chemical photography will become digital photography.
- Your car will be assisted by computer control and fly-by-wire technology i.e. only wires will connect the accelerator to the carburettor, and a computer will be the decision-making connection.
- Household appliances will become 'intelligent'. The automatic and programmable bread-making machine is the first example.
- People involved in intellectual occupations will be able to do most of their work at home.
- Gold collar workers will make more money than their bosses.
- The Internet will change the way goods are made, marketed and delivered.

On the factory floor a new family of machines is making its way into the workplace. This group of machines is generally referred to as robots. In a loose, generalized way, today's robot can be described as a general-purpose, programmable manipulator, the emphasis being both on manipulation and programmability. Mobility is not yet considered overly important but will become increasingly so as we learn more about how to make machines intelligent and mobile. Making machines mobile requires a more thorough and sophisticated understanding of how we perceive our immediate environment and how we react to it. We do not have this understanding at this time and so we cannot write programs to react to it. It is turning out to be much more complicated than we thought it was. We can say we do not understand mobility with some confidence because it is obvious to us that even creatures with tiny brains can navigate environments similar to those that our machines cannot manage, so computing power in itself is probably not the problem – how to use this computing power (the necessary software) is.

It is important to have an understanding of robotics because today's robot is the first programmable general-purpose manipulator. This is a description that very aptly describes the average human worker. As such robots can be expected to do the work that we human beings do – not all the work that we do but some of it – and every day we can expect that these machines will do more and more. Early emphasis will, as always, be on dangerous, dirty, repetitive and boring work. As these tasks come under hand, and as our skill in designing, making and programming robots develops, both more mundane and more skilled tasks will be addressed.

Having the ability to run motors with computers allows us to have unprecedented control over motion. Here we are not talking about just the **on/off** and **reverse** control of motors that we have always had, but of absolute control over the operation of the motor. We can now control the time of operation, the operational sequencing, the speed, the acceleration, the torque and the power of the motor. We can now have all of this control instantaneously, based on complicated calculations, made at lightning fast speeds. This in turn translates into programmability and versatility and gives us the first glimpses of the intelligent machines of tomorrow.

The developments that are making this all possible are:

- The speed and flexibility of modern computers
- The low cost of computers and of memory products
- Mastering the ability to control motors
- The availability of sophisticated software products and the increase in the population of engineers who understand these products

Whenever the necessary components and technologies become available, someone puts them together to create a useful machine. The robot is a logical expression of the ready availability of the above products and technologies.

As previously stated, this book is written for amateur engineers – engineers and tinkerers who are interested in learning about robots at a level that gives them some real understanding of how these machines actually work and how they are controlled. However, I have avoided the use of any formulae and you will not have to understand any complicated circuit diagrams or other highly technical concepts. You do not have to be a great engineer, designer or a software whiz to understand what is being discussed. Everything will be explained in plain everyday English.

The book is divided into two parts. The first part explains simply what robots are and how they actually work. The mechanical components, the electronic components and the software are discussed. The second part describes the construction of a biped, walking robot that you can make in your home shop and program with a personal computer through a serial interface. This interface uses only two wires to communicate with the robot and is similar to the serial interface used by computers to run most serial printers. This is a common interface that most computers already have built into them and is also the interface that you use with a modem. The appendices include a short glossary of robotic terms, a table of ASCII values, information on the Scott Edwards controller, details of the program diskettes available, drawing and construction notes (in metric and imperial) and component supplier information.

When we talk about robots, what we are really talking about is machines that do what human beings would normally be expected to do. These machines mimic the operation of human beings or certain parts of human beings. Most shop floor robots are the emulation of one arm of a human being.

- Their motors are the human muscles
- The general-purpose computer is the human brain
- Robotic vision is the human eye
- Synthesized speech is the human voice
- Automated mass spectrometry can serve as human smell and taste

We combine these elements in various ways to create the robot that we need to do the work that needs to be done. The discipline is still very much in its infancy and anyone interested in the technology can make an important contribution.

Most of us are more mechanically inclined as opposed to being electronically inclined. To this we have to add the unfortunate fact that we never see the part of the robot that has the electronics in it when we see robots on television or in the movies, so naturally we tend to think of a robot as a mostly mechanical contrivance. If the truth be known, the robot is really a computer with a relatively few mechanical components attached to it! By this I mean that the computer component of the average robot has at least *5,000 times* as many discrete electronic components in it than there are discrete mechanical components in the robot. Luckily for us these electronic components come neatly packaged in a box and they are relatively inexpensive – we call them general-purpose, desktop or personal computers. Fortunately, they are now also relatively easy to use.

The most common robot in use by industry today is the **robot arm** as used on the assembly line shop floor. These arms are used to weld, package, paint, position and assemble a host of products that we use every day. Everything from integrated circuits, printed circuit boards and VCR tapes to automobiles are included in the items now either wholly or partially assembled and made by robots. In Japan, robots are even decorating cakes with speed, repeatability and precision.

Basically a robot arm is a series of linkages that are connected in such a way that a servo motor can be used to control each joint or separate movement of the machine. This is not unlike the muscles in your arm though, of course, not nearly as complicated or as flexible. The operation of each joint on the robot arm does not have to be independent although there are advantages to independent operation. If the operation is not independent, the computer can be programmed to sort that out in the software in such a way that for all practical purposes the operation can be considered to be independent. The controlling computer, the brain of the robot, is programmed to control the various motors on the robot in a way that performs useful work. This book is about how this is done.

After reading this book you should be able to have an informed discussion with someone who knows almost nothing, or almost everything, or something in between, about robots. If you are so inclined you will be able to actually build and program the walking robot that is described. It can be programmed to walk on its two feet like a human (or a bird). Surprisingly, but understandably, the gait is not quite what one might have expected – simplifying the joints and muscle structure changes the gait. Keep in mind also that each builder will use his or her own techniques for programming the robot to walk so we can expect that the walk of each robot built will differ slightly.

The robot described for construction uses eight model aircraft servo motors as used for the radio control of a model aircraft. These motors are controlled by a dedicated single chip microcomputer that in turn is controlled from your personal computer in such a way, that to the servo motors, the controller looks like the radio receiver that normally controls them. This is the most inexpensive way to provide the control we need at this time (early 1997). The robot frame or skeleton is made from 3mm (⅛in.) aircraft grade plywood available from your hobby/model aircraft supply store. All the work can be done on your kitchen table with a few simple hand tools and no special skills are required. If you consider yourself a handy person who likes to build things I imagine you already have all the tools that you will need and I expect that you will have no difficulty in making, assembling and programming the robot.

The robot is powered by two batteries – one battery is on board the robot and the other can be placed nearby.

Although all discussion of programming in the book uses the BASIC language, you can program the robot in any language that you are familiar with or have available to you. BASIC is an English-like language that is very easy to learn and is provided with most computers as a part of the basic software components.

A two-wire interface controls the robot from your personal computer. Although all the commands needed to run the motors are very simple, the algorithms that you design and create to program the robot to walk can be as simple or as complicated as you care to make them. I will show you how.

The computer required does not need to be either large or fast – an older unit will be just fine as long as it has a serial interface (RS-232 standard) and the software needed to program it.

Welcome to the fascinating world of robots.

CHAPTER TWO

History and future

The history of robots is the history of the evolution of machines. Today's robots and their controlling computers represent the most evolved of all machines. Manufacturing a robot takes state-of-the-art computers, machining techniques, cutting tools and software. Robots represent the machine designer's work as the state of the art.

There are a number of people and events that influenced the appearance of robots on today's shop floors. In this chapter I will cover a few salient events in the interest of informational completeness. I have picked contributors to the discipline in an unconventional way in that the people I selected reflect my feelings that it is really the ideas that govern what happens, and so it is the men and women who had the ideas who are the important ones. Many others have made important contributions but I felt that a discussion of their work would be more appropriate in an academic, as opposed to a popular, introduction to robotics.

John Napier (1550–1617). Napier's bones were the earliest mechanical manifestation of the automation of a calculation process and were thus the first proof that it was possible to get a mechanical answer to a mathematical problem without having to make intellectual judgements. Napier was the Scottish mathematician who was responsible for logarithms. His bones were usually made of ivory (thus bones) and consisted of small square logs with markings on them on all four of the long sides. The bones allowed logarithms to be calculated by turning the logs as specified by the number whose logarithm was to be calculated. The markings that appeared as the logs were manipulated and the number under consideration determined what was done next.

Isaac Newton (1642–1727). Newton and **Rene Descartes** (1596–1650) invented the calculus that is the singular mathematical invention of the millennium. Before that, Vyas's invention of the zero in India and the development of El Jebra (algebra to us) by the Arabs were the precursors.

Joseph Marie Jacquard (1752–1834). The invention that made the greatest leap forward in the design of machines as it relates to robots and automation is without a doubt Jacquard's 19th century, punched card controlled, loom which he patented in 1804. Jacquard, a Frenchman, perfected his machine in 1809 and it was mass produced. After the Jacquard loom, nothing important happened, along the lines of automation, for nearly a hundred years. The major innovation in Jacquard's loom was the use of punched cards to control the patterns produced in the cloth that was woven. No-one had considered that it would be possible to build a machine that would change what the machine (the loom) did by changing some cards that were an integral but physically minor part of the machine. The concept that governs, and is therefore the most important part of this, is the idea that the weaving is to be controlled by the cards (as representation of information) and not the weaver (as the enterer of information as he wove). The responsibility had been transferred to the machine. Man now began to serve the machine in a radical new way. The skill level needed of the operator was reduced and the sophistication needed to make the machines was increased. This is a theme that we see repeated again and again as we follow the progress of automation through the next two centuries. Today the skill and information needed to make some of our machines (Pentium processors), is so great that even if everything needed was written down for us, we could not manufacture the microprocessors. In some very high-tech companies the death of one person can mean the end of the corporation as we knew it (e.g. Seymour Cray of Cray Research, super computers). Where the robot does the work, the skill of the worker is zero ... the worker and his skills are no longer needed.

Herman Hollerith. The next use of punched cards was to provide a way of handling the large amount of information generated by the 1890 US Census. This use was undertaken by Herman Hollerith, a businessman who worked with the US Census Bureau to tabulate the census. Until the demise of the punched card a few years ago these cards were referred to as either IBM cards or Hollerith cards. Hollerith felt he needed to use cards to ensure that information could be entered into the system rapidly. The International Business Machines Corporation (IBM) was formed from the company that made the machines that Hollerith designed for his work and, as we now know, IBM went on to become the world's premier maker of business machines and computers. Today punched cards have been replaced by floppy disks as a means of holding and transferring information. Where cards are still used they have a magnetic stripe on them and are no longer punched. The magnetic stripe can hold many times more information (about 2,000 characters in most uses) than the 80 or so characters that a punched card holds.

In order to lend itself to manipulation by a calculating engine (a computer) a process has to be able to be represented by a mathematical or some other non ambiguous, logical expression. This makes the contributions made by mathematicians and natural philosophers important to the development of computers and thus of robots.

Charles Babbage (1792–1871). In my mind the next honour goes to the Englishman Charles Babbage. Babbage was a mathematician as well as a mechanical genius. He was a graduate of Cambridge and a fellow of the Royal Society. In 1642, the French mathematician and philosopher **Blaise Pascal** invented the first calculator based on wheels and gears. Babbage is the person who first grasped that mathematics had a mechanical analogue and so postulated that it would be possible to build a calculating engine that could calculate answers to complicated mathematical problems, a mechanical device that would do what up to then only biological man had done. The fact that Babbage was unable to finish his calculating engine is of minor consequence to us today. Of interest to us here is his understanding that the process could be accomplished mechanically. We should not allow the fact that he did not fully understand its immensity to cloud the importance of his intellectual achievement. Although Babbage had a mechanical engine in mind, the ideas put forth are applicable to all calculating engines, even those of today – the huge super computers that can undertake millions upon millions of calculation in a second. Babbage incorporated the use of (Jacquard's) punched cards in his calculating engine. Babbage's engine has now been built and may be seen at the British Museum in London.

George Boole (1815–1864), an English logician and mathematician, worked out all the intricacies of what we now call Boolean algebra in his honour. Boolean algebra specifies how binary mathematics works. Since computers use zeros and ones to represent their universe, binary mathematics is the system they use.

The seminal work of describing the operation of a programmable computer was done by **Alan Mathison Turing** (1912–1954) in England in 1937 and **John von Neuman** (1903–1957) a Hungarian (later a naturalized American) in the United States. Both these men were mathematicians and expectedly, in the modern world, both were theoreticians and thinkers, and therefore dangerous men. Dangerous as in revolution – not the revolution of guns but that of ideas. Neither man ever built a computer but their ideas proved that the computations were possible. Proof meaning that there was no doubt in the minds of reasonable men about it after they had put down their pencils. They proved that there was no question that it could be done. The work is seminal because it heralds the information age. Theirs was the first trumpet heard. The proof that we are in the information age is that it is now much more important to know *how* to do something than it is to actually *do* it, because once you know how, you can hire workers in the appropriate skills/costs market to do the work. The fact that this is true is driving the development of robots. The undeclared concept that drives this is "if labour is expensive, we will strive to eliminate the labour content of the product". The concept is never heard stated as above because the declaration made is in economic terms and engineering terms and never in political or social terms.

John Bardeen (1908–1991). Singer received 50 cents for every sewing machine that was made under his patents and that was a lot of money in his time. If John Bardeen, **Walter H Brittain** and **William B Shockley** (the inventors of the transistor who won the Nobel prize in 1956) had a tenth of a cent for every transistor ever made – and a tenth of a cent is nothing today – they would soon have all the money the world. If I had to select one of the three I would single out John Bardeen for the transistor and for his theories on superconductivity. He was awarded two Nobel prizes in physics during his lifetime. The invention of the transistor is undoubtedly the technological event of the century, if not the millennium, and John Bardeen is the man of the century (though *Time* magazine will probably miss this in its selection at the end of the millennium). The microscope allowed us to see smaller things, the telescope let us see farther. The transistor allows us to think faster and to perform unfathomable calculations in seconds. It made computers, miniaturisation, space travel and everything else that goes with them possible. Without John Bardeen's, Brittain's and Shockley's transistor, the robot as we know it today (and will know tomorrow) would not have been possible. Almost all the early Silicon Valley firms (including Intel and Fairchild Semiconductor) that became successful were started by the students of Shockley, in itself a great contribution to civilisation in general and electronics in particular.

In a way we could say that, in an age where everything depends on information, the transistor allows us to manage information with facility and speed.

The transistor itself was the result of work done at Bell Laboratories, the research facility where cutting edge research was undertaken by the Bell (as in Alexander Graham) Telephone Company, the giant American company that had an enduring interest in switching electrical signals. The telephone system being a giant web of wires connected by an immense array of switches, the means of switching wires as rapidly, reliably and as efficiently as possible was of immense interest to the telephone company.

In summary then:

- The transistor was invented at Bell Labs in 1947–8
- The first commercial transistors became available in the 1950s
- The first integrated circuits appeared in the 1960s
- The first microprocessor was the Intel 4004
- The first high volume, 8 bit microprocessor, the Intel 8008 was introduced to the market in the 1970s
- The first 4 function calculators became common in the late 1970s
- The Microsoft Corporation was started by Bill Gates and Paul Allen in 1975
- The first computer kits were marketed in 1976 (the Altair)
- The Apple computer was first marketed in 1977
- The IBM–PC was introduced in 1981
- The Apple Macintosh was introduced in early 1984
- John Bardeen died in 1991, his death was preceded by that of Shockley and his by that of Brittain
- The Intel Pentium processor, the 5th generation of 80XX type Intel microprocessors appeared in computers in the second half of 1996

Now let us move on to more specific historical information about the development and automation of machines in the last one hundred years or so.

Henry Maudslay (1771–1831). The lathe always has been, and still is, considered the basic machine tool. Henry Maudslay's lathe is generally accepted as the first sophisticated metal cutting lathe. Maudslay added the slide rest, a major improvement, to the lathe when he was still working for Joseph Bramah. He made accurate screwcutting possible and with it the manufacture of screws, nuts and accurate micrometers. He trained some of the eminent machine tool scientists of the day. Sir Joseph Whitworth, whose name is associated with the standardisation of screw thread forms, worked in his shops and laboratories as did James Nasmyth (steam engine developments).

Karel Capek (1890–1938). Karel Capek (pronounced "chop'ek") was a Czechoslovakian author. He did not make any engineering or software contribution but did give us the word robot in his play *RUR* (*Rossum's Universal Robots*). By robot he meant someone doing indentured, inhuman, repetitive work, forced labour or a serf. The word robotics is first thought to have been used by science fiction writer Isaac Asimov (1920–1992) author of over a hundred sci-fi books and the laws of robotics. The laws of robotics are stated as follows:

- **Law Zero**: A robot may not injure humanity, or, through inaction, allow humanity to come to harm.
- **Law One**: A robot may not injure a human being, or, through inaction, allow a human being to come to harm, unless this would violate a higher order law.
- **Law Two**: A robot must obey orders given it by human beings, except where such order would conflict with a higher order law.
- **Law Three**: A robot must protect its own existence as long as such protection does not conflict with a higher order law.

George Devol and **Joseph Engelberger** (1930–) developed the first industrial robots called the Unimates. They were manufactured by their Unimation (Universal Automation) Corporation of Danbury, CT, USA in the 1950s and 1960s. Devol held the patents for some parts transfer machines that were the basis for the development of the robots. These robots were also made under licence by Kawasaki in Japan. Unimation is now owned by Staubli of Switzerland after passing through the hands of Condec and the Westinghouse Corporation. Engineers who once worked for Unimation started Adept, the only major American manufacturer of industrial robots in the US at this time. Adept manufactures some very fast direct drive (by the motor, no belts and gears) SCARA robots and some very sophisticated vision systems.

A mobile robot called Shakey was developed at the Stanford Research Institute (SRI) during the 1960s. It navigated a fairly complicated but structured indoor environment with some success and is credited with being the inspiration for the development of the AGVs of the 1990s.

The present

As computers get faster and faster they can process more and more information in the same amount of time. Speed is necessary because we have not yet really worked out how to make a computer that uses a number of processors to work on the same task. There are computers with more than one processor in them but these processors are not all working on the same task at the same time (we call this parallel processing). They have specific duties but the main processing is still done with one processor. There is a limit to how much one processor can do because electricity will move down a wire only so fast. At about 500 megahertz (500,000,000 cycles per second) the speed of electricity starts to become a limiting consideration. We already have computers that are running at half that speed on computer store shelves. Some improvements can be gained by using 64 bit and 128 bit microprocessors and 128 bits seems to be the limit for now. After that we will have to master parallel processing. The problem is not hardware, meaning that we can now make whatever we may need, but philosophical, meaning that we have not yet worked out in our minds what we need to do to solve the problem. We need someone like Alan Turing or John von Neuman to think it out. Interestingly enough each of us have everything we need to solve this problem – our brains, paper, pencils. In fairness I should say that it is not clear that the problem can be solved in conventional terms though it also needs to be said that no-one has offered proof that this is indeed the case.

When we talk about 500 MHz processors we are talking about the main processing chip in the computer, the Central Processing Unit (CPU). The peripheral cards and much other circuitry on the mother board is still running at between 5 and 20 MHz because of other considerations. This seems to be the limit for peripherals at this time although currently there are lots of engineers working hard to speed up this end of things.

In robotics our interest has two sides to it. On the one hand we already know how to run motors, on the other hand we do not have enough information available fast enough to decide what the motors should do. There are two handicaps involved in this. One is that it takes a certain amount of time to analyse any piece of information no matter how simple or complicated that information and the other is that we have to understand how to analyse the data to get the information we want from it which is not always simple. Robotic vision is an example of this. We know how to capture an image but we are still novices at interpreting the image to get the information we want from it. The problem is both hardware and software related. A computer captured image is an array of pixels (Pixel=PICture ELement), each with colour information attached to it. This has to be processed in a way that will give us useful information. It seems to be apparent that computers will not see and recognize objects in the same way that we do because the computers and cameras we use (our brains and eyes) are radically different from the digital computers and cameras that robotic vision systems use. Automated vision systems are tremendously useful for face recognition, fingerprint identification, bin picking, label placement verification on products, optical character recognition, automatic recognition of suspicious items at airports and many other applications. Although all these tasks are now being undertaken by information processing engines (the vision part of robotics), the way these machines do this is radically different from the way humans perform the same task. However these differences should not be allowed to distract us: we fly with speed and safety but the machines we use do not flap their wings. We travel over the ground in cushioned comfort but none of the machines we employ either hop, walk, trot or gallop. There are no air conditioned horses!

Let us consider a specific shop floor problem/example as encountered in the problem generally called the 'bin picking' problem.

The task can more specifically be described as follows. A bin is being filled with some plastic parts that are coming off a conveyor being fed from a moulding machine. Our task is to program a robot to pick a part from the bin and place it in a packaging machine. The easiest solution would be to never allow the parts to get mixed up and in all sorts of orientations in the first place i.e. handle the part correctly after it comes out of the moulding machine while it is still properly oriented. This, unfortunately, is not possible for a lot of reasons (all the problems have to do with slowing the overall processes down too much) so a different solution is needed. Both mechanical orienting machines and human operators are currently used to address this problem.

What we need is a vision system that can tell the robot to pick the most appropriate part up in the same way as a human being would do. The vision system has to decide which part is to be picked up, how is it oriented, whether it is trapped under another part or not, whether the handle that we want to grasp the part with is available to the robot gripper and what to do if no suitable part can be identified. Every task in the process is difficult and we may have less than half a second to make all the decisions. The decision-making process itself can start only after the robot picks up the last part it identified or immediately after the last part that was dropped into the bin has settled down. This we cannot do with the knowhow we have at this time, however, progress is being made and solutions will be formulated.

Chapter 10 introduces you to the rudiments of robotic vision. It discusses the most elementary aspects of vision such as finding edges and defining outlines and shows you how a vision language is defined. These are the concepts that have to be built upon to create a viable vision system.

Work is in progress to create both an electronic retina and the electronic equivalent of a brain cell. Hopefully these can be combined by the millions to assemble a computer that will, more easily, be able to recognize objects and do useful work. Self-programming software will solve pattern recognition tasks.

As we will see in later chapters, we need a comprehensive vision language before we can properly use vision systems. The work is waiting to be done and any person with the "right stuff" can make significant contributions to the effort. Again, this too is brainwork and interestingly enough, this (how to think) is something that is not taught at universities in a formal way because we have not yet formalized what we know about it. We can reasonably expect that this too will come to pass.

The future

As far as technology is concerned it is not possible to make specific predictions about the future in the long term. In the short term we can expect the following developments to occur in robotics and its related disciplines:

- More powerful computers will allow robots to become more intelligent.
- Software as well as hardware developments will make sophisticated vision systems inexpensive and therefore more commonplace. Systems that learn by seeing will be developed. Software developments will allow software to be told 'what to do' rather than being told 'how to do' as is done now.
- There will be a huge increase in the general population of robots and other intelligent machines.
- The price of robots will continue to come down.
- Both smaller and larger robots will appear.
- The robotic operating system will implement artificial intelligence, fuzzy logic and similar techniques to allow robots to 'learn' from their experience.
- There will be a strong demand for technicians, engineers and scientists who can repair, design and do research as related to robots.
- Defence and space exploration considerations will continue to fuel robotic and remote operation (tele-robotics) research. We will all benefit from this work.
- Robotic languages will continue to become more and more powerful and English-like. A definitive robotic language will emerge. This does not exist today but is suggested by the fact that most robotic languages have many similarities.
- Words that have robotic connotations will continue to be added to every language.
- Further on, the work week will get shorter and there will be more time for leisure activities. As people spend more time in the open spaces they will insist on the aggressive protection of species and the environment.
- Permanent magnets will become more and more powerful and this in turn will allow smaller more powerful motors to be made for robotic applications. Piezo-electric material will also contribute. Higher displacement piezo materials will be invented.
- Smaller linear and segmented motors will become commonplace.
- Motors with encoders attached to them will become standard off-the-shelf items. Even the most common of motors will have microprocessor control on them to conserve energy and provide better, more efficient control. Appliance motors will lead the way.
- Integrated circuits dedicated to the comprehensive control of motors will become more readily available. They will be easier to use and will be built into every motor. It will be required by the law (to conserve energy).
- The number of people who work with robots and other intelligent automated machines will rocket.
- A utility robot that can be used in the average home will not become a reality in the near future because the problem is not yet understood adequately and therefore cannot be solved with the tools we have at hand. Conceivable solutions are too expensive to allow effective marketing.

Surprisingly, ethical and political considerations about the use of robots will be the most important aspects of robotics that will need addressing. I will close with some examples:

- How should we share the work that needs to be done?
- Whose or what work will get automated?
- How fast should we automate our blue collar industries?

- What will we do with redundant workers?
- Should certain international corporate entities be allowed to get a stranglehold on certain critical segments of an industry?
- How will taxation have to be changed to accommodate and respond to massive automation?
- How does education have to change to accommodate and serve the needs of the information age?
- At what age will workers need to retire (or work less, work longer)?
- How often will workers need to be retrained?
- What facilities will be needed by workers working fewer hours a week?
- How will organized labour respond to the new work environment?
- When is it acceptable for robots to be used in combat? This becomes much more serious when two or three sides have combat robots. (Incidentally, this violates the laws of robotics postulated by Asimov.)

CHAPTER THREE

The modern robot

The modern robot, as used on the shop floor today, is a powerful one-armed manipulator with an appropriate gripper or tooling. It is usually a six-axis robot and is fixed either to the shop floor or to the machine that it serves. The robot is controlled from a powerful computer that is located quite close to it. This computer's cabinet contains all the logic components and amplifiers needed to run the robot. The computer is usually also connected to other computers in the factory with high-speed communication lines.

Most shop floor robots can pick up work pieces and tools that weigh over one hundred kilograms (two hundred and twenty pounds) and place them within about 1mm (0.040in.) of the desired location with repeatability. They can move the loads at speed of about 1 metre (3 feet) per second and put them down as softly as you please. Grippers or robot hands of every description allow all manner of things to be manipulated and controlled – the engineer's need, the designer's imagination and the customer's cash book seem to be the only limits on what can be made available to accomplish the tasks at hand.

There are three distinct component groups within any sophisticated robot(ic) system. They compare to the human being as follows:

	Robot part	**Human equivalent**
Group 1	The hardware	The human body
	Robot arm	Human arm
	Robot gripper	Human hand
	Vision system	Human eyes
Group 2	Computer electronics	The brain
Group 3	The software	The education

Each robot must have each of these three basic components. Each of the components is minimally connected to the other meaning that it could be replaced by a completely different unit and the system could still be made to work with comparatively little effort. In a robot these three systems are made to work together to create a useful machine.

The mechanical part of the robot, the part that we are most familiar with, is the part that does the physical work. It too can be made in many different ways but is usually designed to do a specific family of tasks within a specified envelope that is determined by the physical size of the robot. On the shop floor this is a robot arm that sits on the side of the assembly line and performs operations on the manufactured components as they go by it. Automatically Guided Vehicles (AGVs) form the bulk of the mobile robot population. Their main use is in the delivery of raw material components to machines i.e. they provide an intelligent, mobile, programmable conveyor function.

The movable part of the robot, the robot arm itself, is a series of linkages that are so connected that they function as a manipulator or arm but the mechanism is nowhere near as complicated or as flexible at the human arm. A motor controls each joint or movement. The operation of each joint does not have to be independent but there are definite advantages to independent operation. If the operation is not independent, the computer can be used to sort that out in the software in such a way that for our purposes the operation could be considered independent. However, this makes the task more computationally intensive because calculations may now have to be made before each and every move and this time is no longer available for other critical computations.

The robot system is not dependent on the computer that controls it – any computer powerful enough to do the job will be adequate to perform the function. As far as the robot is concerned, all we are doing is processing information and it does not matter how this is done as long as the right results are available when they are needed. The computer can have any architecture and any design internally and we would have no way of knowing what it was by watching the operation of the robot. However, this does not mean that this is either trivial or easy to do.

The software is connected to the system minimally and becomes an integral part of the system only after it is loaded into the computer memory. It can be written in any language, in myriads of ways, and still be made to work. Before the software is loaded into the computer, it can be completely disconnected from the system. It is this detachment or disconnect ability that makes the system programmable and flexible – we can load whatever software we want into the system when we want to. If the software was an integral part of the robot, it would compromise the flexibility of the system.

Typical robot specifications

See the Mitsubishi robot specifications listed on the facing page.

Types of robots

Robots can be divided into families according to the type of work that they do. The major divide among robots is between mobile robots and stationary robots. Since the development of mobile robots is still in its infancy, almost the entire genre is currently being represented by AGVs. Research on other forms of locomotion is being undertaken at every major university with an engineering school and we can expect that mobile robots will become more and more common as time goes on.

The present robot population can be categorized as follows:

- All robots
  - Mobile robots
    - Wheeled robots
      - AGVs
        - Mail delivery
        - Hospital use
        - Shop floor transportation between machine tools
      - Entertainment robots (these are not true robots at this time)
        - Greeters at shows and conventions

CONTROLLER SPECIFICATIONS

Model	CR-E356
Control Method	PRP control, CP Control
No. of Axis Controlled	Maximum 6 axes
Main Function	Joint, linear, arc interpolation; Palletizing routine; Cut-in control; Branch off; Subroutine position Arithmetic function (by MELFA BASIC III)
Programming Language	Rixan's RoboWare-WindowsTM based GUI Movemaster command / MELFA BASIC III (Teaching play-back method. Automatic program.)
Memory Volume	For MELFA BASIC III No. of points: 1800 points/program No. of steps: 3600 steps/program
	For Movemaster Command No. of points: 999 points/program No. of steps: 4000 steps/program For Teaching Play-back: 2000 steps
Program Making Method	Personal computer or teaching box.
Position Teaching	Teaching box or personal computer.
Input / Output	General: Input 20 points (Max. 60 pts.) Output: 16 points (Max. 48 pts.) Exclusive: Defined in general I/O by user. Hand: Optional Input 6, Output 6 (Standard 0) E-Stop: 1 on the back of controller
Interfacing	RS232C 1 Port RS422 1 Port (Used for teaching box.) Expansion Slots 3 (One of them is standard equipped I/O card.)
Ambient Temperature	0 degrees - 40 degrees C (No dew drop)
Ambient Humidity	45 -85%
Power Source	3 PH AC 170V - 253V 50/60Hz 3.5 KVA
Construction	Rack installation is possible with rack. Anchoring adapter optional.
Outside Dimensions	422 W x 516 D x 202 H mm
Weight	23 kg.

Controller specifications for the Mitsubishi robots. There is a lot of interesting information in these specifications. (Courtesy: Rixan, US distributor for Mitsubishi)

MECHANICAL SPECIFICATIONS

Model	Unit	RV-E5NJ	RV-E4N
Number of Axis		5 Axes	6 Axes
Drive Method		AC Servo	AC Servo
Encoder		Absolute Encoder	Absolute Encoder
Motor Capacity	W	J1-J6 200/400/200/100/100/100	
Brake		All axes with brake.	
Payload (Max.)	1 kg.	4 (5)	3 (4)
Arm Length (L1+L2)	mm	250 + 280	250 + 250
Waist Offset	mm	100	100
No. 1 Arm	mm	250	250
Max. Reach Radius (P Axis)	mm	630	634
Operation Range Degree	J1	(+ 160)	
	J2	230 (-90—+160)	
	J3	270(-130—+140)	175(-15—+160)
	J4	-	(+160)
	J5		(+120)
	J6		(+200)
Maximum Speed Degree/s	J1	216	192
	J2	270	270
	J3	270	270
	J4	-	270
	J5	270	270
	J6	432	432
Max. Resultant Speed	mm/s	5700	5800
Repeatability	mm	(+0.03)	(+0.03)
Body Weight	kg.	45	48
Tool Wiring		Input 6 /Output 6/ Extra 4	Input 6/ Output 6/ Extra 4
Tool Air Piping		Primary 06 x 2 pcs	Secondary 04 x 6 pcs
Mounting Inverted		Standard unit may be used.	
Wall Mounted		Standard unit may be used with slight restrictions. (J1:+30 degree limit)	
Clean Room Model		0.3u Class 10 & 100 Available	
Oil or Water Mist		IP 54F Available	

Mechanical specifications for the Mitsubishi robots. (Courtesy: Rixan, US distributor for Mitsubishi)

- Show business
  - Movies
    - R2D2 in *Star Wars*
  - Television robots – the dog in *Dr Who*
- Walking robots
  - One legged hoppers
    - Experimentation and adaptation/ learning research
  - Two legged robots
    - Show business
      - Movies
        - C3PO in *Star Wars*
  - Four legged robots
    - Research
    - Transporters
  - Six or more legged robots
    - Research
    - Transporters
- Underwater robots
  - Exploration
  - Salvage

- Defence
- Flying/aircraft robots
  - Defence
    - Missiles
    - Cruise missiles
    - Bombers
    - Intelligence gathering
  - Weather
    - Data gathering
  - Satellites
    - Communications
    - Data gathering
- Stationary robots
  - Manipulate objects
    - Assembly
    - Packaging
    - Feeding machinery
      - Presses
    - Unloading machinery
      - Castings
      - Investments
      - Presses
  - Manipulate tools
    - Welding
    - Painting
    - Measurement
    - Grinding
    - Polishing
    - Plotters
    - Machining robots
      - CNC milling machines
      - CNC lathes
      - Other CNC machines
  - Assist in process robots
    - Surgery
    - Positioning
      - Telescopes

Defining a robot

Essentially whatever we all agree to call a robot, is a robot. We tend to add robotic as an adjective to describe machines that have been automated to act automatically or autonomously. We might call an automated vehicle a robotic jeep. Industrial robots are called robotic arms and machine vision is referred to as robotic vision.

The first thing we need to agree upon is the definition of a robot. We will try to agree on as general and broad a description as we can so that the discussion can be as broad as possible. Here are some properties that all robots share:

- They all have computers to control them
- They all have components that move in some way
- They all have servo motors on them
- They all have a user interface to allow us to interact with them even if the interface consists of nothing more than a start button or a keyswitch
- They can all be programmed for the tasks at hand
- They all interact with their environment with input and output signals
- They all handle something in some way

Here are some properties that are *not* important to the definition of a robot:

- Size and shape of the machine
- Type of computer used to control the robot
- The software used to control the robot
- Type of power used to run the motors (pneumatic, hydraulic or electrical)
- Mechanical configuration (XYZ, articulated, spherical, cylindrical)
- Duty (what the robot does)
- Manufacturer (the organization that makes the robot)

As time goes on the distinction between computer peripherals and robots will begin to blur and more machines will be controlled by computers. Is a printer a robot that writes or is it a typewriter that is controlled by a computer? Is a plotter a robot or a printer? What if all the plotter ever does is write letters? Is a CNC machine a robot? We have to ask ourselves these questions in order to understand what we mean by the word robot. In the future new words will have to be coined to describe various computer-controlled machines. New words are already appearing because in the final analysis not everything controlled by a computer can be called a peripheral or a robot. Only a few years ago a 'plotter' was person.

How we categorize any object or machine has a lot to do with how we look at or perceive it. To primitive people, everything looks like a collection of mis-shapen iron. In northern India, any machine that is not understood is called a 'chan-koopie' which was initially used for a differential chain hoist and literally translated means 'chain-funnel', meaning a mess of chains that pour out of something! Now chan-koopie is used for anything new and uncomprehended, not unlike our calling everything controlled by a computer a robot or calling a new invention a gizmo.

Under rigid analysis, a Computer Numerically Controlled (CNC) milling machine is a specialized robot that manipulates rotating tools along very specific paths in order to produce accurately machined parts. The path that the tools are to follow is specified in a computer program written in a specific language designed for describing the movement of tools in a three-dimensional space. In a study undertaken in Japan in the 1980s to determine the population of robots in various countries, the Japanese classified their CNC machines as robots, which of course they are. However, today we would not classify them as robots which means that the definition of robot (and CNC machine) is changing rather rapidly with time!

We tend to focus on two human capabilities when we define machines as robots. One is the ability to manipulate objects as we do with our hands and arms and the other is the ability to move about, our mobility. Mobility is of interest because in order to move about autonomously we need to interact with the environment in some sort of intelligent way. We do not as yet understand this in a comprehensive way – only when someone describes or designs a language that can adequately specify the task will we fully understand it. We will not be able to describe the language until we understand the process. (Chapter 10 on vision is relevant to understanding this concept.) It may be that we need some sensors, that will help in the process, that have yet not been invented. There is also some indication that much more powerful computers are needed to process the large amount of (visual) information that must be processed to negotiate a complicated environment. We may have to add transmitters to the environment to allow us to better navigate it automatically. The Geo Positioning Satellite systems deployed for military use by both the US and Russian defence establishments represent such transmitters on a more global scale. Similar, local transmitters (a minimum of 3 are needed) within an office building or complex would allow a mail delivery robot to know where it was to within a few centimetres at all times. (That, a memory of the floor plans and primitive obstacle avoidance software would allow autonomous navigation to be implemented.)

Vision is still not considered an integral part of robotics by the lay observer but is very much a part of robotics to the robotic researcher. We accept that movie and comic book robots have vision but this facility has not yet been provided to everyday robots on the shop floor. It is coming, soon. Chapter 10 is devoted to giving you an introduction to robotic vision.

It is worth noting that although playing chess is very 'human intensive', we do not call chess-playing computers robots. We call them 'logic engines' that play chess or we call them 'computers that play chess' but we never call them robots. If however, we were to add a rudimentary robot arm to manipulate the chess pieces, a mundane task as compared to the ability to play chess, we would all agree that it was indeed a chess-playing robot. This proves to us that manipulation is an important ingredient in our willingness to call a machine a robot. (As I write this *Deep Blue*, the IBM chess-playing super-computer has just defeated Gary Kasparov the chess grand master in a seven-game series, the first time that a machine has *bettered* an acknowledged human specialist although Kasparov did complain of distractions! For the record it was a draw to the last game when Kasparov resigned). It is worth noting that we often refer to vision systems as robotic vision even when no manipulations or movements are involved!

Conclusions

- We are agreed that a robot is a programmable, computer-controlled machine that manipulates products and/or tools to do work.
- The work is generally accepted as being of a repetitive nature.
- The device has the ability to make decisions and can interact intelligently with its environment.
- The device can both receive and send information to its environment.
- The device may or may not be mobile.

This is not the official definition of a robot as stipulated by the Robot Institute of America (RIA) but it is effectively the actual meaning of the official definition.

> A re-programmable, multi-functional manipulator designed to move material, parts, tools, or specialized devices through various programmed motions for the performance of a variety of tasks.
>
> Robot Institute of America, 1979

And a broader definition:

> An automatic device that performs functions normally ascribed to humans or a machine in the form of a human.
>
> Webster

Today both these definitions are rather dated – robots are much more.

Robots as workers

We have an abiding interest in building machines that will do the work that we do. It is how we make life easier, more productive and work more interesting. As such these machines must be designed to work in the workplace and to manipulate the kinds of instruments (tools, machines) that human beings manipulate. As of today there are neither any giant robots or any microscopic ones – we do not (directly) work in those realms. These robots will arrive on the scene but it will take time. Giant robots are needed for moving large amounts of dirt (earth, for reclamation projects) and tiny robots are needed for electronic work and in the future will have application in the practice of medicine.

Another idea that pervades the workplace is our overwhelming interest in doing as little as we can to get the job done. This is true of even the most hard working among us. We can call this laziness or a desire to be extremely efficient with our resources depending upon our frame of reference. One way to get the job done is to have someone else do it – what easier way could there be than to have a machine do the work, day and night, without complaint. Basically that is what the industrial robot of today is: a pick and place machine with a little sophistication added here and there. This indicates that the industry is in its early stages because the use of intelligence to allow the machine to adapt to, and learn from, the task being performed is just beginning to be implemented.

If robots are to do the work we do, they will have to be about our size and to work like us. The ideal, most flexible robot is still the human being. Let us write down a few positive and negative qualities of these human robots.

Positive

- Understands human languages
- Versatile and easily trained
- Intelligent and responsive
- Large quantities available all over the world
- No special fuels or energy needed
- Easy to instruct (program)
- Relatively long, useful, work life
- Usually docile
- Self replicating

Negative

- Tires easily (needs segmented 8-hour day)
- Takes a long time to program (25 years to usefulness!)
- Software tends to get corrupted (forgets, joins unions)
- Relatively fragile, easily injured
- Hard to replace damaged parts
- Expensive to repair
- Some reliability problems have been reported
- Does not do well on repetitive tasks (gets bored and is forgetful)
- Needs to be maintained after end of useful life (pensions)

You get the idea.

The robots that we design have to augment the positive and eliminate the negative attributes of human beings. Almost the total effort is in these two directions.

The salient difference between the automatic machines of today and the automatic machines of yesterday is that the machines of today are programmable. What they do depends on the *information* that we put into them. The same machine can be programmed to do a relative large number of different tasks. Only the software needs to be changed and that can be done in minutes if not seconds. The machines of tomorrow will add intelligence – massive intelligence eventually. They will be able to optimize their work and react intelligently to all predictable and most unpredictable disturbances in their work environment. Unpredictable disturbances can be relatively easy to react to by shutting down, sounding an alarm, summoning a human supervisor, or rejecting the part. It is the minute changes that occur from cycle to cycle and from part to part that are harder to handle without error because they are more subtle and thus harder to define, detect and decide how to react to.

The robot is the machine that replaces the human being in the workplace. Although there are robots that act as autonomous vehicles (AGVs) in factories, offices and hospitals, these will soon no longer be called robots. New names will be needed for all kinds of robots because not everything can be described with the word robot. A whole new vocabulary is developing to describe these machines in all languages.

The developments related to electricity and electronics created similar needs for new words in their time.

Robot intelligence

It is a lot more complicated than this but at this stage of our understanding it is useful to look at this as follows.

In machines (computers), intelligence is the implementation of sophisticated 'IF...THEN ...' strategies in which the course of action taken depends on what has already happened. It looks like intelligence but it is really rigid logic even when some randomness, range and flexibility has been added to the decision-making process to make it less rigid. We make the mistake of calling it Artificial Intelligence (AI). It should be more properly called Machine Intelligence (MI) or Robotic Intelligence (RI) because there is nothing artificial about it. (For that matter there is really nothing intelligent about it either but it is useful to think about it as 'intelligence'.)

IF...THEN... strategies can be made very complicated and it is this ability to be complicated that makes them useful. The complication can be intense enough to make it impossible for a human being to understand the computer code if he or she does not already know what the code is all about and maybe not even then if the proper documentation does not exist. The code can best be generated by software programs that understand instructions that are more English-like in their nature and therefore easier for human beings to work with. This allows programs that are easier for the programmers to implement (write) to be converted to code that is executed more rapidly by the robots.

The following too is more complicated than what is stated, but for the purposes of this introduction this is a useful way to look at it.

Today, most robot language programming is done in a language called 'C' which is used because it has only about 28 instructions in it. I say about 28 because 28 instructions are defined but not all are used! All other instructions (thousands of them) are built up from these 28 instructions. There is no real limit to what can be built up with these 28 kernels and many very sophisticated versions of the language are available. (Separate instruction sets address different tasks.)

Having only 28 instructions means that the language is relatively easy to write (or port over) for a new computer design. All that has to be done is to implement these 28 instructions. The language is so useful that small microprocessors that execute this specific instruction set have been designed.

Standard 'C' libraries have been formulated and there are specialized libraries for the manipulation of images in a vision system and for the control of more than one motor simultaneously. Integrated circuit chip vendors provide libraries that make it easier to use their products. Special libraries and exotic databases that address special needs can be purchased from software developers and vendors.

'C' has a flexible structure that is well suited to the handling of complicated IF...THEN... structures and so works well for the control of robots. Also being a fast language makes it a good choice for robotic control languages because robot control is a real time application.

Mechanical configuration of robots

The motions required of a robot are dictated by the task or family of tasks that the robot is designed to perform. Of course it would be ideal if one sophisticated robot design could do everything we needed – not unlike the desktop computer where one basic design pretty much lets us manage any type of information that we want to manipulate (even so we still need 4 bit processors and supercomputers). All we would then need would be the right software (not a small order in itself). We would then build only this one robot, we could make a lot of them and the production costs would rival those of computers and automobiles i.e. they would be very inexpensive. Unfortunately it is not possible to build just this robot if for no other reason than the mundane fact that one robot will not meet all of our size requirements, not to mention the computational power that would be needed to do everything we would have to do with just one robot. Robots are made in many shapes and sizes and the software is optimized to serve the needs of the specific robot.

Two basic factors govern the motion and

abilities of the robot – the geometry of the design and the sophistication of the software.

Robot geometry

In three-space, the everyday three-dimensional environment that we are used to, there are a number of ways to design a robot that will reach all points in its work environment. As a rule you need one motor for each degree of freedom that you want to specify. So a minimum of three motors is needed to reach a location in three space (X, Y and Z co-ordinates). Another three motors are needed to orient the hand in the three possible orientations (roll, pitch and yaw). This makes the basic universal robot a six-axis robot. The human arm and hand with some assistance from the waist is a six-axis mechanism. Interestingly enough some of the axes have very limited motion but we do not normally feel inhibited by this. We do not

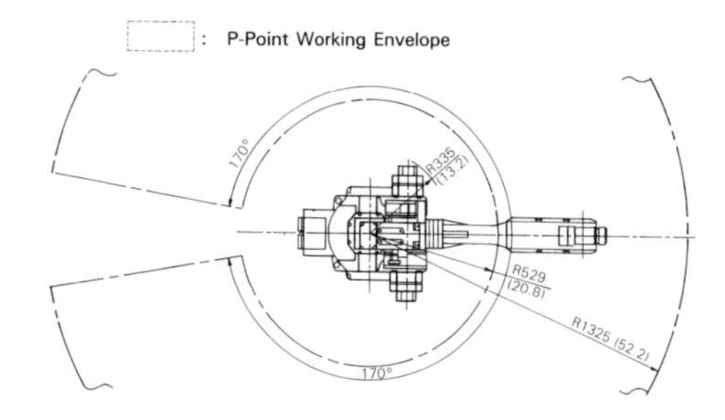

The work envelope of the Motoman SK6 manipulator as seen from above the robot. There is a small area behind the robot that cannot be reached. This does not cause any problems under normal circumstances. (Courtesy: Motoman Inc., USA)

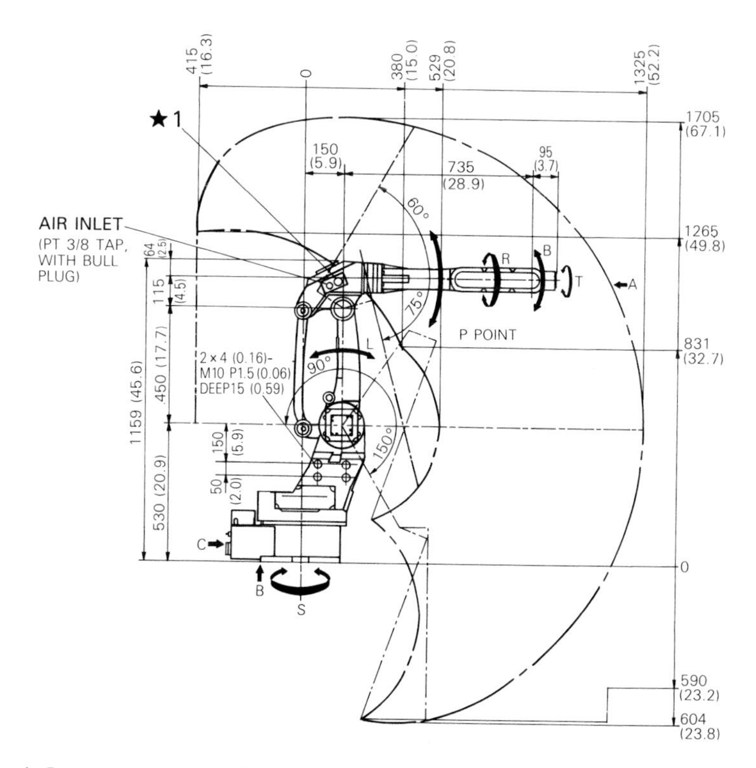

Motoman (Yaskawa in Japan) is a large manufacturer of robots. The diagram shows the work envelope of the Motoman SK6 manipulator as seen from the side. Note how the robot base sits back from the robot arm so that the base does not interfere with the work area. (Courtesy: Motoman Inc., USA)

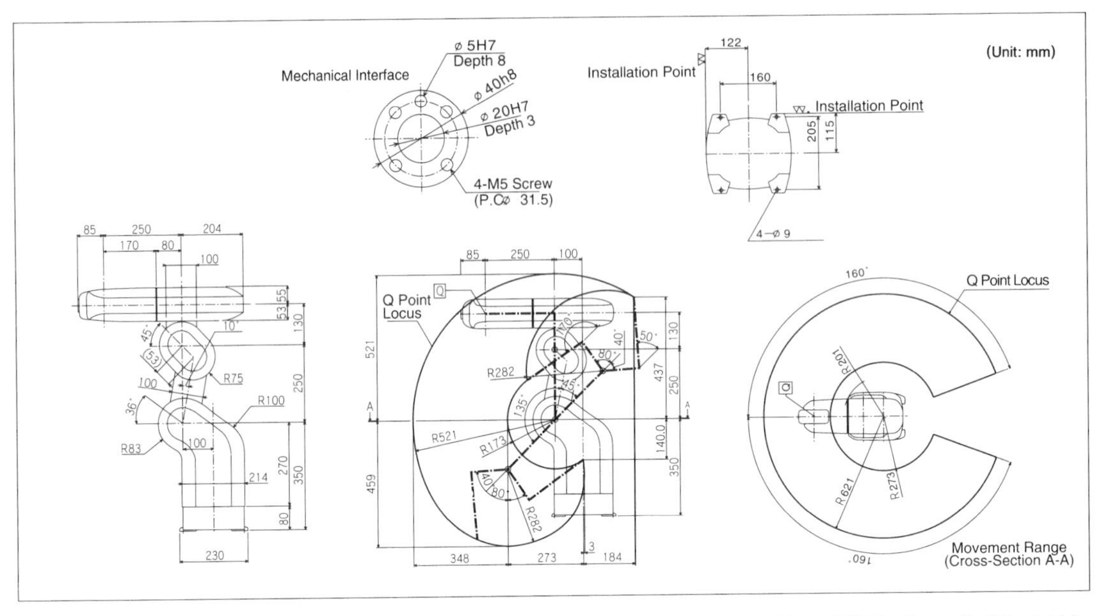

Dimensions and work envelope of the Mitsubishi RV-E2M Movemaster robot. (Courtesy: Rixan, US distributor for Mitsubishi)

work behind ourselves very well and the human arm mechanism is optimized for accessing the right front quadrant. The right hand is oriented to face its work partner, the left hand.

Notes on the human arm

As mechanical design observations about the human arm let us note the following:

- The distance from the shoulder to the elbow is greater than the distance from the elbow to the wrist.
- The distance from the elbow to the wrist is greater than the distance from the wrist to the knuckles.
- The distance from the knuckles to the first finger joint is greater than the distance from the first finger joint to the second finger joint.
- The distance from the second finger joint to the fingertip is the smallest distance on the mechanism.

The resolution of the system gets finer and finer as we get closer and closer to the gripper and the work at hand. We also know that there are more and more nerves in the system as we move from the shoulder to the fingertip. Evolution has optimized the system to place both the resolution and the sensor peaks at the end of the arm, the point where the action is taking place. This is also where the eyes are focused during intensive and highly skilled work. This is expressed at its peak in a surgical procedure where the highest manipulative, visual and cerebral skills are applied to one task.

On the other hand, the largest motors in the system are dedicated to the operating the largest joints with the coarsest resolutions. As we move to the fingertips, the power available becomes less and less.

It is also worth noting that the biological system is designed with the structural members essentially on the outside and the muscle/ motors on the inside. This prevents damage to the mechanism or at least minimizes it. Not all the tendons are on the insides but the powerful ones are. We can see the tendons on the back of the hand but their use is just to open the fingers, there is not much power needed here. The power to grip is provided by muscles on the other side, the inside of the hand.

The other observation to be made is that after the wrist, a considerable flexibility is provided by splitting the palm, by opposing the thumb to the fingers, by removing one digit from the thumb and by duplicating the fingers. Providing fingers of different lengths is a further refinement. The power to run the hand mechanism (the muscles) are in the forearm and not in the fingers. This is why wrist motion is so limited.

A large portion, but not all, of the feedback that the arm needs to operate proficiently is provided by the eyes. Blind workers can do useful work but they are severely handicapped for work in the workaday factory. We need to understand how this affects our designs. Today our robots are still more like blind workers than sighted ones and a large effort is aimed at eliminating this deficiency by funding aggressive research on vision systems.

The above discussion gives us a framework that allows us to think of the human arm as a robotic mechanism. This arm has done everything we have needed for millions of years. Let us see what this rather sophisticated design tells us about the robot arms that engineers design.

Industrial robots

The motions that we want the robot that we design to undertake are dictated by the work that we want the robot to do. Once the task has been studied adequately we can start on the design. The design that will be built will be an

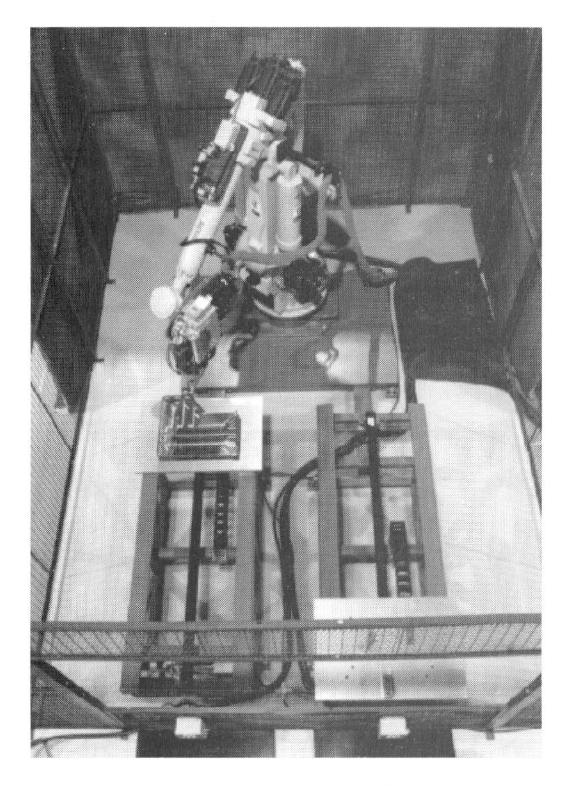

A Motoman robot in a spot welding application. Note that there are two work stations so that one can be loaded with work while work is being done on the other. Each is on a slide. Note also the welding curtains and safety wire mesh. (Courtesy: Motoman Inc., USA)

A Motoman robot in a deburring application. The robot manipulates a high-speed pneumatic grinder to clean up castings prior to further machining. (Courtesy: Motoman Inc., USA)

A Motoman SK6 robot in an arc welding application. the welding rod is fed in automatically and co-ordinated by the robot controller. All aspects of welding (arc detection, puddle size, depth of weld, welding current etc.) can be detected and controlled by the robot controller. (Courtesy: Motoman Inc., USA)

expression of the *minimum* capabilities needed to get the work done. The reach of each axis, the number of axes, the capabilities of the computer, the memory needed and the number of sensors to mention just some of the major design parameters, will all be *minimized* to build the most economical robot possible.

Basically a robot has to be able to move the part that it is handling or its tooling in a way that will permit it to do the work that needs to be done. Since all the movement is in normal, three-dimensional space, there are a number of ways that a robot can be designed that will allow it to reach all the positions that it has to.

The geometry selected will determine how the robot will operate and how it will be used. Robot geometries are defined by the geometric shapes that the robot's design mimics. The most common robot configurations are as follows:

- Articulated geometry
- Cylindrical geometry
- Spherical geometry
- Orthogonal XYZ geometry
- Gantry arrangements

Articulated geometry

Articulated robot arms act like the human arm. This is a flexible design that allows the most 'human arm like' movements. An articulated robot cannot make all the movements that a human arm can but for all practical purposes it can do everything that the human arm can do. Most welding and 'pick and place' robots follow this arrangement. The gripper is positioned in orthogonal XYZ space with three axes. Once the gripper is positioned, it has to be oriented in the three possible ways that it can be moved (roll, pitch and yaw). These three entities are usually specified by three angular quantities.

Cylindrical geometry

A cylindrical configuration dictates a robot whose axes are designed to be specified as cylindrical co-ordinates. This usually means an axis that moves up and down like a cylinder and another axis that moves in and out like a radius vector. A third axis specifies the angle of the

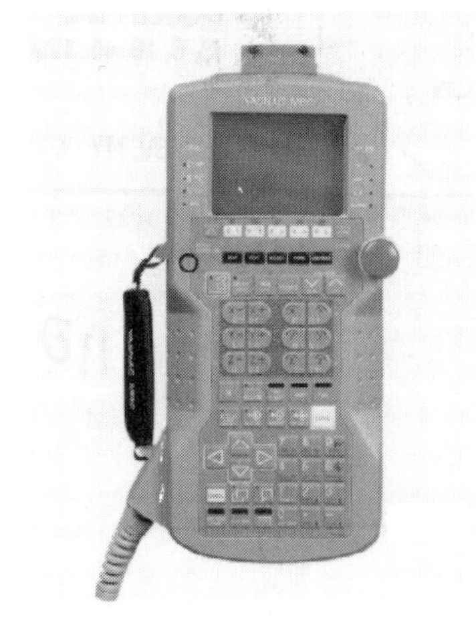

A Motoman teach pendant. Teach pendants are used to teach a robot the positions where the work will be done. This is usually much easier than trying to do it by specifying co-ordinates. Teach pendants are also used to edit robot positions to make them more accurate. (Courtesy: Motoman Inc., USA)

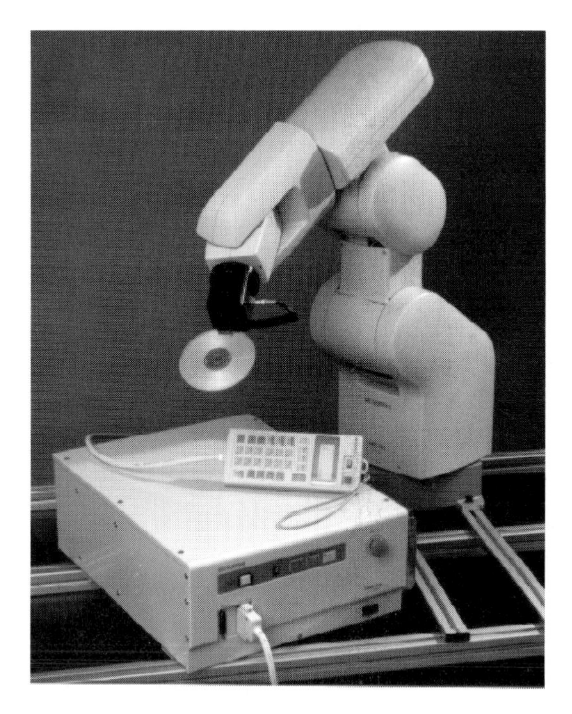

The Mitsubishi RV-E2M Movemaster table-top robot with teach pendant and controller. This is a small sophisticated table-top robot. (Courtesy: Rixan, US distributor for Mitsubishi)

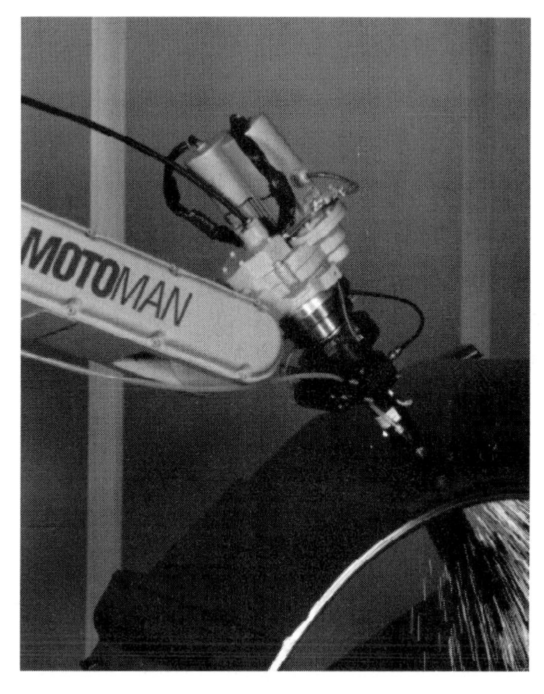

A laser head controlled by a robot. In this application the beam of the laser is trepanning the plate. Lasers can cut half inch plate with relative ease and with a very clean cut. (Courtesy: Motoman Inc., USA)

A welding application. The robot work area in a welding application is always shielded from human eyes to minimize exposure to ultraviolet light. Ultraviolet light is invisible to the human eye but is focused by it. It is near the X-ray spectrum and can severely burn the retina. Never look directly at an arc (the pain does not occur until a few hours after exposure). (Courtesy: Motoman Inc., USA)

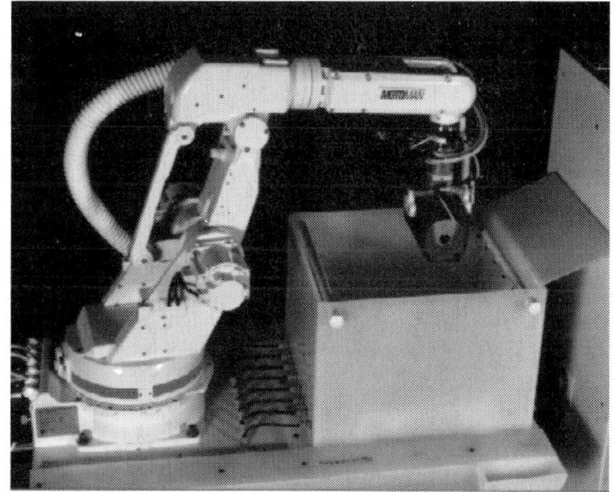

A clean room robot handling a container full of disks that will be used as computer hard disk memories after they have been fully fabricated and then assembled into the drives.

A material handling application. Note the counterbalancing springs along each side of the main body of the robot and the dead weight behind it. Counterbalancing makes it easier for the motors to control the robot arm. The workload is not counterbalanced – only the robot itself. (Courtesy: Motoman Inc., USA)

A SCARA (Selective Compliance Articulated Robot Arm) robot in a palletising application. Such applications are usually provided as pre-engineered solutions by the robot manufacturer. (Courtesy: Motoman Inc., USA)

radial axis. These three numbers specify the location in space. You still have the three specifications for the orientation of the gripper to work with but they are usually not specified as cylindrical co-ordinates.

Spherical geometry

In a spherical co-ordinate robot the two angles and a radial specification specify the point is space. The same comments as above apply to the gripper orientation.

Orthogonal XYZ geometry

An orthogonal robot is an XYZ machine. It has three sides that are arranged at right angles to

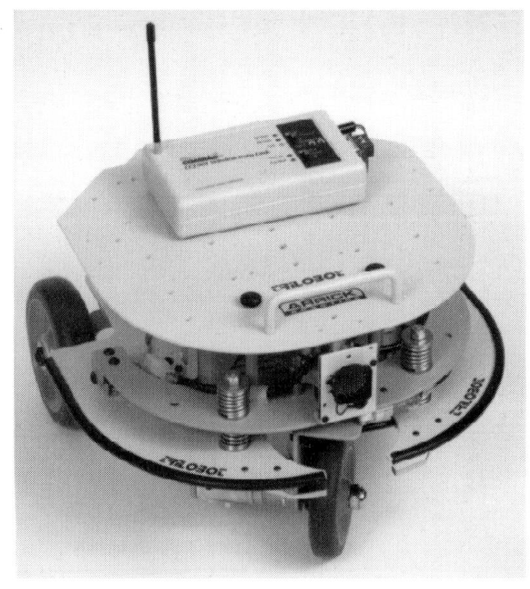

A mobile robot manufactured by Arrick Robotics. This is an autonomous unit that can be controlled from a personal computer. It uses a radio link to talk back and forth between the robot and the computer. Note the steerable front wheel and the sonic sensor above it. This robot is about 14 inches (35cm) in diameter. It is suitable for experiments in intelligent mobile robotics by students. (Courtesy: Arrick Robotics, USA)

one another. By specifying a number for each axis you can specify a co-ordinate in space. The same comments as above apply to the gripper orientation.

Gantry arrangements

Gantry robots have a robot gripper suspended from a gantry that covers a large space. The gantry moves the base of the robot in the X and the Y direction. The robot is suspended from the gantry and can reach any work under the

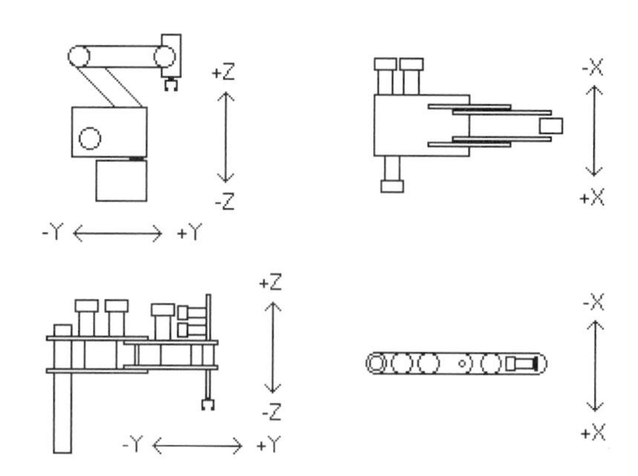

Figure 3.1 Axis designations in articulated and SCARA (Selective Compliance Articulated Robot Arm) robots.

gantry. A tool crib storage and retrieval system is suitable for a gantry which allows a very large number of tools to be stored and retrieved automatically, all under computer control. The emphasis is on serving a large area as against extreme precision.

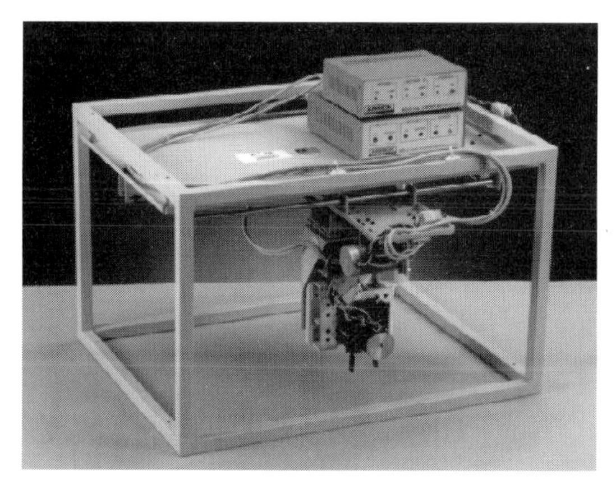

An Arrick Robotics gantry system suitable for use by students studying robotic assembly operations. This is a small table-top system. (Courtesy: Arrick Robotics, USA)

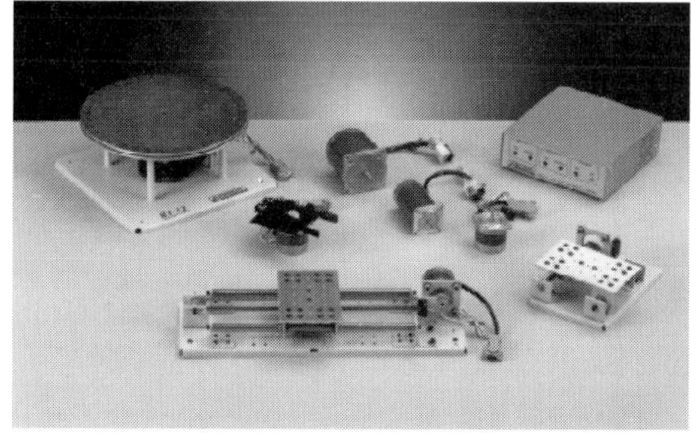

Various accessories for the Arrick robotic system. These are suitable for use by students in making up robotic components and for work cells. (Courtesy: Arrick Robotics, USA)

Grippers

The design of robotic grippers is a discipline unto itself and will keep pace with developments in robotics as time goes on. Sophisticated grippers have microprocessors dedicated to just their control.

The gripper that a robot uses is designed to manipulate the objects or tooling that the robot will be working with and most robots can have the gripper replaced with relative ease. Most grippers implement only an 'open' and a 'close' function. Although this is adequate for a large number of applications, the ability to control the force of the gripper and to detect the presence, or even the size, of the object in the gripper is available on the more sophisticated grippers. As mentioned in the software section elsewhere in the book, these functions can only be implemented if the controller and the soft-

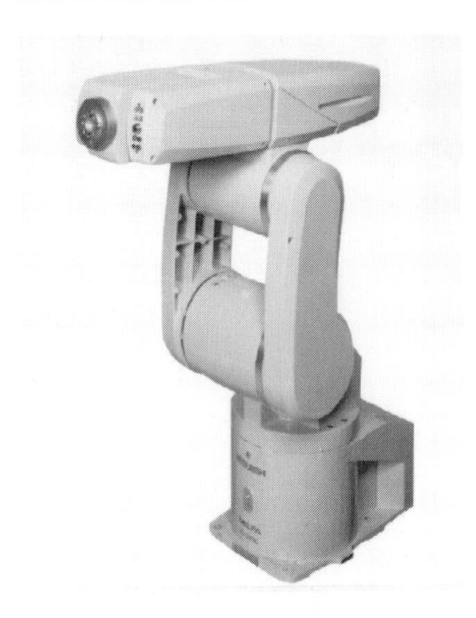

The 6 axis Mitsubishi RV-E4N robot. This small robot can pick up a 4kg load. Note that the gripper (hand) is not considered a standard part of the robot. It will be selected by the user as needed to suit what is to be handled. Note also the connectors for hand sensors, power etc. (Courtesy: Rixan, US distributor for Mitsubishi)

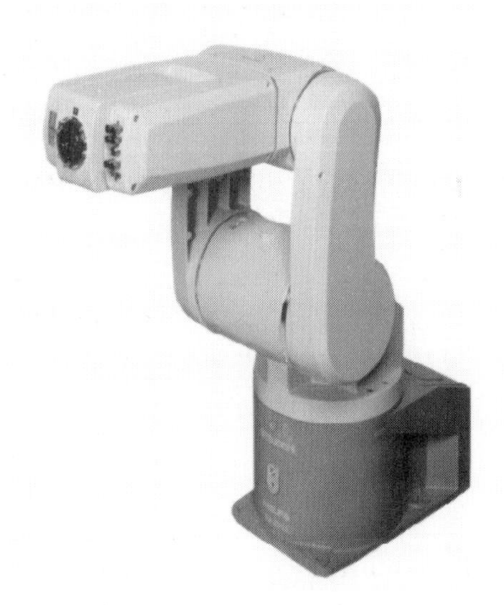

The Mitsubishi RV-E5NJ robot is a slightly lighter, 5 axis version of the RV-E4N robot. These robots are very fast (over 5.5 metres per second). Note: the use of computer aided design (CAD) has made it possible to design and make much smoother-looking robots than used to be the case. Also note the 'arm forward' design. (Courtesy: Rixan, US distributor for Mitsubishi)

ware for the robot have the ability to address these functions.

Almost all grippers fall into the categories:

- Vacuum operated
- Pneumatically operated
- Electrically operated

Vacuum-operated grippers

The simplest of all grippers, these allow the robot to pick up parts that have a flat surface on them. Small delicate parts often need vacuum grippers and they are also used for large sheet stock for the metalworking and woodworking industries.

Pneumatically operated grippers

Pneumatic grippers allow simple open/close control. The fingers can have all sorts of shapes and configurations and they can be supplied as two, three and four finger units. Controlling the pneumatic pressure allows the force of the gripper to be controlled. Parallel motion of the fingers is available as are grippers that hold parts by opening as opposed to closing the fingers.

Electrically operated grippers

The most sophisticated of the grippers, they allow the greatest flexibility of use and require the most complex software. They also need the most maintenance because the more there is, the more there is to go wrong. Feedback, in the form of three force vectors that can be processed to comprehend the forces at the gripper, are sometimes provided on the more sophisticated units. This allows compliance in assembly operations as well as in other operations that are difficult to undertake without some feedback from the task being performed.

Roll, pitch and yaw

Once a gripper has be positioned in space, it has to be given the proper orientation. The orientation is specified by specifying the roll, the pitch and the yaw of the gripper. These three terms are adopted from aircraft terminology and are defined as follows:

- Roll is the rotation along the axis of motion
- Pitch is the up and down motion of the gripper tip as it moves towards its target location
- Yaw is the left-to-right movement of the gripper tip

The human hand has fairly limited motion in these three specifications – about 90 degrees of roll and pitch and about 40 degrees of yaw – but then again the human worker can move around and has a huge brain.

Roll, pitch and yaw each need their own motor.

Software considerations

This cannot be overemphasized:

The most important part of the robot is the software.

Software determines what you can do with the hardware and how you do it. If the hardware needed to perform a function does not exist the function cannot be executed and if the software does not address the hardware provided in an appropriate way, there is not much you can do with the hardware, meaning that if the software does not address the hardware *in the way need for your specific application* you will not be able to use the hardware effectively. In other words the hardware and software must be carefully integrated in any sophisticated system.

Let us consider the example of a printer as a specialized robot. The printer driver in the computer is the software that contains the commands to manipulate the printer. If there is no colour capability in the printer, you cannot print in colour. Equally, if the printer can print in colour but the driver has no colour commands implemented in it you cannot print in colour. As another example, if there is no command to back the paper up into the printer or the paper feed motor cannot be reversed, you cannot back the paper up and print over what has been already been printed. One part of the problem is that there was a time when no-one thought either about printing in colour or about actually backing the paper up in a printer, the other is the fact that these are sophistications that were added as the printer technology matured.

So it has been with robots. Early in the development of the technology the emphasis was on repeatability and the reliability that would allow useful work to be done. Only later could we address the finer points of robotics. Vision is a whole new level of sophistication in robotics. As far as robots are concerned this is a software tool, meaning that we understand that hardware too is needed but that the software overwhelms it to the point that we do not need to discuss the hardware. Truly useful and powerful vision is just beginning to make its appearance as a robotic enhancement.

In vision systems, the systems need such intimate integration that it is not really possible to have a vision system that is not integrated into the robot computer. The problem is that there is not a sufficiently defined language that allows one computer to tell the other what it is seeing in real time, not unlike having to describe what to do in a vision-intensive task to a blind worker – even the English language does not suffice. Under these circumstances it is preferable to hire a sighted worker. So it is with robots. Getting one with an integrated vision system makes it much easier to get the job done (nothing else really works).

Sensors

Sensors that the robot responds to can be located either on the robot itself, on the gripper or in the robot's immediate environment. They tell the robot controller either about the robot itself, its immediate environment or about what is currently in the gripper.

A more detailed discussion of sensors is undertaken in Chapter 7 on input and output. Motor-related sensors are discussed in greater detail in Chapter 6 on motors and encoders.

CHAPTER FOUR

Mobile robots

The mobile robot on today's shop floor is the Automatically Guided Vehicle (AGV). We will look at the operation of AGVs as the basis for understanding the use and operation of mobile robots. AGVs are rudimentary mobile robots and are the only guided vehicles currently doing useful work on the office and shop floor. In this introductory discussion, we will not consider cruise missiles, earth satellite stations or other defence related robots, which are, of course, also very sophisticated mobile robots.

Mobile robots are assumed to have one obvious property – they can move around in their environment without being attached to anything else. What is not quite as obvious is that this places an unprecedented demand for resources in all but the most simple devices. We can look at any transportation vehicle be it a bicycle, a car, an aeroplane or a ship as a mobile robot in which the controlling computer is the human pilot. It is the replacement of this human computer that is difficult to undertake. The human being provides not just the computational power but also the manipulation interface between the instruments and the actuators i.e. the human operator has the ability to not only read the instruments but also to move the appropriate levers and press the appropriate buttons to keep the vehicle operating in the appropriate way. The human operator is both the computer and the servo motor many times over. (On the bicycle man even provides the artificial horizon function that allows balancing to take place.)

The situation is aggravated by the fact that these human computers are so inexpensive that we are using not just one but many of them on

Rocla, Finland. AGV used to transport paper rolls automatically in a factory environment. (Courtesy: Rocla/Mentor, USA)

some vehicles. These computers can communicate with one another and the electronic communication system with relative ease (all over the world, in English!). To do this with digital computers is a major effort. At the present level of technology, we are doing this by drastically reducing the scope of the work done. The AGV is a reduced scope, mobile device.

We are nowhere near having mobile robots with arms running around doing useful work.

Example

The situation can be more easily managed by defining the tasks to be undertaken more specifically. Let us take the example of a group of AGVs in a factory application to learn how these robots as they exist today are used.

Let us assume that the function of this family of AGVs is to transport castings that are being machined, between a vertical machining centre, a horizontal machining centre and a loading/unloading station all located a few metres (or yards) apart in the same manufacturing plant. To simplify the discussion of the operation, let us assume that the AGVs move along a looped path and stop at each of the work stations. If the path was not a loop it would add the complication that the AGVs would somehow have to be returned to the beginning of the line. All other conditions would remain the same. In Figure 4.1 I have shown a loop but I will ignore the turns in our discussions.

Once the mobile robot, the AGV, has been turned on, it is designed to keep moving from station to station in a loop if there is nothing telling it to stop. This makes sure that a machine stops at a point where it is as far down the line as it can be. The movement is always along the prescribed path, be it a guide wire in the floor, a laser beam up high or even dead reckoning for short distances. The AGV keeps moving unless one of the following conditions takes place:

- Some obstruction actuates its proximity sensors
- A machine that it is interacting with inhibits its motion temporarily
- Its work is completed
- A general-purpose safety signal inhibits all motion
- The guide wire (radio, laser, positioning) signal is lost
- It runs out of power away from a charging station

Let us take a look at each of these conditions one at a time to see how they function.

Some obstruction actuates its proximity sensors

Bumpers, proximity sensors and receivers are provided on AGVs to allow them to be shut down if an obstruction blocks their path. This is by and large a safety requirement but also serves in areas where the machines have backed up one behind the other. Usually all the stop signals are sorted by priority and severity and the appropriate action is taken. On-board intelligence determines what needs to be done for each condition because when on the move, the machine cannot be connected to anything and radio communications are not considered desirable.

A machine that it is interacting with inhibits its motion temporarily

When the AGV arrives at a work station, the machine that it is serving takes over its control. It inhibits the movement of the AGV while it loads and unloads it. The inhibiting signal can be as simple as an actuator i.e. a part of the docking mechanism that turns the ability of the AGV to move off. As long as the machine is docked with the AGV, there is no reason for the

AGV to move. When the work is completed, the docking mechanism releases the AGV and it is free to move to its next destination.

Its work is completed

At the end of a production cycle when all the work has been completed, we need to turn off the AGVs since there is no reason for them to continue circling from machine to machine with no work to be done. A signal to indicate this condition is provided to the AGV and it shuts off after docking to a charging station. If a home station has been designated, the AGV will keep moving until it gets to its designated home station. Automation and programmability allow for the implementation of sophisticated features like these.

A general-purpose safety signal inhibits all motion

All systems need a general-purpose shut down signal as there are times when every machine needs to be shut down. To the human work population, the 5.00pm siren is such a signal. Everyone is directed to stop work and go home

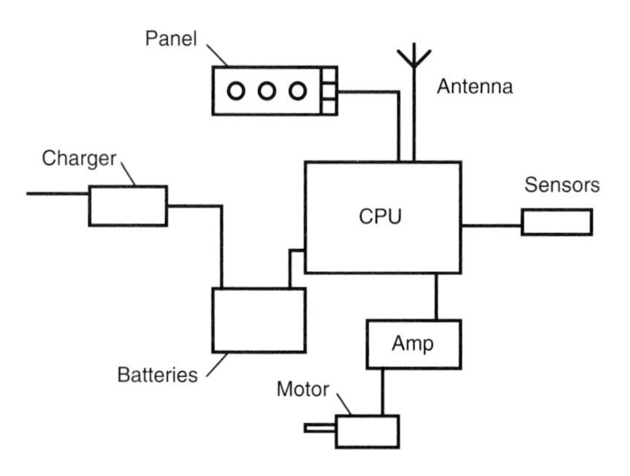

Figure 4.1 Block diagram of major AGV components.

in an orderly manner. Automated systems need similar signals for similar implementations. There is usually also a manual equivalent of this at each machine. If this switch is actuated, the machine becomes dormant.

The guide wire (radio, laser, positioning) signal is lost

If the guiding signal get turned off for any of a number or reasons, it will not be possible for the AGVs to perform their work properly. It is better to shut them down where they are as opposed to letting them to bump their way around the factory. There are a number of situations like the failure of the guide signals that indicate that the systems should be shut down immediately. These signals are prioritized and handled appropriately.

It runs out of power away from a charging station

This is one of those conditions that we can usually predict because batteries run down slowly and predictably. Hopefully this will never happen but in an automated system, every possibility has to be addressed in a logically complete way and resolved. We have to take all possibilities into account. The best solution is to remove the AGV from the system and make repairs before the machine goes down completely. If a low-voltage situation occurs on the AGV, a detection system built into the controls routes the AGV out of the chain immediately, automatically or has the computers summon an operator to do so. Each comprehensive system provides a station where all the AGVs can be routed when out of service and for maintenance purposes. There is no way to address the possibility of sudden power loss caused by a blown fuse or other such occurrence and such

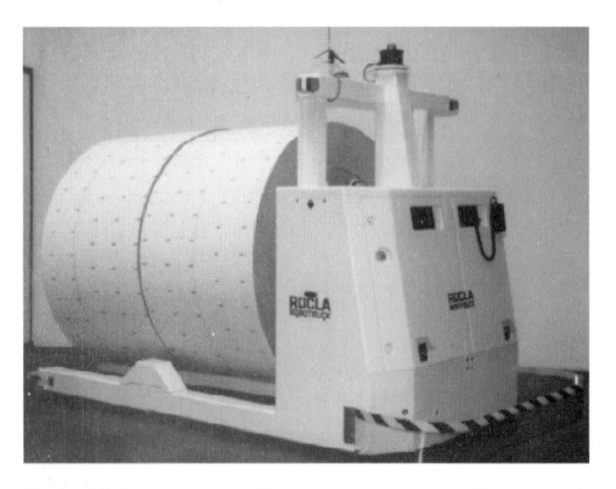

Rocla, Finland. AGV used to transport paper rolls automatically in a factory environment. Note the hand-held pendant on right front for controlling the AGV manually. (Courtesy: Rocla/ Mentor, USA)

situations are best avoided with proper maintenance.

Computer interfacing

In automated machines, the rule of thumb is that each and every signal is first read by a computer and every output is then actuated by the computer. There are no exceptions to this rule except for some power system connections that have to be made active before the computers themselves can be turned on. Shut down is handled by the computers with a parallel manual shut down provided for emergency conditions. This means that even if a simple switch is to turn on a minor light, the switch is first read by the computer and the computer then turns on the light. Doing it this way allows all interlocks to be programmable which makes them easy to change and to tie into. Anything that is hard wired cannot be changed without changing the wiring and so is to be avoided. On shut down there is a parallel manual shut down to make sure that the system will be shut down even if the computer logic has broken down. Normally the computer is operational and handles the shut down in an orderly fashion and the manual system is for back-up purposes only.

Loading and unloading pallets

The basic AGV is a wheeled vehicle with a pallet platform that holds two pallets. The pallet platform can be rotated 180 degrees to allow either pallet to be positioned at either location. As we will see, this scheme allows the pallets to be loaded and unloaded with greater ease.

At each work station the finished work on the pallet in the processing machine is unloaded onto the AGV, and a pallet with work to be done is loaded onto the processing machine. After this, at the processing machine, work is performed on the workpieces on the pallet just received and the AGV takes the finished work to the next station.

Parts that are to be machined are mounted on very accurately machined, identical pallets. The transfer machinery on the Computer Numerically Controlled (CNC) units and on the

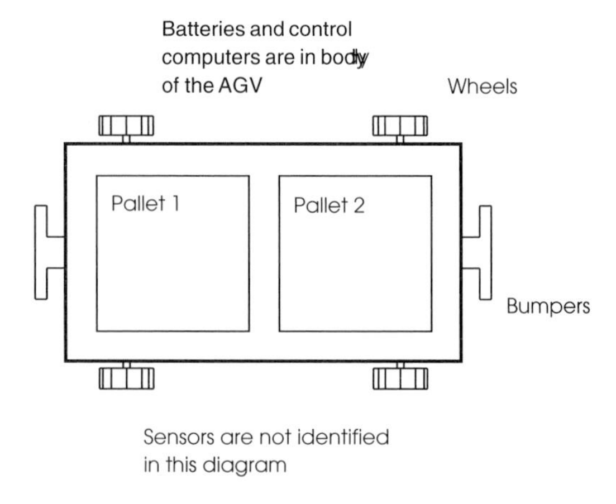

Figure 4.2 A simplified diagram of an AGV for serving machining centres.

AGVs handles these pallets only. The load/unload machinery has no way of knowing what might be mounted on the pallets and the system is designed so that it does not make any difference to the load/unload process. Since the pallets do not change, the system is easier to design and maintain if it is done in this way. The machining centres machine whatever happens to be on the pallets, be it one part of a number of parts. The CNC machining is controlled by software and the software is easy to change. The pallets themselves may have the parts loaded onto them automatically or manually depending on the difficulty of automating the process and the value of the cargo. We would not want an extremely valuable jet engine casing, on which many thousands of man hours of work has already been done, to be misaligned and thus ruined during the next machining operation. Robots not withstanding, the judgement of the human operator is still an important ingredient in any complicated process and will continue to be so for the foreseeable future.

Discussion of operations

Let us assume that there are eight AGVs in the system under consideration as shown in Figure 4.3. One AGV is in the process of being loaded/unloaded at the vertical machining centre (VMC), one in the process of being loaded/unloaded at the horizontal machining centre

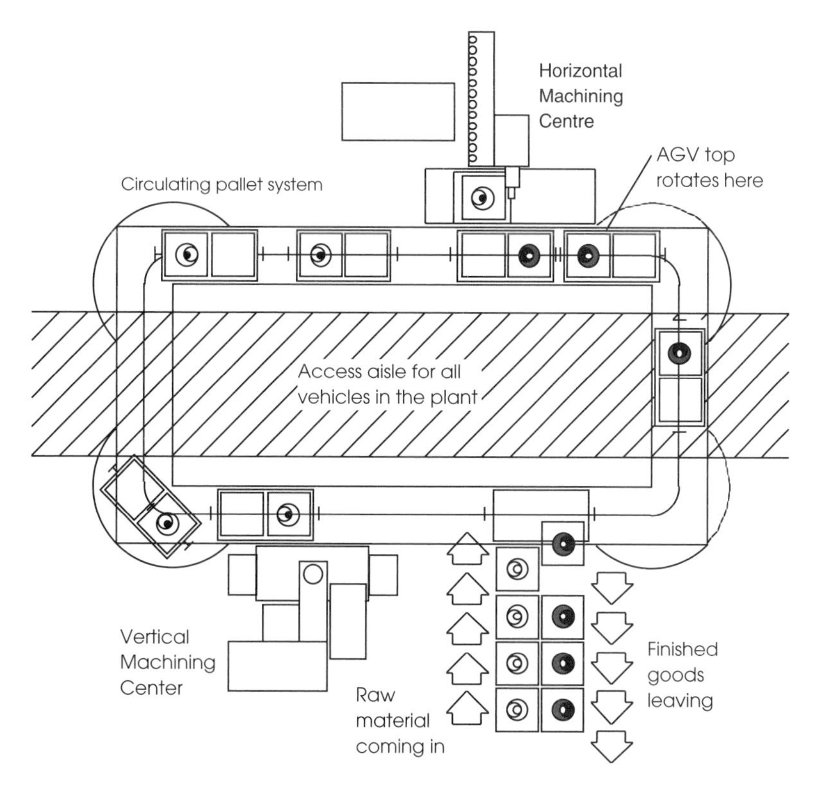

Figure 4.3 Overall schematic layout of a simplified system (clockwise motion). An empty pallet position always leads in the system shown.

(HMC) and one is shown being transferred at the load/unload station at the lower right. These machines are considered to be busy as shown. We need one AGV to be ready to service the VMC and one more ready to service the HMC so that there will be no delays. The three machines that are in the wait stations make sure that there will not be any delays in the process. Two other machines are spares for maintenance and repairs. For our purposes, we will assume that once an AGV leaves one machining centre, it is waiting to be unloaded at the next machining centre. This is a valid assumption in that the short distance between the machines can be traversed in a short time. If not, we would have to add more AGVs so that they could be in transit.

Either the HMC or the VMC will have a shorter cycle time. This will cause the AGVs to collect at the machine with the longer cycle time. We will provide charging stations at the slower machine if they are to be provided at one machine only. For the greatest flexibility, we would provide them at both machines. While the AGV machines are waiting here, their batteries will be charged – docking stations would be provided for this function. The AGVs move from docking station to docking station as they move toward each machining centre and they are charged at each station. Alternatively, the AGVs could be charged at night or they may have battery packs that can be changed at each shift change. The important thing to understand is that there are many levels of automation. It is not an all-or-nothing proposition and even when we think everything is automated, the chances are that it is not.

Note that at the present time there are no factories (to my knowledge) where one button starts the whole process going although we now have the knowhow to create a factory where just one button would start the entire plant running without human intervention – the expense would be too great. There are a number of factories that use very few human operators, and most of these are there to make sure that the robots that do the work stay operational. Plants that make VCR tapes are examples of this. This is a relatively simple, low cost, high volume, high-quality product that is amenable to completely automatic assembly. The human beings at these plants are there to make sure that the robots do not malfunction and to service them but they do not perform any direct manufacturing functions.

At each machining centre we must have a docking system that will hold the pallet such that it can be transferred to the machining centre table. The machining centre will first eject the pallet that it is working on to the finished parts pallet location and then accept the new pallet from the AGV. The AGV moves away once the pallet with the raw material has been removed. It then rotates its top so that the empty position is again leading, ready to accept the next processed part at the next station. Doing this eliminates the need to back an AGV up. Backing up can be a real problem if a group of AGVs has bumped to a stop behind an AGV.

Most AGVs that serve machines have two pallet stations on them – one to hold unfinished parts and one ready to hold finished parts. In the above case the finished pallet from the

A Mentor AGV being used at Kennecott Copper. This AGV was initially designed to be wire guided but has now been converted to guidance by laser. (Courtesy: Mentor, USA)

machining centre would be moved to the finished parts station and then the unfinished parts pallet would be loaded into the machining centre. This scheme also has the advantage that empty pallets do not have to be moved back to the loading station via a separate system.

When an AGV has to move from station to station, it follows a specified path which is a line on the floor, a wire buried in the floor or a laser beam that is beamed down the aisle, high above obstructions. The most common system today is the wire buried in the floor. Most manufacturers are moving towards beam guided and radio positioned systems because these are easier to work with than a buried system.

Buried wire systems have the guide wire buried a few inches into the floor. The wire emits a signal at a frequency that the AGV can detect. Various schemes that allow the vehicle to stay centred on the wire are employed. Other emitters along the path, sensors on the AGV and even mechanical guides allow the AGV to make turns at the appropriate locations.

Sensors on the AGV itself allow the machine to detect obstructions that may be placed in its path. These include collision detectors or bumpers on the vehicle itself and signals that come from the environment. If the path of the AGV crosses aisles that are to be used by other machines or human beings, it becomes necessary to provide a way for the two systems to operate in the same space without interfering with one another. If there is another vehicle in the AGV space, the AGV is inhibited. If an AGV is in the aisle, some signal is provided to other vehicles so they will not enter the space. This can be done with something as simple as a red light or by lowering a barrier across the aisle depending on the degree of safety desired.

When the AGV arrives at a docking station, a sequence similar to the following takes place.

The AGV has to determine that the target docking station is not occupied by another machine before it can enter the docking area. The receiving machine provides a signal that indicates that it is ready to receive the AGV when the previous AGV has moved out of the way and the machine itself has finished machining the part(s) it is working on. This signal is active whenever the machine is able to accept a new AGV. If the signal is not present the AGV waits, out of the way, until it is. The system is designed to guarantee that if the signal is present, the docking station is empty, and it is designed to be fail safe.

A Mentor AGV capable of carrying a 30,000kg (60,000lb) pallet in use at Boeing Aircraft in Auburn, Washington, USA. (Courtesy: Mentor, USA)

Once in the docking station, the system locks the two machines together and transfers the finished part pallet to the empty pallet station on the AGV. This empties the machining centre. The AGV is then moved forward (or the machine table is moved back) to present the unmachined part pallet and the machines lock together again. The unmachined part pallet is then transferred to the milling machine. Once the transfer is complete, the AGV is released.

As soon as the AGV clears the machine work area and is in an open space (allocated for this purpose) it rotates the top to make sure that the empty pallet station is in front. This makes the AGV ready to accept the next processed part at the next machining station.

How do machines know when to interact with each other?

Simple handshaking. When I hand you a cup of tea a lot of handshaking takes place between us to make sure that the tea does not get spilt during the transfer. Some of it is done with words, some of it is with gestures and some of it is with our eyes, but it is all some sort of handshaking (communication). There might even be some dead reckoning and this is where the tea is likely to get spilled if a mistake is made. Dead reckoning is always to be avoided.

Pallet transfer between machines takes place in a similar way. Let us go over it one step at a time to see how it is done.

Let us assume that we start with a machining centre ready to receive an AGV with a part on a pallet, ready to be machined.

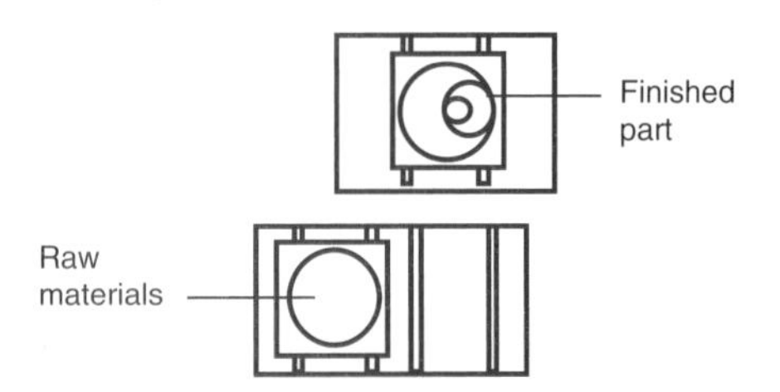

Figure 4.4 An AGV arrives at the machining centre and is ready to be pulled into the docking position.

The AGV arrives at the machining centre and signals the machine that it is ready to be pulled in. The milling machine pulls the AGV in and locks it into position.

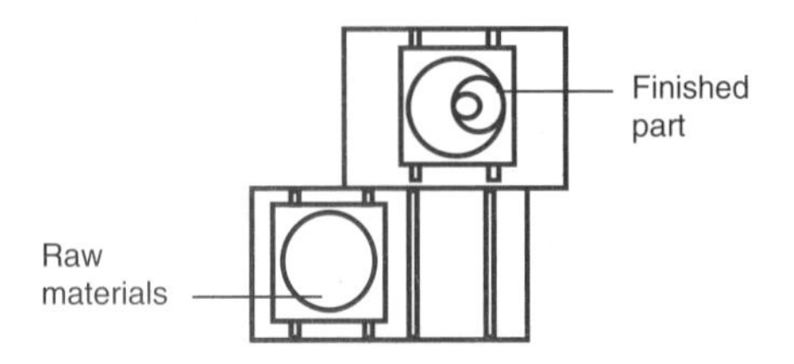

Figure 4.5 The AGV is pulled into the locking position. The ways on the table and the AGV line up ready to transfer the machined parts and pallet to the AGV.

Proper alignment and locking are confirmed with appropriate sensors and the pallet is moved onto the locked in AGV.

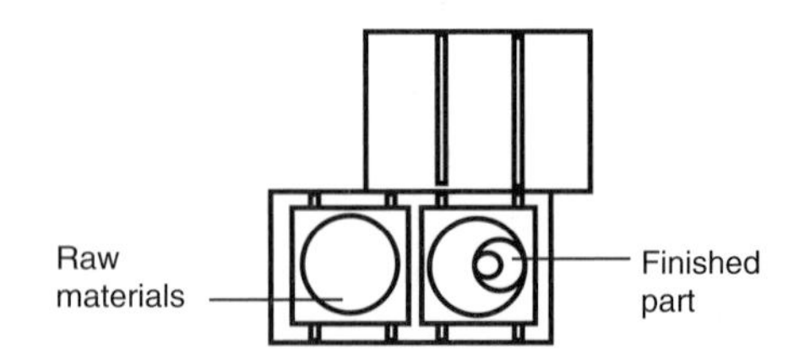

Figure 4.6 The machined pallet is pushed onto the AGV. The machining centre is now empty and ready for a new pallet to be pushed onto it.

The AGV is released and the system moves it forward (or the machine table back) to align the raw materials pallet with the ways on the machining centre. Once aligned the AGV again signals the milling machine that it is ready to be pulled in.

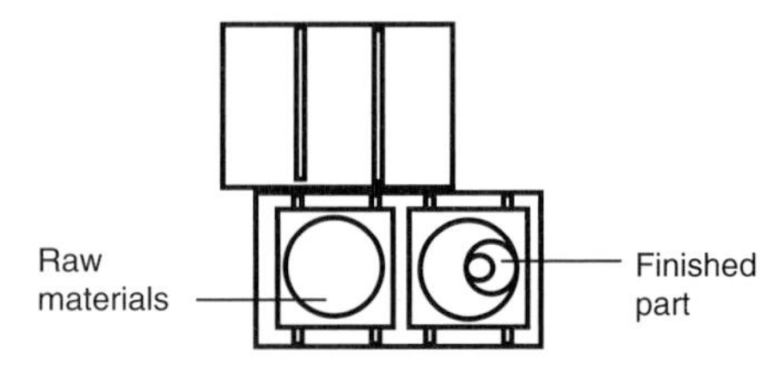

Figure 4.7 The AGV is repositioned and pulled in to allow the raw materials on the fresh pallet to be transferred to the machining centre.

The fresh pallet is pushed over onto the machining centre and the machining centre is signalled that the pallet has been pushed over all the way.

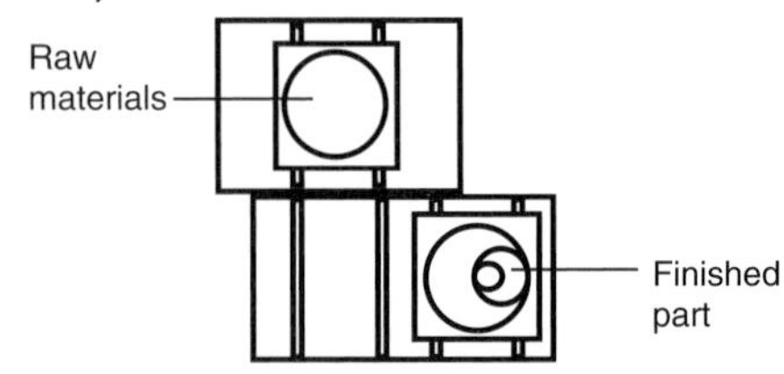

Figure 4.8 The unmachined parts and the pallet on which they are on are pushed into position on the machining centre. the pallet is locked on the machining centre.

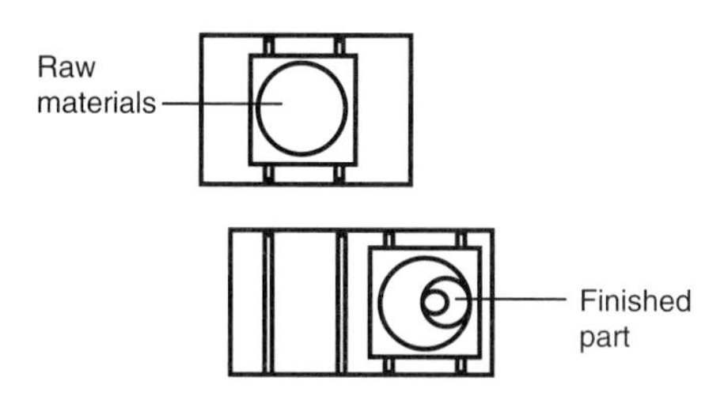

Figure 4.9 The AGV is pushed away from the milling machine and can move on to the next machining station. Machining starts.

The machining centre releases the AGV.

The AGV moves away from the milling machine.

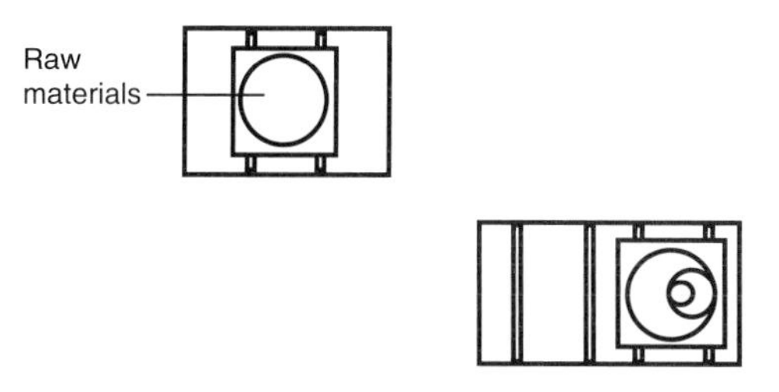

Figure 4.10 The AGV moves away from the milling machine table. Machining is in progress at the milling machine.

After clearing the milling machine the top of the AGV is rotated so that an empty station is in the leading position.

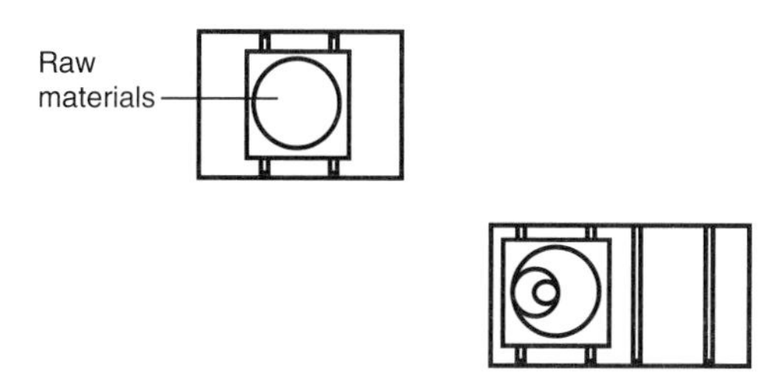

Figure 4.11 The AGV top is rotated to present an empty pallet station to the next machining station ready to receive the finished parts. The complete sequence is ready to be repeated.

The logic that controls a mobile machine can be resident on the machine or at a remote location. If the intelligence is at a remote location, two-way radio communications have to be maintained between the machine and the computer. If there are a lot of machines, this becomes difficult because a lot of radio channels are required and reliability is compromised. The preferred system is an on-board system and the preferred situation is to have the vehicle completely independent of external intelligence. It responds to signals in its environment without requiring any interpretation from an outside source (not unlike a human being). If something gets in the way of the vehicle, the vehicle stops and waits until the obstruction is removed. If the obstruction is not removed within an acceptable time, it may initiate an alarm to the supervisory system or even to a human operator.

Providing autonomy makes the system safer as well as easier to maintain. If each AGV is independent, replacing a defective unit is just a matter of removing it. The system takes up the slack automatically. When the repaired unit is put back into operation, the system responds to the addition without operator intervention.

When an AGV arrives at its destination, the first thing the receiving station does is determine if there is actually a part on the pallet that it is about to receive and confirms that it is the correct part. A system similar to a barcode system can provide this information. If either of these conditions is not met, the pallet is not unloaded from the AGV, the AGV moves away and the next AGV moves into position. Here again the idea is that no matter what else is happening anywhere else in the plant, it should have nothing to do with what this particular work station and AGV are doing. Keeping it compartmentalized and as simple as possible (in a fairly complicated system) is the goal. The ability to select pallets according to their cargo allows the system to serve a number of machines with the same AGV system in a situation where all the machines do not have to work on each part being moved through the system. This is the basis for Flexible Manufacturing System (FMS) technology. In an FMS system, any machine can perform its processes on any pallet from any AGV at any time without creating a problem.

All the fixed machines have the ability to communicate with the central computer. Whenever a machine starts working on a part, finishes a part or rejects a part etc., it informs the central computer of its actions. This information goes into an active database that can be interrogated by all systems and humans who need to know. This includes human operators who are interested only in the status of the factory at all times. This allows them to see what is going on at all points in the plant at all times in real time. Information read from the AGVs is also transmitted to the central computer at each docking station. This allows AGVs to communicate with the main computers. The information received and sent is in bursts as is necessitated by the mobile, stop and go nature of the operations but this is adequate.

An AGV arrives at a location approximately, meaning that it is approximately in position when the arrival signal is actuated. Fixed base arms then pull the AGV into the exact position at the docking mechanism using pins and aligning fixtures. Both mechanical and electronic docking takes place. Pneumatic and hydraulic lines may also be connected. Other sensors determine that the docking took place perfectly as was expected. If swarf or something else gets in the way, the docking will not be right and the pallet transfer will not take place properly. This is detected at the docking and the appropriate actions are taken.

Discussion of identification systems

Let us take a close look at exactly how the identification system works as an AGV moves from one station to the next. The operation at each station is identical so that once we understand the operation at one station we will be able to understand the operation at all of them.

On each pallet there are two identifications – the ID of the pallet and the ID of the part or parts mounted on the pallet. The design assumption is that any AGV can be removed from or added to the system at any time and that it will not disrupt the system. This is necessary because we do not know when an AGV might break down. Once a unit breaks down, the most expedient thing to do is to simply get it out of the process. Once it has been repaired we want to be able to add it back into the process at the most convenient location. The system is designed to undertake these activities without problems. Having identifications of the pallets and workpieces lets the various systems anticipate the arrival of components and to take corrective actions when there are unexpected arrivals. This also allows the system to inform the main computers about what is going on so that they can send the information to relevant locations to allow corrective measures to be undertaken.

Having an adequate identification system also allows all processing machines to be fed from the same AGV line as discussed above. Those pallets that do not have the right parts on them are simply passed onto the next section. They will be processed when they get to the proper processing machine. Having just one line feeding all the machines allows any machine to pass a pallet to any other machine completely automatically and this can be done in any sequence.

CHAPTER FIVE

Running motors

A robot is an electro-mechanical contrivance that can be looked upon as a set of linkages, chains, castings and gears connected to a number of servo motors and a computer. Since it is the computerized control of these motors that makes the operation of the robot what it is, understanding how these motors are controlled is the key to understanding how robots actually work.

The motors used to control robots are called servo motors. Servo has its root in the Latin *servus* for slave. The concept is that the motor does what it is told to do by (i.e. is a slave to) a changing signal called an error signal. In more formal terms, the motor responds to a continually changing error signal by trying to make the error signal disappear or be made zero. Whatever the motor is connected to affects the magnitude of the error signal and the motor is made to work or move in the direction that will reduce the error signal. Some external (to the motor load) device is also able to manipulate the error signal over a period of time. Since the motor is designed to follow the signal we can make the motor do useful work by programming the error signal.

This gives us the ability to more than just start and stop the motor. We can now tell the motor exactly when to start, how fast to speed up, how fast to run, how long to run, how to slow down and exactly when and where to stop. We can tell the motor to repeat the cycle as often as we like, we can have it cycle just once and we can modify the cycle at will while the cycle is in progress. This allows us to make the operation of the motor dependent on any condition within the controlling computer or on any signal that can be read by the computer.

Both alternating current (AC) and direct current (DC) motors can be used as servo motors and both can be controlled with high precision with the technology now available. Hydraulic systems and pneumatic systems can also be made into servo systems. As a matter of fact any power source that can be properly modulated (i.e. have its power varied) can be turned into a servo system. Any force that can be controlled by a smaller force can be used as a motor.

I will consider only permanent magnet, direct current (PMDC) motors in this introductory text. Both permanent magnet and wound field motors can be used in robots and the control of either is essentially similar. AC motors require more complicated techniques to control them. These are necessitated by the alternating current nature of the power that they use and there is no great learning benefit in discussing how they are controlled at this stage of our understanding. AC motors have the major advantage of not having brushes (that arc, pit and wear out) to maintain and AC has the advantage that its power (the voltage) is easily transformed with a transformer.

Piezo-electric motor development is still in its infancy and will not be discussed either. Piezo-electric materials change their size when an electric field is placed across them. The displacements realised are small but very strong forces are created. Special techniques are needed to turn these small expansions and contractions into useful motion. Piezo-electric motors have an advantage when relatively small (and very fast), very strong motions are needed. As the technology develops, piezo-electric motors will have an important place in robotics. New research in this technology is aimed at increasing the displacements that these materials exhibit when excited. This will make these materials easier to use in motors.

At the present level of technological development, electric motors are put into motion by creating opposing and attracting magnetic fields. This is the only method of driving electric motors that is of interest to us in the context of robotics. The magnetic fields are manipulated sequentially to rotate a shaft attached to the

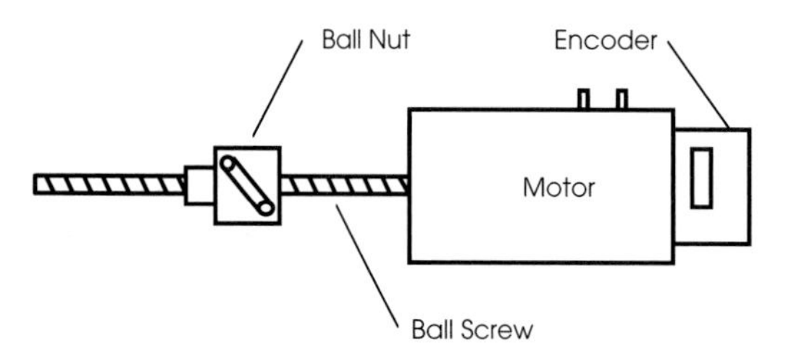

Figure 5.1 The components of a typical servo motor installation. Gearboxes are usually avoided to eliminate backlash problems.

rotating armature. Since at least one of the magnetic fields is created by passing an electric current through a winding, and we are proficient at controlling electricity, we can control the operation of the motor by controlling the electricity going through its windings.

The following motor designs are suitable for use in robots.

Rotating servo motors

These are usually DC motors with some form of position encoder attached to the motor shaft, usually an incremental optical encoder, to serve as a feedback signal to give us the position and speed of the motor. Having this feedback allows us to vary the power to the motor and to stop the motor when it has moved to its desired destination.

Linear servo motors

These motors use the same technology as the rotating motors except that in these motors the armatures and fields are arranged in a straight line as opposed to being in a circle. Imagine cutting a regular motor along a radial plane, opening it up and laying it flat on the table. The field, the armature and the commutator are all in straight lines now and the motor armature moves across the field in a straight line. (Appropriate physical constraints and guides have to be added to allow this to take place properly.)

Stepper motors

Stepper motors move a small segment of a circle each time the current feeding arrangement to the motor is changed. There are a number of independent windings in the motor and there is usually a sequence of four electrical changes –

the motor moves a step during each change. You can also have half steps and micro steps which are created electronically. Stepper motors usually move between 0.9 and 15 degrees in each step and they do not usually use feedback encoders because we can count how many steps the motor has moved as we send it the steps. The problem is that if the motor gets overloaded, it can slip and the count is then compromised. Stepper motors usually have low speed and low torque characteristics and at certain (relative low) speeds their mechanical-electrical harmonic characteristics can cause them to become unstable. By and large stepper motors have been replaced with servo motors for robotic applications. Their main use is in office machines and other low power applications.

When a motor is running we have an interest in how fast it is running and how far it has moved. To get this information we have to attach something to the motor shaft that will relay rotational information to us. There are a number of ways to do this and the most common among them are as follows.

Incremental optical encoders

Incremental encoders provide signals that a computer can count as they rotate. The signal consists of two square waves that are 90 degrees out of phase with one another. An index signal is provided on some encoders to allow positioning at a specific location with a rotation.

Absolute encoders

Absolute encoders provide a way of determining the position of a shaft, within a 360-degree envelope. They use a number of encoded rings placed in a common centre.

Potentiometers

A potentiometer mounted to the axis of motion can be read to provide an analogue equivalent of the position of the axis. This information is then compared to a desired value and the motor motion is adjusted accordingly.

Synchros and resolvers

Synchros and resolvers use coils mounted to the shaft and the body of the motor to determine the position of the two with respect to one another. One coil is excited and the degree of excitation in the other coil is measured. The excitation tells us how the two coils are positioned with respect to each other. The information then has to be converted to digital information so that a computer can read it. All this is too cumbersome and optical encoders have become the positioning devices of choice.

Encoders and potentiometers are also made as linear models for measuring straight line motion. These devices are discussed in greater detail in Chapter 6.

Model aircraft type servo motors

Radio controlled model aircraft use tiny servo motors that are positioned by converting the length of the pulse fed to them into the position of the output shaft of the servo. These servo motors consist of motor, a gearbox, a potentiometer and a small integrated circuit. The integrated circuit converts the length of the incoming pulse to a desired output shaft position as represented by the shaft-mounted potentiometer. If the position of the potentiometer does not match the desired shaft position, the motor is turned either forwards of backwards until the potentiometer reaches the desired

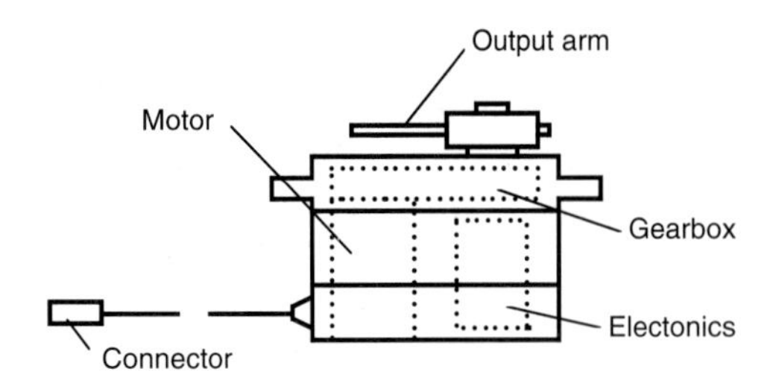

Figure 5.2 A model R/C servo motor.

position. The current to the motor is then turned off. The situation is monitored constantly so that the correction is taking place at all times.

The positioning accuracy achieved depends on the accuracy of the potentiometer and the accuracy of the length of pulse received. A resolution of about one half of a degree can be achieved with most model aircraft servos.

It takes only three wires to run these servo motors – the power line, the pulse signal line and a common ground. These are the servo motors we will use to power the robot that we will discuss making in the second part of this book.

Since model aircraft servo motors operate on the principle of converting a known pulse width to a motor output shaft position, these motors are relatively easy to use if a source that can generate pulses of short duration can be created. This can be done quite easily with the small single chip microcomputers now on the market. A pulse width of between 0.001 seconds (1ms) and 0.002 seconds (2ms) determines the position of the output shaft. A pulse of 0.001ms moves the shaft to one end of its travel and a pulse of 2 ms moves it to the other end. The pulses have to be repeated about 60 times a second.

Varying the motor speed

The next concept that we need to understand is that of running motors at varying speeds on command. Once we understand the concept of variable speed we will understand that a motor can be slowed down as it nears an intended destination and stopped when it gets to where it is supposed to be. If it overshoots, we can even reverse the motor and come back to where we have to be although, of course, it is better not to overshoot.

In order for the motor move to be predictable it is made to follow a trapezoidal profile. In this mode of operation, the motor accelerates at a fixed rate until it reaches its operational velocity. It then runs at that velocity for as long as needed and then decelerates at a fixed rate until it stops. The computer calculates the energy needed by the motor to do the work in the time that it needs to be done. All motors that are to be operated in synchronization with another motor have to accelerate and decelerate for the same length of time as the lead motor to keep their encoder counts in sync.

For very short moves there is no constant speed operation. The motor accelerates and then de-accelerates and stops – it never gets up to the running speed. This move profile is referred to as a triangular move (as compared to the trapezoidal move above).

It is also to be appreciated that it is very hard to run a motor at a very slow speed. Imagine trying to run a motor at one revolution a day (gears not allowed). If we wanted to adjust the speed every second we would need $24 \times 60 \times 60 =$ 86,400 encoder counts per revolution just to get one count per second (so we have a signal to read) and we probably need 1,000 times that for really smooth motion. It would depend on what we thought was smooth enough because a jerky move every second is not very smooth. So let us assume that we have an encoder that gives us just the minimal 86,400,000 counts for now. If we also wanted to be able to run this motor at 3,000 revolutions per minute at its top speed, we will have to count encoder counts for 3,000/60 times 86,400,000 or 4,320,000,000 counts per second.

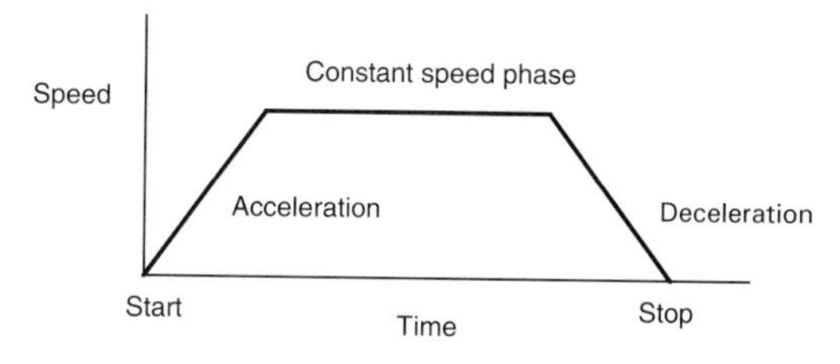

Figure 5.3 A trapezoidal motor move.

Although not impossible, this causes problems. Minimum speed, maximum speed and encoder counts are interrelated.

Although we are used to thinking of AC motors as being relatively fixed speed motors, both AC and DC motors can be run at varying speeds and be reversed. Again to simplify our discussion we will discuss DC motors only.

As mentioned earlier, the speed of a DC motor is dependent on the energy that is provided to the motor and on the load on the motor. The more energy that we provide to the motor, the faster it will run and the lower the load, the faster it will run. As the motor armature spins within the magnet field of the field magnets, it acts as a generator and generates a back voltage referred to as a back Electro Motive Force (EMF). This voltage counteracts the voltage being applied to the motor. The final speed attained by the motor is determined by the back EMF generated by the armature as it spins in the field, the forward voltage applied to the motor terminals and the load on the motor. When the back EMF matches the forward EMF at the terminals minus the effect of the load on the motor, the motor can go no faster.

There are two ways of varying the energy to a DC motor. We can vary either the voltage or the current applied to the motor and there are a number of ways of doing this.

Analogue techniques depend on changing the voltage across the motor leads to control the speed of the motor. We will not discuss analogue techniques here because high performance servo motors controlled by computers now use the digital techniques that we are interested in.

Digital techniques use a power supply with a fixed voltage and then turn the voltage off for a part of the time to vary the speed of the motor. This is done thousands of times a second, usually between 15,000 and 40,000 times a second.

When we use a motor in a servo application, we are interested in defining a full speed for the motor that uses less than all the energy that the motor can effectively use. For example if we want to run a device at 100 rpm and we have geared the motor to the device with a 20:1 ratio, the full speed of the motor will need to be 2,000 rpm to achieve the speed we want. It is desirable that this full speed be attained when the motor is being given less than about 25% of the energy that it can readily accept (without overheating or having other operational problems). The rest of the energy is to be applied when there is a load on the device. So under normal 'no load' conditions, we could move the device at up to 100 rpm by applying just 25% of the energy possible to the motor. In our 'on/off' method of control, the power would be on 25% of the time and off the other 75% of the time for no-load, full-speed operation. This would give us the reserve power we need to meet the load demands of the application. A 25% duty cycle is not a magic number, the number picked would depend on the loads the device was being designed for. The concept we need to understand is that there needs to be plenty of reserve power available to allow the system to be fully compliant. A compliant system is one that can do what we tell it to do without running out on any of its performance parameters.

You may already know that most of the logic components in a computer work at below 5 volts and at a very low amperage (a few milliamps or microamps). The signals that the computer provides have to be magnified considerably if they are to drive a motor of any size at all. The tiniest hobby motors can be turned on with a simple single transistor controlled from one of these low power 5 volt signals. These are called Transistor-

Transistor Logic (TTL) signals. Anything beyond that needs a more sophisticated amplifier. In commercial application, even small motors used in office machines are controlled by amplifiers more complicated than a single transistor.

As the need for power increases, the size of the transistor increases. A large transistor is essentially a lot of small transistors in parallel. It is of course a lot more complicated than that but that is one way that we can think about it. In fact you can control a larger current by putting 8 or 10 small transistors in parallel with one another. This is tolerable under a hobby situation but would not do for a commercial application. In commercial application, special transistor arrays with safety features added and designed specially for controlling motors are used.

By 40,000 cycles a second we mean that the motor has to be turned off and then turned back on 40,000 times a second. Although this is fairly easy to do for low power applications, as the power goes up, it becomes harder and harder to do this. The problem has to do with the difficulty of shutting a large current device off abruptly. Like in other systems, once something starts to flow, it does not want to be turned off suddenly – there is always some trailing current to cause problems. Leakages cannot be tolerated because all leakages contribute to a shorting effect (see Chapter 6 on encoders and amplifiers).

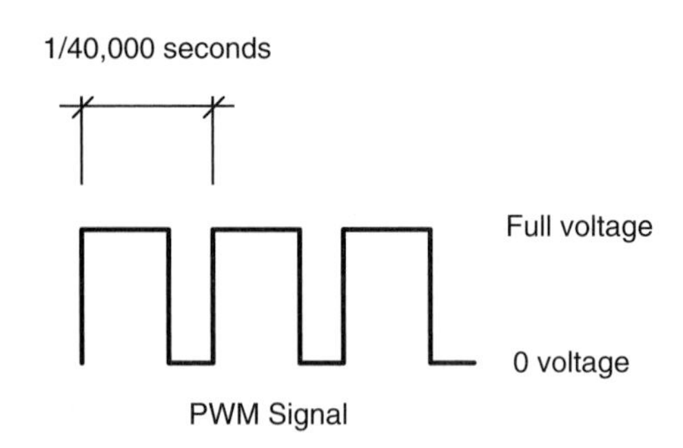

Figure 5.4 Power applied to the motor.

We need three basic inputs to control a motor amplifier.

(1) A signal to enable to the amplifier.
(2) A signal to select direction of motion (forward or backward).
(3) A signal to determine the percentage of full power applied i.e. the pulse width.

Being able to enable a motor amplifier is important to allowing us to guarantee that the amplifier will remain turned off until the computer has come up to a stable condition and is ready to control the motor properly. This is specially important when an amplifier is connected to a robot motor because we must guarantee that the motor does not move until we are absolutely ready for it to move if no damage is to be done. This is achieved by designing the electronics to be fail safe and tying other signals to ground potential until they are ready to be released.

CHAPTER SIX

Encoders and amplifiers

The two ancillary pieces of equipment needed to run a motor with a computer are optical encoders and power amplifiers. Encoders tell us what a motor is doing as regards its rate of motion and the overall revolutions turned, and amplifiers allow us to control the motor itself by controlling the energy supplied to the motor. By combining these two with the speed of a digital computer we can control a motor with precision.

A simple encoding scheme

A simple way to gather positional information would be to connect an arm to a motor in a way that would allow us to count how many times the driving motor had turned to move the arm to any position. Suppose the arm was geared to the motor in such a way that it took 720 turns of the motor to turn the arm through 360 degrees. Then if we knew that the motor had turned 156 turns from a repeatable starting position we would know that the arm was 78 degrees from the starting position. For every revolution that the motor moved, the arm would move half a degree. Since it is relatively easy for a computer to count how often a signal goes on and off in a given time, and it is fairly easy to connect the motor to a signal generator that goes on and off once every revolution, we can read the arm position with the accuracy we want with our computer. Encoders work in a similar but much more sophisticated way.

Encoders

An encoder is any device that encodes or transforms a signal or piece of information in such a way that we can read it with the instrument we intend to use. In our particular case we are interested in transforming the motor rotation into signals that we can read with a computer.

The encoders used with robot motors are usually optical encoders. This means that they use some sort of an optical signal system to provide the information we need. If a computer is going to read a signal it usually means that it is a signal that goes on and off in some fashion with respect to time. Signals that go on and off and have no other states are called digital signals. They may have only two states: on and off, zero and one. The information is in the timing and, of course, there are often millions of zeros and ones that have to be read and sorted out. Since modern computers run at over 100,000,000 Hz (cycles per second) they can sort out very sophisticated signals and analyse complicated signal patterns. (For comparison purposes, the upper or high frequency end of the radio spectrum on the AM radio band is at only 1,400,000 Hz.)

Usually the position of a motor shaft needs to be known with great accuracy to allow accurate positioning. Angular positions often need to be known to within 0.001 degrees for the positioning accuracies needed of today's robot arms. These accuracies can be obtained by providing the motors that drive these arms with devices that divide the position of the motor into thousands of counts per revolution. This is done with optical encoders that divide a circle into over 1,000 divisions. Such an encoder would allow the computer to position the motor within 1/1000 of a revolution. When this is combined with the gearing to the arm, the accuracies needed can be achieved. Backlash in the gearing can be eliminated by using harmonic drives, high precision gearboxes and ball screws.

Optical encoders are made as both incremental and absolute encoders. Let us discuss these one at a time.

Incremental optical encoders

Incremental encoders provide two signals that are 90 degrees out of phase with one another. Each signal is assumed to go on and off for equal amounts of time during each cycle as shown below. The convention states that one complete on and off signal cycle represents a 360-degree rotation.

The second signal is 90 degrees out of phase with the first signal. This is shown schematically in Figure 6.2.

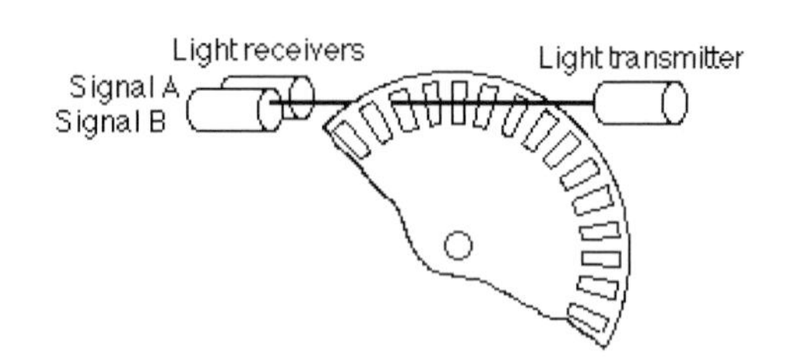

Figure 6.1 Optical encoder construction. Signals A and B will be 90 degrees out of phase. One signal is shown on and one is shown off in this drawing. See also following figures.

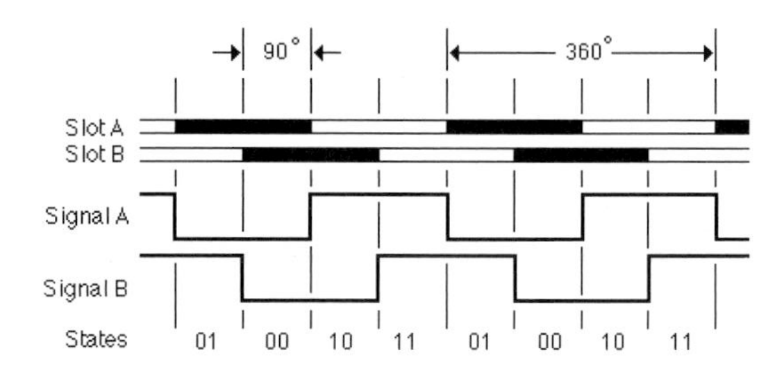

Figure 6.2 Incremental optical encoder signals. Signals are 90 degrees out of phase with one another.

When a motor moves in one direction, one signal leads and when the motor moves in the other direction, the other signal leads. This phenomenon can be recognized by a computer and the information is used by the computer to determine the direction of motion of the motor. An incremental encoder allows the computer to know the travelled position of the motor at all times (i.e. even when many revolutions have been traversed).

Incremental encoders provide signals as long as the motor is moving. These signals are counted to determine the position of the motor. The counting process has to start at a known position if the positional information is to be accurate.

Devices using incremental encoders have to be 'homed' to a known position before one starts counting the encoder counts. Some encoders are provided with a third channel that is used as an index channel which allows the motor to be positioned at a known home position within its circle of rotation upon start up. Coarse positioning is usually provided by a microswitch or an optical flag and the index pulse provides the final position.

Speed is determined by taking two encoder counts a known time apart and then dividing the difference in the counts by the time.

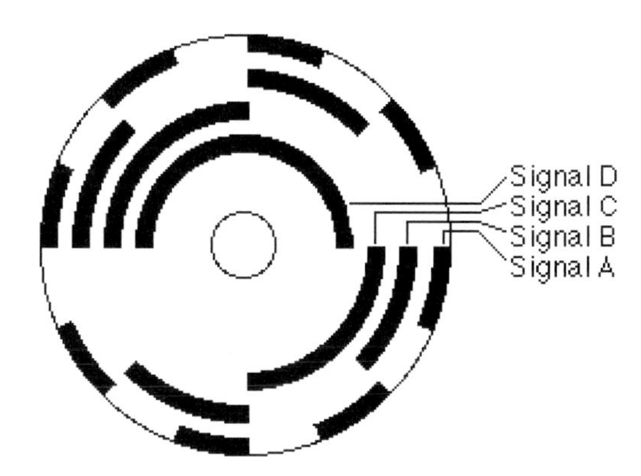

Figure 6.3 Absolute encoder disk. Only 4 signals are shown in this disk. These would give 16 divisions of a circle.

Absolute encoders

Absolute encoders give the position of the axis that they are connected to within one revolution. As such absolute encoders usually are attached not to the motor but to the arm joint of the robot. They have the advantage of providing the arm position at all times without having to be reset to a known position as has to be done with incremental encoders.

Absolute encoders provide a way of determining the position of a shaft, within a 360-degree envelope. They use a number of encoded rings placed in a common centre. Each ring is divided into alternate dark and light segments to provide a binary signal. The rings each have twice as many segments as the previous ring to provide finer and finer positional information as you move away from the centre. All the rings have to be read simultaneously to make sure that the information does not change while the signal is being read. Eight rings provide a resolution of 1 part in 256 in a circle or a resolution of 1.41 degrees. Sixteen rings provide a resolution of one part in 65,536 (256 × 256) or 0.0055 degrees.

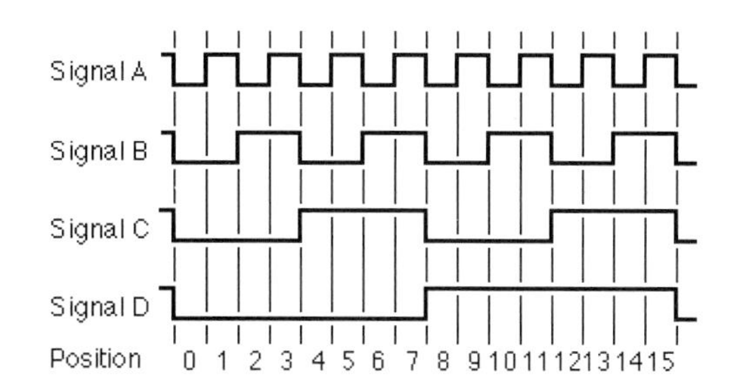

Figure 6.4 Signals from an absolute encoder.

Absolute encoders do not have to be homed and provide accurate positional information as soon as they are turned on.

Potentiometers

A simple way to read the position of the arm is to connect the arm to a variable resistor such that the resistance of the device corresponds in some way to the absolute position of the arm. It does not have to be a linear relationship because the information can be converted to the form needed in the computer with ease.

A potentiometer mounted to the axis of motion can be read to provide an analogue equivalent of the position of the axis. The information provided is absolute as compared to incremental. This information is then compared to a desired value and the motor motion is adjusted accordingly. Analogue signals are converted to digital signals so that computers can process them with speed and facility. Potentiometers are limited by their accuracy and

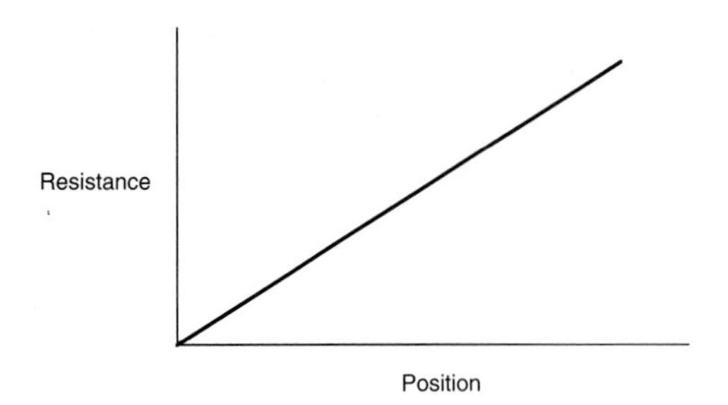

Figure 6.5 Potentiometer signal.

repeatability and because they are mechanical contact devices their accuracy changes as they wear over time.

The accuracy with which we could read the position of the arm depends on the following parameters:

- The sloppiness of the linkages
- The accuracy of the potentiometer
- The accuracy of the device we used to read the potentiometer
- The accuracy with which we can convert the resistance to a digital signal

All encoders can also be made as linear devices. Linear encoders are used by attaching them directly to the tables of a machine tool. Used in this manner, linear encoders have the advantage of not being affected by the backlash in gearboxes connected to motors however they are still affected by the expansion of the machine as it warms up during use. Higher accuracy control can be provided with software that can compensate for the temperature variations of the system.

Running motors

Now that we have an understanding of how positional information can be obtained with the desired accuracy, we need to understand how a motor is positioned to exactly the position we are interested in.

There are two things you need to know about a motor over a period of time – how fast it is running and how long it has been running. If we have these two pieces of information we can determine what the motor has done and what it is currently doing. With this information, and the very accurate clock in the computer, we can do the following:

- Start a motor when we want
- Accelerate it at the rate we want to
- Reach any velocity reasonable for the application
- Main the velocity under varying loads
- Slow the motor down when we want
- Slow the motor at the rate we want
- Stop the motor at the exact point that we want
- The stopping can be based on time
- The stopping can be based on revolutions turned
- The control can be based on internal or external events
- The control algorithm can be changed at will and as often as we want

Encoders as used for motion control are designed to give us two types of information – speed and distance. In the final analysis this is related to the motor shaft. There may be intermediate steps on the way to getting this information but eventually we are talking about the motor, how fast it is running and how long it has been running. The clock for all the time information needed is built into the computer.

Motor control

As mentioned above, the speed of a DC motor can be controlled by changing the amount of energy supplied to the motor. Changing the load on a DC motor also changes its speed (within limits this is not true of certain types of AC motors). The speed of the motor is stabilized by detecting its speed and modifying the energy being supplied to it as needed to maintain the desired speed. In a robot where there is an ever-changing load on the motor because the robot moves the way it does and picks up objects, since accurate positioning is important, these energy corrections have to be made many hundred times a second for each motor on the robot.

There are two basic ways of electrically controlling the speed of a motor. One way is to control the actual voltage to the motor by some analogue method and the other is to turn a fixed voltage on and off rapidly (digitally) to achieve the same result. In a digital system it is easier to turn the signal on and off. This is done to vary the amount of energy being sent to the motor during each time cycle. The technique is referred to as Pulse Width Modulation or PWM – we modify the length of the energy pulse in each cycle.

In a PWM scheme the power to the motor is turned on and off rapidly and as needed to control the speed of the motor. If the signal is on all the time, meaning that the pulse width is long, the motor runs at a high speed. If it is on half the time, the pulse width is 50% and the motor runs at about half speed and if it is not on any of the time, the pulse width is zero and the motor remains off.

The motor has to be turned on and off rapidly to make the operation smooth. A couple of hundred times a second is enough for most

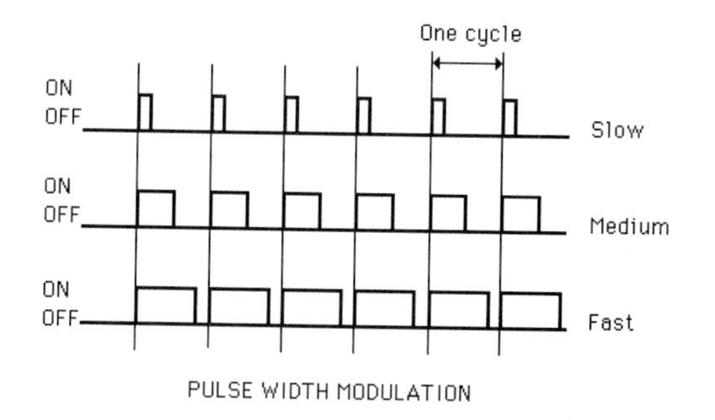

Figure 6.6 PWM signals. Energy is fed to a DC motor.

motors because the mass of the motors and the attached components is enough to average out the speed. However, these frequencies are in the range that human beings can hear and they are very annoying to most of us. Something loose in the motor windings always starts to vibrate and we can hear it. A higher on/off frequency, usually above 20,000 times per second, is therefore chosen. Going to 40,000 Hz (cycles per second) takes it above the hearing range of most domestic animals as well. At 40,000 Hz each full on/off cycle of the motor has to take 1/40,000 of a second. (Square waves are made up of many distinct frequencies so each frequency repeatedly stimulates a very specify part of the inner ear. This gets irritating very rapidly for the average human being.)

Specific difficulties accompany the design of amplifiers that can go on and off this rapidly without creating serious problems. Special, fast switching transistor arrays and special integrated circuits that control and manage these transistors have been developed, however, the design of a high power PWM motor amplifier is a job for an experienced electrical engineer.

The PWM amplifier

The basic PWM motor amplifier is an H bridge (see Figure 6.7). In this bridge, if transistors A and D are turned on, current flows in the motor windings in one direction and the motor runs in the one direction. If these two transistors are turned off and transistors B and C are turned on, the current flows in the other direction and the motor is run in the reverse of the first direction. Note that if transistors A and C or B and D come on at the same time there is a direct short circuit from power to ground and the amplifier is destroyed. It is absolutely necessary that one set of transistors is *shut off completely* before the other set comes on if the above mentioned shorting is to be avoided. The integrated

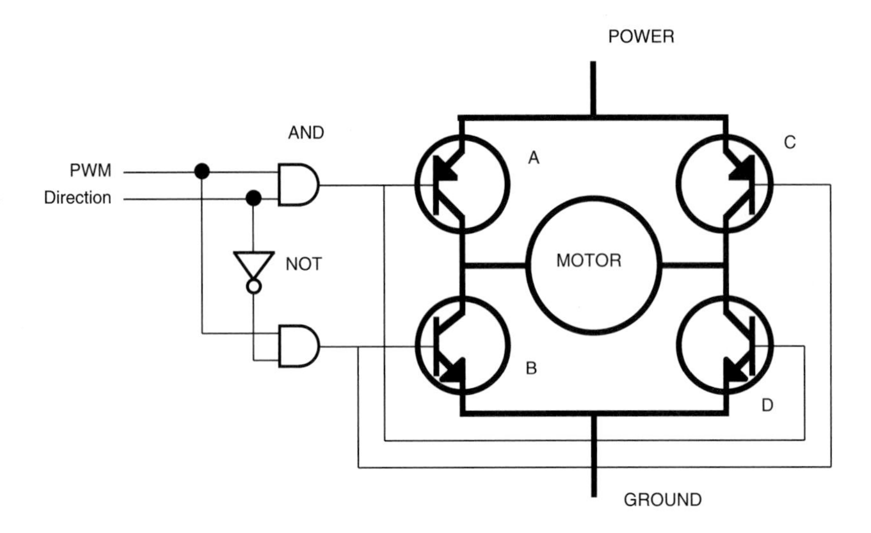

Figure 6.7 A basic H bridge amplifier. In this A, B, C and D are large transistors that act as switches. Either A and D or B and C can be turned on at one time. The power wiring is shown as heavy lines.

circuits mentioned above allow the amplifier designer to manage these conditions in a safe way. This is not as simple as it may appear because the switching of the transistors is taking place very rapidly and it takes time both to turn a transistor on and to turn it off – not necessarily long but a measurable amount of time.

If all the transistors are off, the motor is off.

It is also necessary to control the maximum current delivered to a motor to ensure that it will not be destroyed by overheating. This can be done by monitoring the current in each leg of the H bridge or through the motor itself and shutting the amplifier off if the current is exceeded. It is not usually possible to protect the motors by detecting the heat build-up in the windings because the response time is too long. A short pulse that is capable of destroying the windings without overheating them will not be detected in such a protection scheme. Only temperature rises that take place over a period of time can be guarded against by using a temperature detector buried in the windings.

The software

A servo motor needs to respond to the commands given to it within certain parameters if it is to be useful in a robotic application. A motor would be considered to be *not performing its job* if any of the following conditions were to be present:

(1) It does not turn immediately when power is applied to it.
(2) It does not stop immediately when power is removed from it.
(3) It does not move as fast as it needs to.
(4) It moves faster than commanded to.
(5) Its operation is not repeatable.

The control schemes that are designed to run motors make sure that these conditions do not occur, however, if they do occur, the system is designed to detect them and to annunciate the problem to the operator. Usually if the error between what the motor is commanded to do and what it actually does exceeds a certain number of encoder counts the condition is flagged as a performance error. The encoder

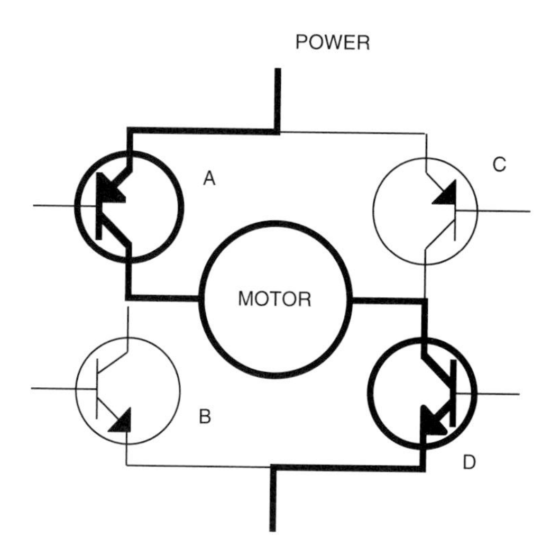

Figure 6.8 The motor turning in one direction.

counts are a measure of the instantaneous position of the motor with respect to time and so can be used to detect performance deviations. Needless to say there are always delays between what is happening, when the readings are taken, when they are interpreted and when corrective action is initiated.

If transistors A and D are turned on, the motor turns in one direction as shown in Figure 6.8. If, on the other hand, transistors B and C are turned on, the motor turns in the other direction as shown in Figure 6.9.

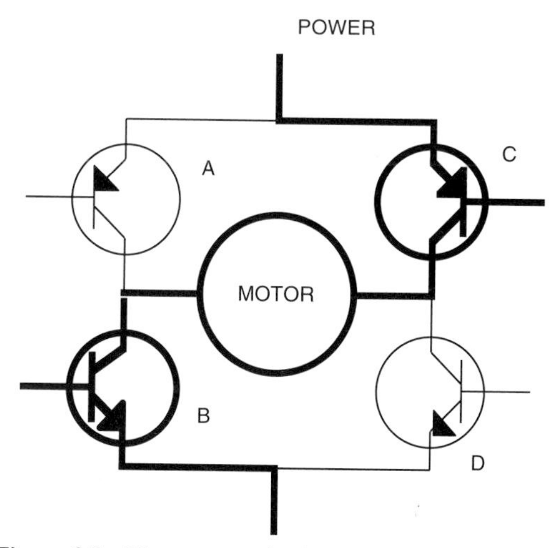

Figure 6.9 The motor turning in the opposite direction.

Logic circuits that are a part of the amplifier make sure that the two sets of transistors can never be turned on at the same time. It is not enough to turn off one set of transistors before turning on the other set – we have to make sure that the first set are actually turned off (and this takes time) before we turn the other set on. Turn off can be estimated with a time delay but is best detected by actually measuring voltages and making decisions based on actual conditions. Transistors can be made to switch more rapidly by not saturating them when switching them on and by dumping the current to the base when turning them off. This is done in hardware not software.

We now know how to run a motor in each of the two possible directions. We now need to consider how to control its speed and rate of acceleration.

Speed control

Motor speed is determined by controlling the percentage of the time that the motor has power applied to it. As we know, the current to the motor is turned on and off fairly rapidly. If the current is off all the time, the motor is off. If the current is on all the time, the motor is at full speed and if the current is on about half the time, the motor runs at about half speed. This control is accomplished with the software.

The response of the motor to the changing energy input to the motor is measured by reading the encoder counts. As the motor turns, the encoder feeds counts into an automatic counter that the computer can read whenever it needs to. The computer uses the information, and the time from its internal clock, to change the pulse width fed to the amplifier to maintain the speed and position of the motor.

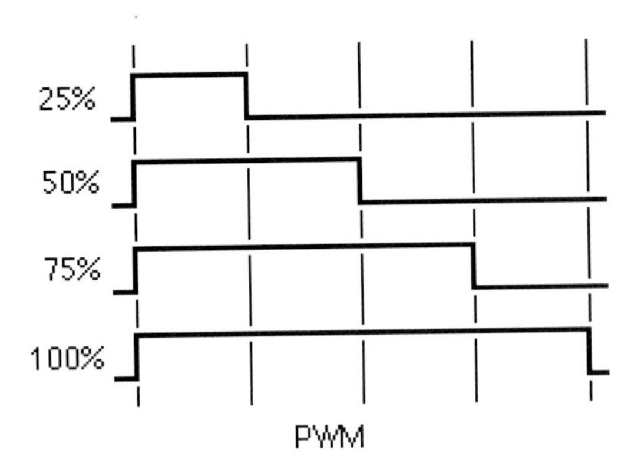

Figure 6.10 The PWM duty cycle. One cycle is shown above.

The English-like language listing of a program to maintain a motor speed with just the integrative function is as follows:

Label 1 Read the position counter
Compare it with the last reading
Calculate the motor speed
If it is faster then desired, lower the current
If it is slower than desired, increase the current
Take care of other functions
Go to Label 1

The code written in a computer language would not look like the above because it would not be so similar to English but would fulfil the same function.

Figure 6.11 shows a software flow diagram that illustrates how the speed of a motor is maintained by the software. The actual scheme is much more complicated and uses a PID loop as explained below.

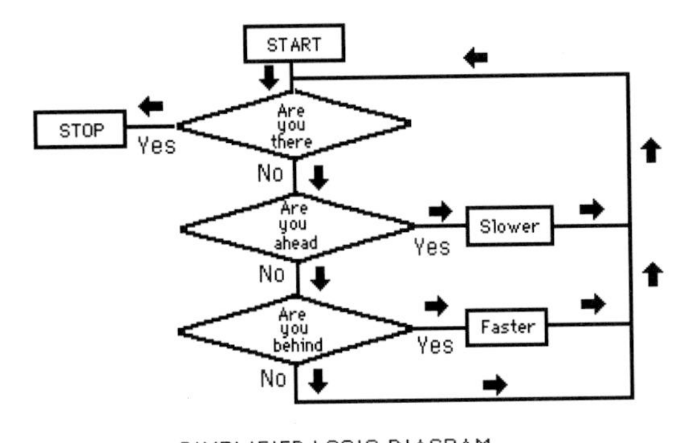

Figure 6.11 Simplified motor velocity software feedback loop.

The PID loop

The basic control loop for a motor consists of a series of expressions that represent the **proportional**, **integrative** and **derivative** components of the energy needed by the motor. This equation is called a PID equation and we often refer to this form of control as PID control. You do not need to know exactly what the expressions are but you need to understand that having three components allows better control of a motor.

Here is a simplified example. Suppose you are driving a car down the road at 80 kph (50 mph). You have in mind a position of the accelerator that is proportional to the speed at which you want to travel. This is the **proportional** component of the power you give the engine. If the car is moving slightly slower than the desired speed, you will start to press on the accelerator slowly over a period of time to speed the car up and make the correction. This is the **integrative** component i.e. you integrate (add to) the

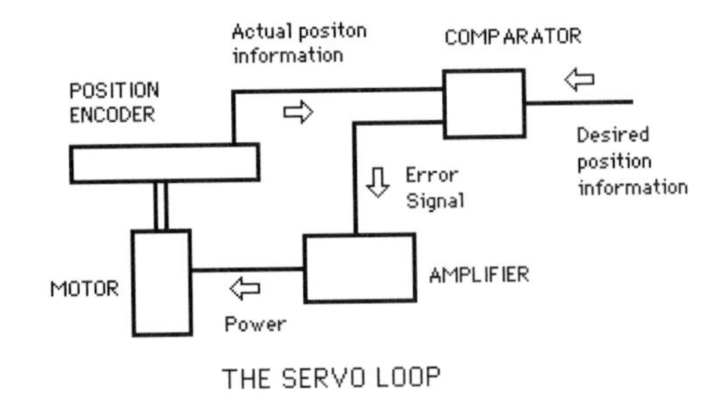

Figure 6.12 Schematic of motor feedback scheme.

increase in the accelerator position over a period of time to make the correction. If you needed to make a sudden change in the speed of the car, you would either floor the accelerator or step on the brake. This is the **derivative** component as it allows for the need for sudden changes in speed. An electric motor is controlled in a similar way in a PID loop.

All the components of the PID loop are handled in a similar manner.

CHAPTER SEVEN

Sensors, input and output

A person, animal, insect or robotic system interacts with its environment by being influenced by it in some ways and influencing it in others. In the case of a robot, information flows into the robot as signals it receives and flows out of the robot as signals that the robot sends out. After a short general discussion we will cover these two concepts one at a time.

General

Only that information for which we have appropriate sensors can be received and only that information for which we have appropriate transmitters can be transmitted. All other information is essentially irrelevant to the machine.

During any interaction there are two flows of information; there is the information that is received and the information that is transmitted. As the environment around the robot changes, it affects the sensors that are a part of the robot. These changes are brought about by both the changes in the environment and the fact that the robot is moving within the environment. There are still other sensors that are on the robot itself and these are actuated to inform the controller of internal conditions. An example would be the actuation of a limit switch on an axis or the actuation of a microswitch mounted on the gripper to indicate the successful gripping of a part. These are handled internally by the robot.

Only those things that affect the robot and its operations are of interest to the robot operating system. All other phenomena is ignored.

Sensors used with robots fall into the following categories. These are listed in 'distance to robot' categories:

- Contact or tactile sensors
  - Force sensors
  - Size sensors
  - Microswitches
  - Tape switches
- Near proximity sensors
  - Fluidic sensors
  - Eddy current proximity sensors
  - Magnetic field proximity sensors
    - Hall effect sensors
    - Magnetic attraction reed switches

- Optical proximity sensors
  - Interrupted light beam
  - Modulated light beam
  - Reflected light
  - Infra-red sensors
- Distance sensors
  - Acoustical sensing
  - Vision
  - Radar

The environmental signals to the robot enter the robot through its sensor systems. These may be in the form of whiskers, bumpers, micro-switches, reflective sensors, microphones, ranging devices and the like. If an appropriate sensor does not exist, the robot cannot detect the signal. If the robot does not have a microphone built into the system, it cannot receive any information that has been encoded as an acoustical signal. It is also worth mentioning that having a microphone is not enough. All but the simplest tones will also need to be stored for analysis and the appropriate software to analyse the sound received will have to be provided to be a part of the system.

Output devices may be classified as follows:

- Light signals
  - Visible light
  - Infra red
- Electrical signals
  - Digital signals
  - Analogue signals
  - Communication streams
  - Radio frequency signals for ranging
- Acoustical signals
  - Tones
  - Words
  - Ultrasonic signals for ranging
- Other signals
  - Pneumatic signals for pneumatic devices
  - Hydraulic signals for hydraulic devices
  - Probes

The information the robot sends to its environment leaves the robot in the form of signals that the robot emits. These can be in the form of electrical signals on wires, the physical closing and opening of relays, lights, sounds and radio signals broadcast in a specific way or some another form of communication (i.e. to a computer device).

What can be treated as input will depend on the sensors that the robot has built into it. What the robot can transmit will depend on the output devices that the robot has built into it. If it does not have a speaker, it cannot transmit audio information. If the sensors and transmitters are inhibited, for whatever reason, they cannot be used and the inhibition can be intentional or accidental.

Inputs and outputs are not always isolated. It is often the case that a robot emits a signal and then reads the response from the environment. We use a Light Emitting Diode (LED) and a photo-transistor together to provide an inexpensive way of getting proximity information and we use sound waves in a sonar configuration to get information about the immediate environment. (Long distance sensing is not of immediate interest to us in an introductory robotic text.)

Input sensors

Of the five traditional senses, robots can use the following three:

- Touch
- Vision (sight in humans)
- Sound (hearing in humans)

The other two senses, smell and taste, have been used in specialized machines (as mass spectrometer applications) but do not have an application in everyday robotics. During the Vietnam war the American Department of Defense used small portable mass spectrometers to detect the presence of enemy troops in the vicinity. How successful these machines were has not been revealed but we know that the machines did work and can surmise that the same techniques could be used to detect a dangerous chemical (or gas) with a robot if this was relevant to its usefulness.

Touch

Of the senses, touch is by far the most important for use with robots. It allows us to work out solutions to collisions and allows the exploration of the immediate environment. Using touch to explore the environment is what a blind person does and we know from experience that even rudimentary sight makes it much easier for a blind person to move about. So it is with robots. Running into objects and then backing away from them in some intelligent way is not the best way to move around.

However, touch is not restricted to motion in robotics – robots also need to know when they have grasped an object and how tightly they might have to grasp it. Other sensors that are not on the robot can be used to detect the arrival or presence of objects in the work envelope so that the robot can respond accordingly to the situation.

The microswitches

The simplest input device we can provide on a robot is a microswitch. An object that actuates the microswitch tells us that the microswitch has been actuated and nothing more. How we position the microswitch conditions what information we will get from the actuation. This means that a microswitch placed in front of the robot will tell us if the robot runs into something in the direction in which the switch is mounted. Since each microswitch tells us only one thing, we may need a number of microswitches to give us enough information to make it useful. We need to use at least four microswitches to detect collisions, one in front, one in the back one on the left and one on the right. For some applications we may need eight switches to give us more resolution – the exact number will depend on the shape of the robot, the directions in which it moves and its environment. We do not need microswitches where they are not likely to be actuated (because of how they are positioned or how they are affected by robot movement) – a robot that can move forward only does not need to have any microswitches behind it.

Photo-transistors

Photo-transistors can detect frequencies in and near the light and heat spectrums. The frequency does not have to be in the visible light spectrum – infra-red frequencies are used by a large number of photo-transistor detectors and using light that we cannot see makes the system less distracting to us (as the devices go on and off).

A photo-transistor can be used either as an on/off device or as a modulated device (which means that we measure how far the device is turned on). When we want on/off control we usually place the LED directly across from the photo-transistor and detect the signal if the light beam is broken. On most face-to-face installations we are looking for a flag or other device that comes between the two devices. Limit switches and similar devices are created in this way. When we are interested in measuring more diffuse reflections, both the LED and detector (the photo-transistor) can be aimed approximately in the same direction. Reflective schemes can be used to follow an appropriate strip on the floor and to estimate the distance of the robot from an object when in close proximity.

Switches

When we want to detect an object in the path of the robot, we have a number of schemes available to us. Let us start with detecting the closest objects and then move on to detecting objects that are farther away.

A switch that closes when an object comes up against it is an effective way to detect a collision. The problem is that we have to actually run into something before we get a signal and running into things may not be the best thing to do for a number of reasons, not the least of which is the lack of elegance. An additional problem is that this is a rather ineffective way of detecting that we have come too close to an object because this technique does not tell us anything about the object that the robot ran into other than it was strong enough to actuate the switch. The object might have been a little stone or it might be a boulder the size of a house. Increasing the number of the microswitches tells us a bit more about the direction from which the collision came but still tells us nothing about the object itself. In general, microswitches cannot detect the size of an object even if we had a lot of them. However, it should be appreciated that knowing the size of the object is often not important to what we are trying to do.

Infra-red LEDs

If we want to detect an object at a small distance, say a few millimetres or centimetres (inches) away, we can use an infra-red (IR) LED to illuminate the immediate area and use a sensitive photo-transistor as a reflection detector. As soon as we get close to an object some of the IR will reflect into the photo-transistor and create a signal. There is a problem with the reflectivity of some objects – those that are not reflective to IR will be harder to detect. The sensitivity of this scheme can be increased by adding rudimentary optics, using brighter LEDs, sensitive photo-transistors and adding amplifiers.

Vision/light

The ideal sight implementation would support fully fledged vision. This can be provided in an expensive machine but the more run-of-the-mill machines are often limited to having sensors that can detect light and others that can sense refections from close-by objects in the more inexpensive robots.

Light curtains are used as safety devices in the robot environment. They have the advantage of being physically transparent to the robot and so do not inhibit its movement in any way. They are also easily turned off when the robot is not moving or for the part of the cycle when it is working the other direction and thus provide a high degree of flexibility. Most light curtains consist of light beams that are either reflected to or directly matched to photo detectors. Interrupting any beam in the system set of the detector.

Chapter 10 contains a detailed discussion of vision, its various capabilities and functions.

Sound

Sound has the advantages of being both easy to generate, detect and record. The major problem with using sound is that there is a lot of audio noise in the workplace. The effects of noise can be minimized by using high frequencies and by modulating them in some way so that the signal can be more easily discerned.

The use of sound to detect distance consists of emitting a very specific frequency as short bursts and then waiting for the sound generated to bounce back from the surrounding objects. The signal that has to be detected gets weaker and weaker as the object being detected gets farther and farther away. The attenuation of the signal is a function of the square of the distance from the detector. To compensate for this the gain of the amplifier that receives the bounced signal is increased with time during each bounce cycle. Since sound travels quite slowly, a fairly short distance (a few centimetres or inches) can be detected. Small objects beyond 20 metres (66 feet) are harder to detect though this depends somewhat on the size of the object and the background.

Since both the emission of the sound burst and the detection of the reflection are relatively time consuming, this can be done only 20 to 50 times a second. The function is usually delegated to a independent microprocessor.

What are the extremes of what can be achieved? At one extreme we can respond to just about any sound on a binary level (heard–not heard), on the other, we can implement speech recognition. Between them is the ability to respond to specific tones or combination of tones, not unlike what the telephone system does, and to use sound as a ranging signal as was discussed above.

Output

A large part of the reaction to inputs is used within the robot and does not have to be processed and sent out in any other form. The signals are used to make decisions that do not affect the general environment away from the robot.

The output from a robot is designed to match the needs of the devices that it is interfaced with. Almost all of the information transferred to other machines is in the form of electrical signals.

Electronic output can be divided into two families. One family consists of streams of information exchanged with other computer-controlled machines. These signals are usually transmitted in a serial stream on one line not unlike the technique used to run a serial printer. If there is a lot of information to be moved very quickly, parallel communications can be used. In parallel schemes, all 8 bits of a byte are transmitted and received at the same time on 8 lines.

The other family consists of simple off and on signals that are used to indicate the release of parts, the conclusion of work cycles and the like to adjacent machinery.

In general, input comes from machines that are *uphill* from the robot and output goes to machines that are *downhill* from the robot in the production line.

Most robotic controllers also contain the implementation of a Programmable Logic Controller (PLC) like device that can be used for functions that might otherwise have to be provided by a separate PLC. PLCs execute ladder logic which is the implementation of Boolean functions at a real control level. This means that the machine has the ability to execute functions like 'If signal A and B are on and signal C is off start blinking signal K once a second for 15 seconds'.

Sound transmitted and light emitted are usually matched to detectors on the robot itself. They are used for ranging and for alarm functions.

Combining input and output signals

The robot often provides both the input and the output function without active participation from another machine. A reflective IR sensor is an example of this. The robot provides the illumination and also the detector to detect the reflected energy. Having the ability to do this gives the machine the ability to more readily discriminate the signal that it is trying to detect. This is done by turning the output signal on and off very rapidly. If the detected signal does not go on and off at the same time and at the same frequency as the output signal, some other source is activating the detector.

Recognizing voice commands

There are two basic problems associated with understanding speech. One is to understand what was said as actual words and the other is to work out what the words meant – all in essentially real time.

There is no problem with transmitting, receiving, generating and recording audio transmissions. We can do it both well and inexpensively.

Sound comes across the room as a series of pressure waves. It is generally accepted that the human ear responds to frequencies from about 20 Hz to 20,000 Hz. If we sample the sound being received 40,000 times a second (twice the highest frequency) we can recreate what was received and the human ear will find the reproduction completely faithful. Less than 20,000 Hz is sufficient for robotics. This means that we have to record about 20,000 bytes of information for every second of sound that we are interested in. What we record is the instantaneous pressure at the microphone.

There is one other problem – noise, both background noise and noise in the signal itself. Background noise makes conversation in a busy crowd or noisy factory impossible. Signal noise is a bad connection on the phone, a distortion in the signal itself. Other problems are male/female voice recognition complications, accents, cadence, humour and volume. Background noise is by far the biggest problem in any industrial environment.

Next we need to have a way to analyse these 20,000 bytes every second. The analysis is not trivial and it is time consuming. What it means is that we do not have the hardware and software to understand speech with computers. It is pretty well certain that a byte at a time will not be the way sound will be deciphered. Some form of front end filtering has to be used to sort the sound out so that we can handle the information received more efficiently, not unlike how we hear words. We hear words as discrete pieces of sounds rather than as individual waves of sound. In English we use about 100 sounds to make all the words in the language. By first dividing the incoming sound into these 100 sounds makes it much easier to analyse what is being said. (These sounds are called phonemes.)

Once we understand what is being said we have to decipher what it means. This is handled by limiting the vocabulary of the machine. The machine only understands a limited number of words and all combinations of those words can be handled the software.

Voice recognition is now working in the laboratory and limited usage is in place at the telephone company. It needs to be much more powerful and reliable before we can use it effectively in robotics.

CHAPTER EIGHT

Computer and software

A computer is the brain of every robot, it is the logic engine and ultimately the controller. The computer is the second of the required three components that a robot must have, the other two being the mechanical components of the robot and the software. The software determines how the computer will operate or, more specifically, how the robot will respond to programming and its environment.

The robot is told what it has to do with a program that is written in a language that it understands. The computer is the part of the robot that provides the programming function, the decision-making function and the memory function as needed by every programmable machine. Just as the brain is the essence of every human being and our education defines our capabilities so the computer defines what the computer will be able to do for the robot and the software defines how it will do it. Neither can make up for the shortcomings of the other.

The functions provided by a robot's computer are arranged in a slightly different way from the way they are organized in a general-purpose, data-processing computer because controlling a robot is a real time operation. This means that things have to be done when they need to be done. You cannot take your time to finish what you are doing and then come back to do what was needed. When a motor needs to be stopped it has to be done immediately because if it is not stopped when it is supposed to it will over-travel and the results could be disastrous.

Stated more specifically, the computer monitors the operation of a motor at all times and makes hundreds of adjustments every second to ensure that the motor follows the exact trajectory that was programmed for it. It is responsible for starting the motor at the exact time required, accelerating it at the required rate and then maintaining the exact speed needed. When a motor is to be stopped, the computer calculates the necessary trajectories, slows the motor down at the proper rate and stops it exactly where it was supposed to stop. This describes the operation of just one motor and on a robot there are usually half a dozen motors that have to be controlled simultaneously and in complete synchronisation with one another. Besides the motors the computer has to monitor the input lines, control the output lines and make sure that it does not miss any communications duties. At the same time it puts out information to the other machines that it is working with to make sure that they are kept informed of the processes taking place at the robot, all in real time. All these functions keep the computer busy almost all the time. As a matter of fact it is desirable for the most efficient and accurate operation of the robot that the computer be busy all the time. This is effected by increasing the number of calculations made to optimize operations if there is any free time available. The number of calculations can even be varied as the load on the computer varies.

Real time does not mean instantaneously – not much in the world of computers happens instantaneously. It only means that the reaction to the calling condition has to be fast enough to serve the condition adequately and this in turn usually means that it has to be pretty much immediate. No time is to be wasted. To us things might seem to happen instantaneously but in fact they are taking place in a very ordered and disciplined way and all of it was programmed very carefully by someone in the software department at the robot factory.

As the number of things that may need to be taken care of immediately increases, the likelihood that a number of them will become due simultaneously becomes more and more likely. When this happens, the computer becomes too slow to get the job done in time and so some other scheme has to be implemented to decrease the overall response time and to keep it within acceptable limits. There are two ways to handle a number of events that might occur simultaneously and at an unpredictable time.

Think of a classroom full of students any one of whom may need the teacher's attention at any time. One way of making sure that every student who needs attention gets it when he or she needs it is look at each and every student in sequence and ask them if they need attention and if someone does, take care of it right then before moving to the next student. This works well in small classrooms with a few students and is called simple polling. You poll each of the students and service the ones that need attention with whatever they need done.

When the classroom becomes larger and the student population increases, it takes too long to poll all the students and some students who need immediate attention are likely to have to wait too long after the need first arose. Here we can use a technique where we ask the students to raise their hands if they need assistance. You then poll only the students who have their hands up and take care of their needs one by one. The possibility still exists that some long-winded student will tie you up for too long and this can be avoided by polling everyone with their hands up and determining what the priority need of each student is before taking any action. The important tasks are then taken care of first and the less important ones are saved for later. This is called polling the interrupts. If you have a table that tells you who the critical students are you can use that information to determine what to do first.

The way the operating system of the robot works is similar. Some tasks that need instant attention are taken care of immediately while those that can wait for a few milliseconds are taken care of later. The kind of things that need immediate attention are things like the Emergency Stop switch. Usually by the time you decide to press the Emergency Stop button it is too late already but the condition still needs to be terminated immediately for safety reasons. Usually, on most automatic machines, you cannot recover from an emergency stop, meaning that you cannot press the Continue button and continue from where you emergency-stopped the machine. The Feed Hold or Pause button is used for stops from which you intend to continue. The stopping actions that are undertaken during one of these stops are much more orderly than in an emergency stop.

In summary, in a robot control application,

the computer provides the following functions:

- Run the motors (usually 5 or more)
- Read all the encoders
- Set the PWM amplifier gain for all motors
- Monitor the input lines
- Set the output lines
- Receive all communications from one or more ports
- Send information to other machines needing information
- Monitor the control panel of the robot
- Update the CRT on the controller
- Perform all the calculations needed for proper operation
- Parse the instruction in the program
- Detect errors in the program lines

As you can imagine, a fairly powerful computer is needed to do all of the above without any apparent hesitations in the operation of the system. Most robot controllers have at least one 32-bit processor for running them. The usual configuration will have at least two microprocessors with one in charge of the motors and the other in charge of all other functions. With the advent of cheaper and specialized microprocessors additional processing units are being used to control various functions in the machine. For example, in a modern robot, the following functions are handled by separate microprocessors:

- Each motor has a dedicated microprocessor running it. Processors that can run up to eight motors in real time are now available. These processors also read the encoders.
- Almost every computer uses a separate processor to manage the keyboard, even personal computers do this.
- Separate processors like the keyboard processors monitor the front panel and interrupt the main processor only if attention is warranted. This means the main processor does not have to look at the front panel every so often just to see if any control has been actuated.
- Communications with other devices are handled by special processors.
- Input/output functions are handled by separate processors.
- Vision always has its own processor and a shared section of fast memory.
- Printing functions are relegated to a separate processor.

This means that the main processor tells each of the subordinate processors what they need to do in a special language they both understand and then goes on to the next task. If the subordinate processors need attention they interrupt the main processor and tell it what they need when they are asked to. Doing it this way makes it much easier to create a fast and responsive system. A modern industrial robot controller may have as many as sixteen 32-bit processors in it.

A robot is a state machine and although there is a large number of states that it can be in, it can assume only a finite number. Let us look at just one motor on the robot. The motor can go from one extreme of its travel to the other extreme and there are a fixed number of encoder counts between the two positions. There are no other functions that it can perform. Within the two extreme positions it has to follow a given sequence in that it cannot skip from one encoder position to a random position but must go through all the intermediate positions and they must be encountered in order as it moves from one position to the other. All other paths are forbidden and would be recognized as machine failures if the situation was being monitored. The total number of states that the motor can assume is the number of revolutions that it has to move to go from one end of its travel to the other multiplied by the number of encoder counts in one revolution of the motor.

Similarly as a robot moves from one state or position to another state or position it has to move through a pre-determined sequence of positions. If a six-axis robot is moved from one position to another, in which all six motors have to be moved, there is no guarantee that the movement of the tip of the gripper will be in a straight line (as a matter of fact it is most unlikely that the gripper will move in a straight line). Moving the gripper in a straight line involves creating a sequence of moves as described next.

The position of the gripper tip can be calculated if we know the positions of the six motors (relative to a repeatable starting position) on the robot. The equation to do this is a fairly simple one whereby we determine the position of the first joint from the position of the base, and the position of the second joint from the position of the first and so on until we get the position of the final joint which is the gripper tip.

Straight line motion

Robots do not, of course, always need to move in straight lines but there is a definite benefit to such motion in many applications. For one, it is much easier to control a robot that moves only in the X, Y and Z direction when using a teach pendant. Straight line motion is achieved by calculating the direction and distance from position 1 to position 2. The distance is then divided into a reasonable and discrete number of moves and the robot moves from one to the other in the calculated direction and in doing so it moves in an almost straight line. There are a number of algorithms that allow the software to calculate how much each motor has to move to move from one intermediate position to the other. This means that a robot does not move in an exactly straight line but rather it moves in a set of little squiggles that together seem like a straight line to us. The moves are melded into one another by the software to create a smooth move.

All the calculations needed to make a straight line move may not be made in real time. If the time is available, the positions are pre-calculated and placed in arrays while other less demanding activities are being undertaken. These arrays are then executed in real time and in doing so straight line motion is created. The move algorithms tend to even the squiggles out to make the move smoother because each move is blended into the next to avoid having to stop between each pair of mini-moves.

Encoder counts and the computer

A robot needs to have a design parameter that determines the smallest move that it can make. In most cases a high precision robot can move about 0.05mm repeatedly. To do this it might need a theoretical capability of about a tenth to a one hundredth of that. Let us arbitrarily pick a theoretical minimum motion of 0.001mm. There is a minimum 'length of move' that can be made because a motor cannot be moved less than an encoder count. The 0.001mm constant determines how many encoder counts are needed at each motor. The distance moved when any encoder is moved by one count has to be such that it is always under 0.001mm. This will mean that the encoder counts combined with the gearing ratios have to be finer at the joints near the base of the robot as compared to those at the gripper end. If coarser encoding is used for the coarser joints, it can be compensated for in the control algorithms.

Picking encoders with too many counts per revolution can cause the following problems:

- Encoders become very expensive as the line count increases
- Counters for the encoder signals have to be high-speed units
- Jitters can develop if there is any slack in the system bearings and gears
- The more encoder lines there are the more the susceptibility to dirt and noise

Encoders with about 512 to 1024 counts per revolution are both inexpensive, easy to use, rugged and can provide good resolution with the right gearing. Common encoder counts are 64, 100, 128, 360, 400, 500, 512, 1000, 1024, 2048 and 4096. Higher custom numbers can be obtained and counts of a million per revolution are available.

Number of calculations made

The number of calculations made is determined by the speed of the processors, the fastest speed at which the robot moves and the mechanical accuracy needed by the system. As many calculations as there is time for are made.

Speed of movement

In most work situations it is desirable that the work get done as soon as possible. This means that the robot should move as fast as it possibly can. Movement speed is moderated by:

- The weight of the object being handled – the heavier the object is the more difficult it is to overcome inertial and safety problems.
- The distance that the object has to be moved – the distance moved determines the time you have to make the move. On short moves you do not have the time to get the load moving fast.

Velocity, acceleration and jerk

- *Velocity* is the change of position with respect to time
- *Acceleration* is the change in velocity with respect to time
- *Jerk* is the change in acceleration with respect to time

There is always some jerk when you start moving an object. How fast you can accelerate and what path you use to increase the velocity determine the acceleration that you can use. Breakage and safety are the major consideration – jerky motion is undesirable.

The computer is programmed to manage the system to optimize these three functions.

Trapezoidal motion

Most motion is some form of trapezoidal motion. In trapezoidal motion, the motor is accelerated to its operation speed at a fixed acceleration, the speed is then maintained for as long as needed and the motor is then slowed down at a fixed deceleration until it comes to a stop at the desired location.

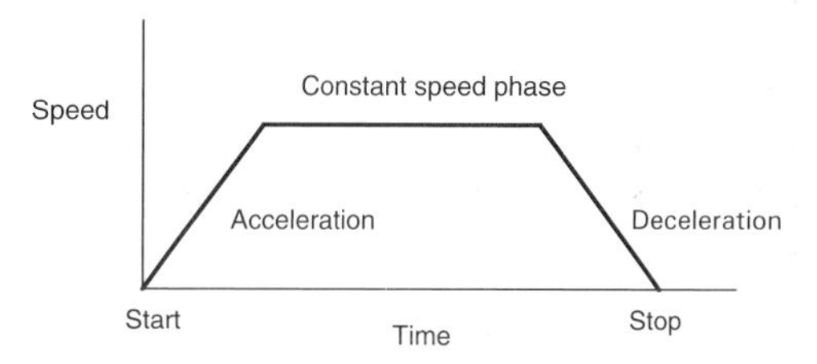

Figure 8.1 A trapezoidal motor move.

All the calculations needed to affect trapezoidal motion are carried out by the computer in real time because the effect of the load cannot be determined until the load is actually picked up.

Not all moves use a trapezoidal trajectory. It is often necessary to use a sine wave trajectory. This trajectory has the advantage in that it exhibits less jerk on starting and stopping and at any other acceleration change points. Newer robot software allows selection of the form of acceleration used by the system.

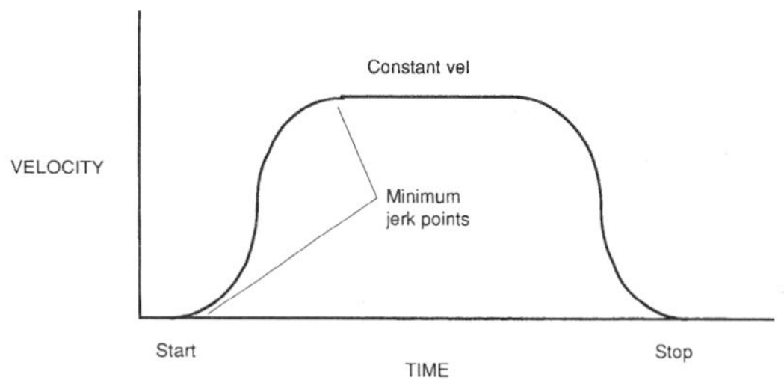

Figure 8.2 Sine wave motion.

Input/output considerations

As the computer monitors the operation of the motors on the robot it also monitors the condition of the input lines. If there is a change in the incoming signals it responds to the change appropriately. Output signals are set as is required by the program in response to work progress.

Housekeeping functions

In any computer-controlled device, there are a number of housekeeping functions that have to be taken into consideration upon start up and before shut down. These include the homing function and the reading of the parameter files that determine the conditions under which the robot will operate.

PWM generation

Since motor motion trajectories are determined by the software, the parallel function of generating the PWM signals needed by the motors is also calculated and updated by the software.

Parameter tables

Within every software system for any programmable machine is a table that contains the information needed by that specific machine to tell it about itself. Robot software is usually designed to run a whole family of machines made by one manufacturer. The parameter tables specify the properties of the specific machine being used. This information includes items like the following:

- Amount of memory in the system
- The maximum overall speed of the processor
- Date of manufacture
- Software version
- Model number
- Type of gripper in use
- Number of motors
- Physical descriptions
  - Arm and segment lengths etc.
  - Type of gripper
- For each motor
  - Maximum acceleration under any condition no matter what
  - Maximum acceleration for the machine as set up
  - Maximum acceleration as a function of the velocity
  - Maximum velocity under any condition no matter what
  - Maximum velocity for the machine as set up
  - Maximum velocity as a function of the length of the move
  - Maximum permitted positive move position
  - Maximum permitted negative move position
  - Home position for the axis (this is a reference position)
- Number of motors
  - Encoder counts per revolution of motor
  - Gearbox ratio of motor or threads per inch of ball screw
  - Minimum encoder count position
  - Maximum encoder count position
  - Encoder count at home position
  - Maximum current allowed to each motor
  - Stall current at motor (to shut down)
  - Motor manufacturer

The velocities and accelerations are also defined within the program on other lines. There are other parameters that might further modify positional parameters. For example, we may not want the arm to move too fast if it is extended all the way out. A multiplier based on the arm angle would make sure that this does not happen.

The software has special commands that allow the parameters to be changed. There is usually a parameter change switch within the cabinet (so it will not be actuated by mistake) that enables the changing of parameters.

CHAPTER NINE

A robot control language

This chapter will be of much greater interest to you after you have built the robot and need to design a language for it. Until then you can skip this chapter – this is the example you will refer to.

This chapter is designed to give you a feel for how one goes about actually controlling a robot with a formal language. What you can do with a robot is limited by the language that the robot understands and the physical attributes of the robot. Here we see how a language is put together and what one needs to control a machine like a robot.

Studying a language gives you insights into how moves are specified, how the robot is reset, how the input and output are controlled etc.

Before we look at the language, let us look at the hardware attributes of the robot for this particular language so that we can see how the two tie together. The description of the hardware is very cursory in this instance to keep it as short as possible – only the information needed to understand what the language is controlling is included:

- 8 motor ports with encoder support
- 2 auxiliary ports (relay-like operation)
- 8 input lines
- 8 output lines
- 8 microswitches (6 on the robot itself)
- A communication port for a host computer
- A teach pendant port to attach a 32-key teach pendant

The robot is a five-axis robot with an electrically operated gripper. The six motors have optical encoders on them. The robot is 76cm (30in.) high to the gripper tips when its hand reaches straight up.

The following commands form the RoboTalk language that controls the above hardware. I designed both RoboTalk and the robot as an introduction to robotic languages, for students of robotics, in the early 1980s. It is a very simple and rudimentary implementation of a robot language designed to be about halfway between Binary Algorithm for the Symbolic Instruction of Computers (BASIC) and VAL. BASIC is an easy to learn computer language. It was one of the first higher level English-like languages used by computers and was developed at Dartmouth University in the USA. The goal was to design an English-like computer language that was easy to use for students

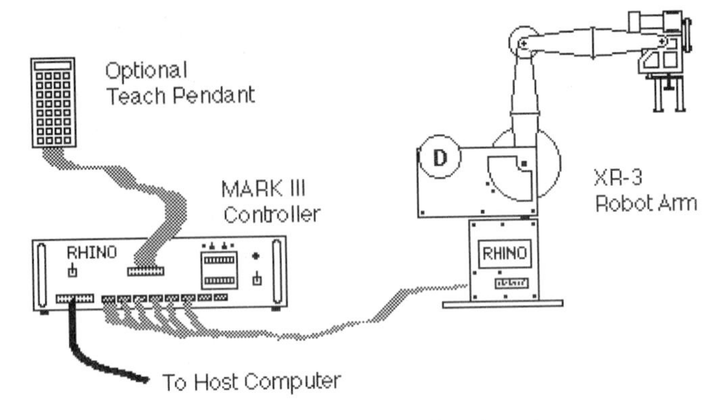

Figure 9.1 The robot, controller and teach pendant.

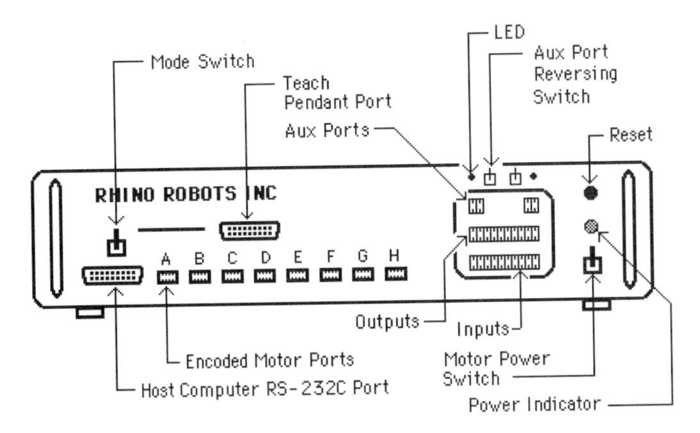

Figure 9.2 The front of the controller.

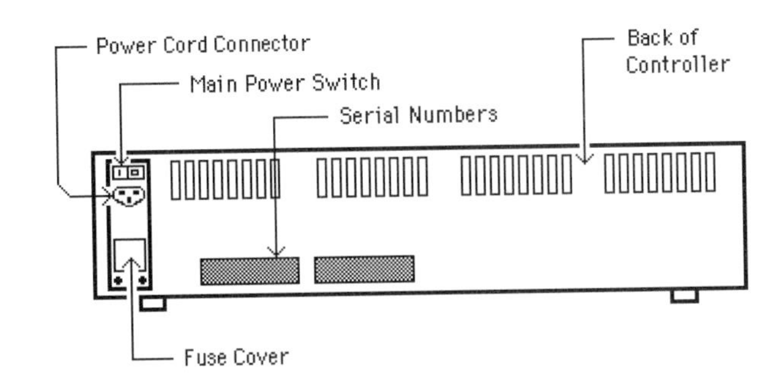

Figure 9.3 The back of the controller.

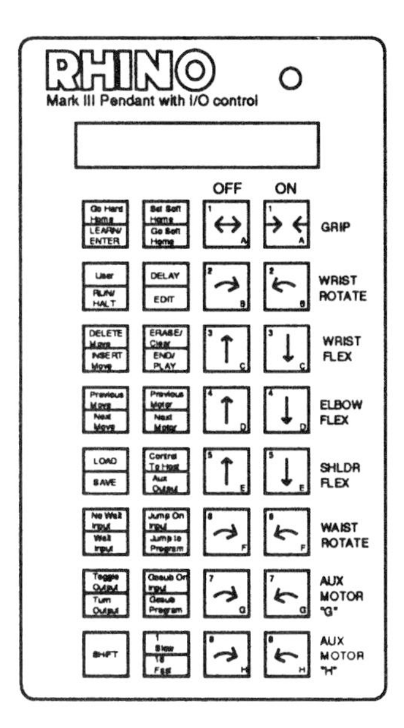

Figure 9.4 The teach pendant.

and first-time computer users (who were not computer literate). VAL is the robot control language developed by Unimation and is used by Kawasaki and Adept for controlling their robots. VAL II is now in use and is a much enhanced version of VAL.

The RoboTalk language has over 50 instructions, commands and functions (plus the editor commands needed to edit a program). As in any robot control language, these instructions and commands can be broken up into three main families.

(1) Program control statements. Program control instructions control the program flow and decision-making process in the program and as such they have no direct affect on the robot itself.

(2) Robot control statements. Robot control statements control the robot in some way. They cause something to happen in the hardware – a motor moves, a signal changes. Actions are always specified but something that we can see does not have to happen. For example a robot already at the home position will not move if told to move to the home position.

(3) Functions. Functions are used to perform calculations and manipulate memory in other ways. The functions affect neither program flow or robot movements directly.

These three families of commands are listed below.

Program control statements

BEEP — CLS
END — ERROR_CHECK
FOR...TO.../NEXT — GET_ANSWER
GOSUB — GOTO
IF...THEN... — IFMICRO...THEN...
IFSIG...THEN... — INPUT
LOCAL — PAUSE
REM — RETURN
SEND — SETI
TROFF — TRON
TYPE — WAITFOR

Robot control statements

ARC — ARCX — AUX
CLEARPATH — CLOSE — GRIP
HARDHOME — HOME — MOVE
MOVE TO — MOVEGH — MOVEGH TO
MOVEP — MOVES — MOVEXS
MOVEX — MOVEX TO — MOVEXP
OFFLINE — OFFSET — OFFSETX
ONLINE — OPEN — OUTSIG
PATH — POINT — SEARCH
SETPATH — SETPATHX — VEL

Functions

ACOS — ASIN — ATAN
COS — SIN — TAN

and the standard +, -, *, and / functions

The rest of this chapter contains a cursory description of each command to give you a feeling for what a robot control language looks like and what it does. In this discussion, the arguments of the commands have been omitted to make the discussion easier to understand. Explanatory paragraphs tell you how the function is useful in a robotic context.

As you study these commands, think about how you might design a language to control the process of walking as done by a robot.

ACOS, ASIN, ATAN – inverse trig. functions
These three functions accept arguments and return the appropriate trigonometric value in degrees. Since these are functions, they cannot be used as commands by themselves but are to be used in assignment statements and expressions. Having these functions available allows you to make calculations that will then be used to effect the operation of the robot.

ARC – point defined circular move
The ARC command moves the robot gripper in an arc or circle from the current position through two stated points. As you are probably aware, a circle can be defined by defining three points that the circle passes through. There is only one circle that will pass through these three points. Since the robot hand is located at one of the points on the circle and the destination is one other point, defining the intermediate point makes the robot move to its destination in a circular arc that passes through the intermediate point. Obstructions can be avoided by using an arc as a move trajectory. The points are defined as named points somewhere else in the program. Defining the points in this way allows you to edit the point specification without having to go to each and every point where the location is referred to and changing all those values.

ARCX – Cartesian circular move
The ARCX command moves the robot in an arc or circle from the current location through two Cartesian locations. This is similar to the ARC command but uses Cartesian co-ordinates to define the points. This is useful for use in computer-generated programs. The computer would have a description of the robot environment in its memory, and this would most probably be in Cartesian co-ordinates.

AUX – Aux port control
The AUX command is used to control the auxiliary ports on the robot controller. In the RoboTalk language the ports can be used to run the motors provided on the robots or on other accessories. These are motors without encoders or relays or any other suitable device. There are two auxiliary ports – port 1 and port 2 – in the RoboTalk language. Other robots and languages have similar capabilities to run motors and control relays. This is necessary to allow the intimate co-ordination of robot and accessory action with ease. If the many devices are run from independent computers, the co-ordination becomes more problematical because it is more difficult to exchange information between two (or more) computers.

BEEP – audio alert
The BEEP command produces a short tone on the host computer's speaker which can be used to alert the operator that a process has been completed or it can be used as an error condition indicator. This is similar to the beep provided on all computers.

CLEARPATH – clear continuous path
CLEARPATH clears the array containing a set of locations or points defined by SETPATH or SETPATHX. These commands are discussed later on in this chapter.

CLOSE – gripper control
CLOSE is used to close the gripper on the robot or to turn on AUX 1 or OUTPUT 1 to operate a non-

standard (pneumatic for example) gripper. The optional argument is the amount the gripper is to be closed in encoder counts if used in the motor mode. If the gripper is to be fully closed, no argument or an argument of −1 can be used.

Since grippers come in many configurations, it is necessary to have a number of ways to actuate them. The above three are not the only means to control a gripper but they are the most common ones used. The method has to match the gripper that you decide to use and the software implemented.

CLS – clear the screen
CLS is used to clear the screen of the host computer. Any information previously written to the screen will be erased and the cursor will be positioned at the upper left-hand corner of the screen. CLS has no effect while the system is in the TRACE mode because that would erase information that is useful in the current context. The use of the screen to display messages and other status information allows the operator to know what is going on within the system. The CRT screen is also used to display all error messages. The screen is where the robot talks to the operator.

COS, SIN, TAN – trigonometric functions
These three functions accept arguments in degrees and return the appropriate trigonometric value. The variable used to take the value should be a floating point type, if not, only an integer value will result. Since these are functions, they cannot be used as commands by themselves but are to be used in assignment statements and expressions. Functions like these increase the utility of the robot by increasing the control that you have over the machine with the program. This is an important point because it allows more powerful control of the robot.

END – end of program
The END command is used to mark the end of the program. Although the physical end of the program will also cause your program to end, the END command can be used to terminate execution at any point in the program. The END command is useful when subroutines are to be used because they are often located after the end of a program. Without the END command, the program could unintentionally execute the first subroutine it encounters.

ERROR_CHECK – lists error stack contents
The ERROR_CHECK command displays all the errors that have been stored in the error stack. After ERROR_CHECK has been executed the error stack will be empty. It is useful to be able to look back and see what errors have occurred within a program to allow one to debug the program. In a powerful language, some errors will not stop the program because they can be considered non-critical. In these powerful systems it might also be possible to turn the stopping feature on and off.

FOR...TO... / NEXT – program loop control
The FOR...TO... command controls the execution of a group of program lines located between the FOR...TO... line and the line containing the NEXT statement. This is the standard looping feature that is provided in almost all computer languages. In a robot language it is useful for doing tasks that have to be repeated a number of times. Stacking and filling boxes are examples that might use this command set.

GET_ANSWER – interrogate controller
The GET_ANSWER command sends an alphanumeric string to the controller and receives and displays the information returned. The string sent to the controller must represent a valid command that has been designed to elicit a specific response. This is a debugging function.

GOSUB – subroutine call
The GOSUB command is used to call a labelled subroutine. This is similar to the standard

subroutine call feature as is provided in almost all computer languages.

GOTO – branch to a label
GOTO is used to transfer program execution to the line with the label (name) specified in the GOTO statement. It should be mentioned that using GOTO commands is now considered bad programming practice because it creates programs that are hard to follow and debug.

GRIP – close gripper and record counts
The GRIP command is an enhanced version of the CLOSE command. It differs from the CLOSE command in that a variable is set, after the command completion, to the number of gripper encoder counts that the gripper is displaced from the fully closed position. This command can be used to gauge the size of the grasped object or to detect if the gripper did indeed grasp anything at all. After the command has been executed the Z (in RoboTalk only) variable can be tested or used in an assignment statement. Commands like this are useful only if you have a gripper that has a motor with an encoder on it. The command would not mean anything if the robot had a pneumatically operated gripper.

HARDHOME – find all microswitches
HARDHOME is used to re-initialize the robot and return it to its hardware home position by actually finding the centre of the microswitches on all the axes under program control. You would normally not use this command once the robot had been initialized. If you wished to return the robot to the hardware home position, you would use the HOME command because it is much faster. Use HARDHOME when you actually want to do a complete hardhome sequence. This will be the case after a crash or in some other situation where a robot might be thought to have lost positional information.

HOME – sends robot to its home position
The HOME command is used to return the robot to the home position i.e. the hardhome position. The robot does not try to find the centre of the microswitches; it moves directly to the position where all the encoder counts are zero. This is much faster than the HARDHOME command and is generally the command you use to return the robot to its home position. The HOME command does not affect the gripper position because if it did the robot might drop what it has in the gripper. This means that HARDHOME must be used if the gripper needs to be reset and then whatever is in the gripper will be released!

IF..THEN... – conditional execution
The IF..THEN... statement is used to test a condition and, if that condition is true, perform the statement after the THEN. If the condition is false, the program execution continues with the line following the IF..THEN... statement. The conditions tested for are mathematical or relational conditions. This is similar to the use of this command in standard computer languages.

IFMICRO...THEN... – conditional execution
IFMICRO is similar to both IF..THEN... and IFSIG...THEN... except that it is used to test the state of the microswitches located on the robot and the encoded motor accessories (if they are attached). The command is used to move the motor to the home position. The program should be written to find where the microswitch is actuated from each direction and then find the centre as the home position.

IFSIG...THEN... – conditional execution
IFSIG...THEN... is similar to the other IF commands except that it is used to test the state of the input signals coming in to the controller from other devices attached to the controller. This is how the robot responds to what is happening in its environment.

INPUT – input from computer keyboard
INPUT allows the user to input, directly from the computer's keyboard, an integer or decimal numerical constant or string and assign that value to a RoboTalk variable. This is useful for entering information in real time in any sophisticated language. It is also useful for debugging and for other maintenance needs.

LOCAL – define local subroutine variable
LOCAL provides a means of using variables in a subroutine that have the same names as variables in the main program but are only defined and visible within the subroutine. Once the subroutine has ended, the variable and its value are no longer viable. LOCAL is useful because it releases the programmer from concerns about variable interaction between the main program and the subroutine calls. If the LOCAL command is not used to specifically make a variable name local to the subroutine in which it is located, the variable will have the same definition and value as it does in the main program. This can cause problems that are very hard to debug.

MOVE – incremental joint move
The MOVE command is used to move the robot's motor(s) a specified number of encoder steps from its current position. It is an incremental or relative move command as opposed to an absolute move command.

MOVE TO – absolute joint move
MOVE TO is similar to MOVE except that it will position the robot motor(s) at the specified number of encoder steps from the home position. Therefore MOVE TO is an absolute move command. This means that the robot will move to the specified encoder position for each motor encoder from its current encoder position, regardless of the current position.

MOVEGH – incremental move command
MOVEGH is similar to MOVE except that it moves the auxiliary G and H motors. It will move the G and H motor encoders the specified number of counts from their current position. This makes MOVEGH an incremental or relative move command. The G and H motors are usually used to control accessories like a belt conveyor and a rotary carousel. This is how accessories are controlled in a robot environment.

MOVEGH TO – absolute move command
MOVEGH TO is similar to MOVE TO except that it is used to control the G and H motors. It will position the G and H motor encoders to the absolute motor count position from their home position. This makes MOVEGH TO an absolute move command. As already stated. the G and H motors are usually used to control accessories like a belt conveyor and a rotary carousel.

MOVEP – move to a point location
The MOVEP statement tells RoboTalk to send the robot to the point (location) specified. The location must be a named point defined with the teach pendant and must be defined as a joint location, not a Cartesian location. The advantage of doing this is that changing the location of a named point changes all references to it. This makes editing a program much easier. A point referred to 50 times does not have to be edited at 50 different locations in the program.

MOVES – defined straight line move
The MOVES (S= straight line) command is used to move the tool tip (gripper tip) in a straight line from the current position to a pre-defined point. Straight line commands are useful in all applications similar to glue application and certain assembly operations. Straight line moves are very computation intensive. See discussion of how a straight line move is executed in Chapter 8 on computers.

MOVEXS – Cartesian straight line move
The MOVEXS command is used to move the tool tip (gripper) in a straight line from the current position to a Cartesian co-ordinate location.

MOVEX TO – absolute move command, Cartesian
MOVEX TO is similar to MOVEX except that it will position the tool tip at the Cartesian position specified as referenced from the robot Cartesian system origin.

MOVEXP – move to a Cartesian location
The MOVEXP statement tells the controller to send the robot to the point location specified. The location must be a named point defined with the teach pendant and must be defined as a Cartesian location, not a joint location; that is, the name of the point must start with the letter 'X'. This is a subtlety of RoboTalk and would not be a requirement in other languages.

OFFLINE – ignore a motor
OFFLINE is used to tell the system that one or more of the motors are not available for use. No attempt is made to move the offlined motors even when a move request for that motor is received. This command prevents the system from hanging up (because an absent motor never gets to the location it is supposed to move to).

OFFSET – encoder position offset
The OFFSET command is used to alter the location of the next motion command by the amount specified for each motor encoder. This is useful in stacking and similar operations. There are more sophisticated ways to do this and this is included in the command set to show the student how these things are done. Having the command allows students to learn how to use it.

OFFSETX – Cartesian position offset
The OFFSETX command is used to alter the location of the next Cartesian motion command by the amount specified for each Cartesian axis.

ONLINE – activate an offlined motor
ONLINE is used to return a motor, that had previously been OFFLINEd (in the same program) back into service.

OPEN – open gripper command
OPEN is used to open the standard gripper on the robot or to turn off AUX1 or OUTPUT1 to operate a non-standard gripper. The optional argument is the amount the gripper is to be opened in motor encoder counts if used in the motor mode. If the gripper is to be fully opened, no argument or an argument of –1 is used. When the robot is initialized, the gripper is closed fully and then opened a set number of encoder counts. This applies to motorized grippers only.

OUTSIG – output signal line control
OUTSIG is used to turn the output signal lines on the robot controller ON and OFF. This is how the robot communicates with the machines around it in the output mode. These are signals going out from the robot as opposed to signals coming into the robot.

PATH – continuous path move
The PATH command is used to initiate a continuous path move that was previously defined using the SETPATH and/or SETPATHX commands. A continuous path is a move that follows a specific path that is arbitrary and cannot be specified as a circular or a straight line move.

PAUSE – delays program execution
PAUSE is used to delay execution of your program for the specified period of time. This is useful for co-ordinating the movement of the robot with other machines and for the time that may be needed to allow the gripper to settle down.

POINT – set location point
The POINT command is used to set a location variable to the present robot's position or to set a location variable to a specified value. This is how the location of points is specified. Most robots let you do this with the teach pendant and with the keyboard by specifying variables. More sophisticated software can create point locations automatically from a database that describes the work environment.

REM – remark, documentation
REM is used to place a comment or remark into the source code of your program. All text between the REM and the end of the line will be ignored by RoboTalk. Adding remarks makes it easier for a person looking at a program listing to understand what the programmer intended to do. Programs should be well documented so that they can be maintained by end users.

RETURN – subroutine return statement
The RETURN statement is used to cause a return from a subroutine. All subroutines must have been called using the GOSUB command. After the RETURN has been executed, program execution will begin with the line immediately following the GOSUB that called the subroutine. This is the standard use of the RETURN command.

SEARCH – conditional move command
The SEARCH command is a high level command that moves a specified axis motor a set number of encoder counts per iteration, incrementing the Z variable by one in each iteration and continues this process until the specified input port matches the programmed state. Commands like this are useful when there are sensors on the grippers and in the work space. It allows the robot to keep moving until the sensor is actuated. These are rudimentary 'intelligent' behaviour commands. Interactive commands like these are built up into intelligent systems.

SEND string – send string to controller
The SEND command sends a string command to the controller. This allows undocumented commands to be sent to the controller. Commands like this add flexibility to the system.

SETI – assignment function
SETI is used to assign a variable an integer value.

SETPATH – set continuous point define
The SETPATH command is used to add a location to a continuous path move.

SETPATHX – set continuous Cartesian define
The SETPATHX command is used to add a location to a continuous path move with a Cartesian point.

TROFF – turn trace mode off
TROFF is used to turn off the trace facility.

TRON – turn trace mode on
TRON is used to activate the trace facility. The trace facility displays the contents of critical section of the memory on the screen as you step through the program. This is used in the debugging process.

TYPE – output to the screen
TYPE is the general output command in RoboTalk. You can use it to output character strings or numeric values to the screen. There are two forms of the command; one for displaying strings, the other for displaying numbers. RoboTalk implements only the most rudimentary ability to print to the screen. The emphasis is on the robot language and not on the ability to manipulate information on the screen.

VEL – set motor velocity
VEL sets a specified motor's velocity. Controlling the motor velocity keeps certain automatic move commands from overspeeding a motor. A motor that overspeeds can cause loss of

encoder counts and can move a heavy part too fast. It is also useful for setting heavy parts down gently.

WAITFOR – wait for signal condition
The WAITFOR command is used to suspend program execution until the specified input signal conditions are in the specified state.

The language that you design for the robot that you build has to reflect the capability of the physical structure of your particular robot. We will discuss the design of the language for your robot in Chapter 15, which is devoted to that subject.

CHAPTER TEN

Robotic vision – an introduction

This chapter provides both cursory and more detailed descriptions of a vision system's commands. Vision will be a **very important** part of all robots with time and understanding how the computer processes an image is of interest to all those with a serious interest in robotic software. If you have a serious interest in robotic vision, read the entire chapter. If you have only a cursory interest, you can read the first part and skip the rest of the chapter.

Why is vision important and what does vision have to do with robotics?

These are good questions because the uses of vision are not intuitively obvious to us. I will answer in a heuristic way rather than directly. Vision is important because a vision system allows us to import more information into the system more rapidly than any other system we currently have at our disposal. To be useful robots need to be intelligent and to be intelligent they need lots and lots of information. Vision provides this information very rapidly. Getting the information from the image is the task at hand.

A vision system, as used in the industrial/manufacturing context, is a combination of hardware and software that allows the user to record a visual image of an object or set of objects and to perform various manipulations on that video data to extract useful information. This information can be used for inspection, quality control, pattern recognition, location, measurements and for many other tasks. The tasks of capturing an image and displaying the image on a monitor are straightforward and use technology that has been around for quite a few years (television was first demonstrated by Farnsworth in the 1930s). The problem is that the task of extracting information from the stored image is a very computationally intensive process that requires mathematical operations on every piece of data that has been stored and then some. Not until the advent of low cost, high-speed computers was vision able to be affordable for use in the everyday manufacturing environment.

A basic vision system consists of a video camera to 'see' the desired object(s), a frame grabber (printed circuit board, electronics etc.) to capture the image, software to manage the hardware, memory components to store the image, a separate vision monitor to display the captured image, a camera stand to mount the camera and the computer and vision software to perform the many calculations (as functions) necessary to extract useful information from the stored image. All in all not a small order.

The theory of vision and all its associated algorithms are beyond the scope of this book, however a brief tutorial of the basics of vision and an explanation of some of the more important terms will be given here to show how even a fairly simple vision systems needs to offer a comprehensive set of commands if it is to allow the user to fully explore and understand the principles of vision. Many textbooks are now available on the more academic aspects of machine vision; you are encouraged to study a book that matches your understanding and interests.

Vision basics

For a vision system to provide useful data it must be able to perform three sequential steps:

- capture an image
- enhance the image
- and extract useful data from the image.

The sophistication of a vision system is dependent on the resolution of the image captured, the speed of these three steps and the amount and types of data extracted from the image. Any comprehensive vision system provides the hardware and software needed to carry out all three steps, with the speed and number of data types needed to use the machine vision system in the context for which it is designed.

The 'video camera' and 'frame grabber printed circuit board' pair is used to convert the different light levels that comprise a visual image into data that a computer can be programmed to understand. Converting an image into a computer compatible data structure requires that the image be broken up into small uniform areas; each small area is considered to be one uniform point of light and is defined by the size of the elements in the hardware at the focal plane of the camera. Each such area is called a pixel (PICture ELement) and represents the smallest area that the vision system can resolve – the more pixels there are in an image the higher the resolution of the system and the smaller the detectable detail. In the vision software the CAPTURE (or similar) command instructs the vision system to take the current vision image from the camera's image plane and store it in the system's memory. **After that it is all software**.

The number of light levels in black and white (no colour information is under discussion here) that a system can detect is described as the number of grey levels. The grey level is simply the resolution of the vision system in detecting the relative brightness of an individual pixel. The workable minimum is 32 grey levels, where the computer dedicates five bits of brightness information for each pixel and each pixel can have a value of from 0 to 31. For such a system, which may have a resolution of 256 by 200 pixels, there are a total of 1,638,400 bits (819,200 bytes) of information ($256 \times 200 \times 32$) for each image captured.

If colour is used, the amount of information explodes and becomes cumbersome to store and manipulate in a small system. Discussing colour adds nothing at the level of this introduction. For our present purposes, colour is just another level of grey although it is, of course, quite a bit more complicated than that. Grey levels address brightness of the pixel only and colour addresses both brightness and the frequency of each pixel and there is more than one frequency at each pixel.

To extract data, the computer must examine and manipulate each of these bytes of information, which, because of the sheer number of them, takes a finite amount of time. To reduce the processing time of the vision system, either a vision co-processor has to be used, a faster computer has to be used or the amount of data to be processed has to be reduced. Since in most situations the computer cannot be changed, researchers in vision have come up with various algorithms to reduce the amount of data without an appreciable loss in the *usability* of the information. One method (at our level of interest) is to reduce the amount of information per pixel is by **binarization**. Binarization examines each pixel and converts its brightness to one of only two levels – on and off or black and white.

Binarization is accomplished by specifying a **threshold** value, a grey level above which a pixel is assigned a value of 31 (fully on), and below which the pixel is assigned a value of 0

Figure 10.1 A grey image (3.5 inch diskette).

Figure 10.2 The above image as a binary image.

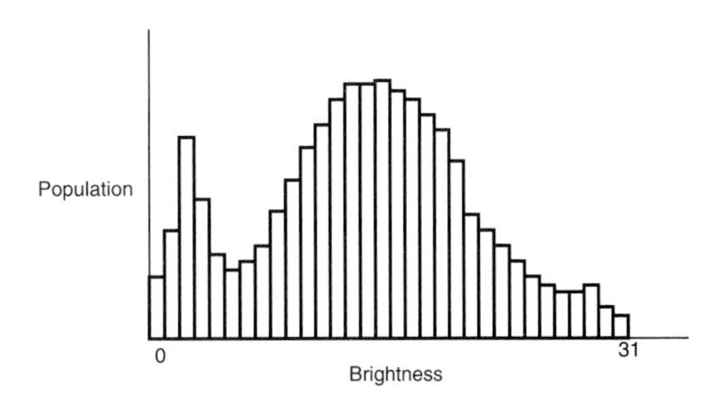

Figure 10.3 A histogram.

(fully off). Specifying the threshold can be done in two ways, automatically by allowing the computer to calculate the appropriate level or manually by specifying the threshold in the binarization command. Both methods use a **histogram** (which is a graphic plot of grey levels verses the number of pixels in each grey level). Using this plot, the system or user can determine the 32 levels which the pixels of the frame fall into and then determine a point between these peaks as the threshold.

A common task for any vision system is the recognition of objects. For an object to be recognisable by the system it must be visually distinct from the background i.e. it must have an edge which is defined as the area where the background stops and the object begins. Edge detection is where much of vision research has taken place – it is also the area where many of the vision algorithms are applied. To make edge detection reliable in the absence of optimum lighting or in the presence of suitable contrast requires the use of edge enhancement routines.

Convolution is one such technique (or routine). The concept of convolution is based on replacing a pixel's grey level value with a weighted sum of its surrounding pixels. The table of weights which are to be applied to the neighbouring pixels is called a **kernel**. There are a number of standard kernels that have been developed for use in vision. These emphasize either the speed or the quality of edge enhancement. These standard kernels have their values set such that only pixels that lie on an edge of an object will have their values increased after the convolution has taken place, both the background and interior space will have their values reduced. In this way the vision system detects or enhances only edges of objects. See the convolution command described later.

Once an object has been detected the vision system determines various parameters for the object. This allows the vision system programmer to use this information to compare the object with a desired object or a list of objects. The SEGMENT command computes a list of parameters for each object such as area, number of holes, minimum X position, maximum X position, minimum Y position, maximum Y position, angle of orientation, X position of the object's centroid , Y position of the centroid and more. These values are then used to determine what is being looked at and what is to be done to the object seen. See the SEGMENT command for details.

The term 'window' will appear throughout the command descriptions. A window is any rectangular subset of an entire frame and each rectangular window is defined by specifying the co-ordinates of two opposite corners. By default two windows are predefined, the first window,

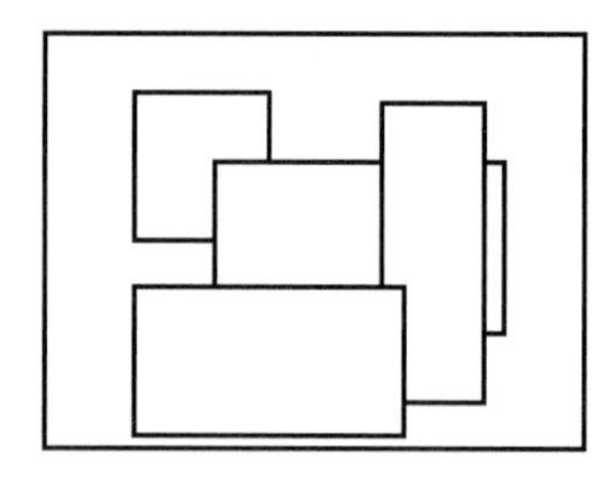

Figure 10.4 Windows on a computer screen.

window number 1, is called the **display window** which is the entire frame image of the frame grabber board. The display window is displayed continually on the vision monitor when the system is in the LIVE mode. A second window, **window number 2** called the **storage window**, is a block of memory allocated in the computer's memory area. This allows a transient image to be stored in a stable memory area where it can be manipulated mathematically. Windows are classified as a display window or a storage window depending on which memory area they reference. Keep in mind that though the information in window 1 is of a transient nature it can be captured and transferred to other sections of computer memory for later evaluation.

Figure 10.5 gives us an overview of the hardware aspects of the vision system.

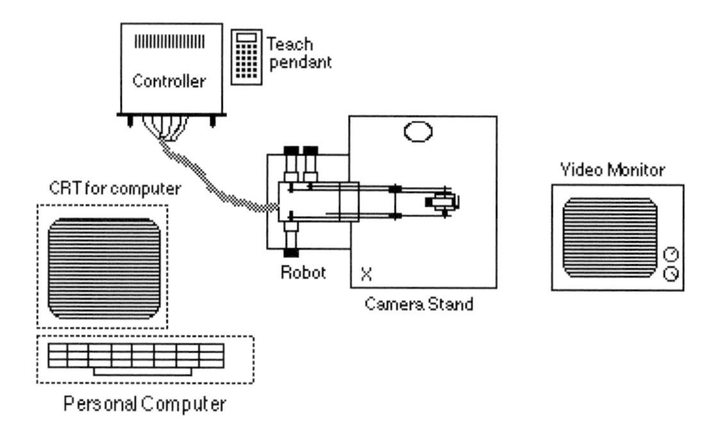

Figure 10.5 A laboratory vision equipment layout in plan.

Next let us take a look at the **vision instruction set** for an educational vision system. These instructions are from the RoboTalk language and represent a rudimentary instruction set. Sophisticated industrial systems have powerful instruction sets that allow much more comprehensive control over image manipulation.

The next few descriptions give you a quick overview of the kind of commands a vision system uses. The later discussion is in much greater detail and can be ignored if you do not have a great interest in robotic vision.

VISINIT
Initializes the vision system and sets the camera to the live mode. Every control system needs a way to reset it to make sure that you are starting out from a known condition.

CAPTURE
This will capture a video frame in the capture board's display memory. This is the act of moving the information from the camera to the memory area.

LIVE
This selects the live mode on the capture board so that input from the camera is displayed directly on the monitor, in real time.

CALIBRATE
Calibrates the home position and the ratio of pixels in the board image to world co-ordinates so that the robot can actually interact with what is seen by the camera. The user is prompted to place an object with the upper right corner over a known point in front of the camera and press return. Then the user is prompted to type in the X and Y world co-ordinates of the point.

HISTOGRAM
Will display a pop-up screen with a bar graph of the number of pixels in the display memory having each of 32 grey level values. An array which is accessible through RoboTalk is filled with the 32 numbers.

BINARIZE
Binarizes an image in display memory with a given grey level value as the threshold.

SEGMENT
Makes a list of the objects in a frame, along with their characteristics.

OBJECT.CHARACTERISTIC
Here OBJECT is an integer variable with the value of 1 up to OBJECTS, where OBJECTS is the returned number of objects. Characteristic is one of: AREA: HOLES: MINX: MAXX: MINY: MAXY: ANGLE: CENTERX: CENTERY: NAME.

CONVOLVE
Performs convolution on a captured frame for edge enhancement and/or filtering.

DILATE
Performs dilation on a captured and binarized frame. Parameters are as in the convolve command. Dark pixels are dilated.

ERODE
Performs erosion on a captured and binarized frame.

GETK
Gets a kernel from the user and assigns it to the number specified in the kernel parameter. Numbers assigned as defaults are: 1 – Sobel magnitude, 2 – Sobel directional, 3 – Roberts magnitude, 4 – Roberts directional. The directional kernels are actually two kernels each, but they are assigned one number.

SAVEK
Saves a kernel to a disk file.

LEARN
Saves identification information in memory for a frame of objects. The user is prompted to type in the name of each object in the frame.

REMEMBER
Writes a frame of learned objects to a disk file specified in filename.

RECALL
Retrieves a frame of learned objects from a disk file specified in filename.

MATCH
Matches an object to the frame of objects already learned (or recalled).

WINDOW
Sets up a window in the display memory or storage memory. There are two memory areas: the DISPLAY memory which is displayed when in capture mode and is on the ICB board, and the STORAGE memory, which is not on the board, but in RAM on the computer. Storage memory is the same size as display memory and can be used in commands.

SAVEW
Saves a window to a file.

GETW
Gets a window's contents from a file.

PIXMATH
Performs pixel operations on windows. The operation is one of the following: AND, OR, NOT, XOR, ADD, SUB, MUL, DIV, MIN, MAX, MOV, LUT, SWITCH.

SETLUT
Displays the contents of the look up table, and then prompts the user to type in the 32 values of the look up table.

DRAW_LINE
Draws a line in the display memory.

ERASE_LINE
Erases a line drawn with DRAW_LINE.

GET_INTERSECTS
Gets the number of pixel transitions in the display memory along a line.

COLOR
Highlights an object with a specified colour.

LABEL
Labels a point in display memory with a string variable, quote, integer or decimal variable.

More detailed descriptions and notes (optional reading, very heavy)

Understanding computer vision will be a new experience for almost all readers. As such, the operation of the vision system is not going to be obvious to you. This means that almost everything about computer-based vision has to be learned from the ground up.

It is important to understand that the vision commands constitute a set of powerful tools. *They do not constitute a solution – they are the tools to create a solution.* The solutions have to be created by the user because each problem needs a unique solution.

In any problem, a part of the solution is to simplify the problem so that it can be solved. This may consist of breaking the problem up into smaller parts so that it is easier to manage or a number of other techniques may be used. The same is true in vision. The most important thing you can do is to simplify the task before vision is applied to the system. As expertise in the work with vision systems is gained, more complicated tasks will be able to be solved. Start with one object at a time before moving on to many objects and build up the vision program slowly.

Lighting plays an important role in vision because it affects what the camera sees. Strive for good uniform lighting that is constant. Constancy is the most important aspect of the lighting system as far as a vision system is concerned.

In the following list of vision commands, the commands are listed in capital letters and the parameters follow. If the parameter is optional it is shown between brackets, otherwise it is not optional.

BINARIZE

When you capture an image, it is made up of a grid of picture elements or pixels. Each pixel is digitized so that it is assigned a number value between 0 and 31 depending on its brightness level (we are discussing black and white images only at this time). This number is referred to as the pixel's grey level – 0 is completely black and 31 is completely white. When an image or frame of an object is taken, a method for determining which pixels belong to the object and which do not must be found. In other words, a way of distinguishing between foreground and background must be found. One way to do this is to pick one grey level value, and set all pixels with grey levels below that value to 0 and all pixels with grey levels above that value to 31. This is known as binarizing the image, because the result is an image with two grey levels (black and white) – a binary image. The grey level value picked as the dividing line is known as the threshold and is specifiable.

The general form of the command is:

```
BINARIZE [<window>][,<threshold>]
```

The **window parameter** indicates the subwindow of the display that will be used. If no parameter is provided for window, the display window (1) is assumed. See the WINDOW command for a more detailed explanation and discussion.

If no **threshold** value is given in the binarize command, a suitable value for the threshold will be picked based on a histogram of the image, otherwise the threshold parameter given is used as the threshold.

CALIBRATE

The CALIBRATE command co-ordinates the 2-dimensional vision system with the robot in 2 space. Without the CALIBRATE command, the vision system does not know where the camera is with respect to the area seen by the camera, so that values in millimetres and inches are meaningless.

Calibration is necessary because the system permits the user to move the camera with respect to the robot. If we knew the camera position was fixed at all times we would not have to do this. The price for doing this would be less flexibility. Once the vision system knows where the camera is with respect to the robot, we can translate pixels in the camera image into millimetre or inch measurements that the robot can relate to.

One way to calibrate the system would be to have the user measure exactly where the camera is and how it is rotated. This is tedious and subject to errors. Instead we take a snapshot of objects for which the millimetre or inch positions can be determined. These positions can be determined by being taught to the robot with the teach pendant.

The general form of the command is:

```
CALIBRATE [<threshold>][, <window>]
```

The optional **threshold parameter** is used as a threshold for binarizing the image used for the calibration. If it is not given, an adaptive binarization is used. See the BINARIZE command for more information about using a threshold to binarize an image.

The optional **window parameter** is used to allow the user to set a slightly smaller window than the display in case there is noise at the edges of the field of view. If it is not given then the entire field of view is used. See the WINDOW command for more information on windows.

CALIBRATE_F

The CALIBRATE_F command can (in some cases) be used in place of the CALIBRATE command, thus avoiding much of the tedious and time consuming calibration procedure.

When the CALIBRATE_F command is used, calibration data is taken from a disk file named CALIBRAT.DAT rather than from taught points. The data has to have been stored in the file before it can be recalled. The data is only valid for one location of the robot with respect to the vision system.

The general form of the command is:

```
CALIBRATE_F
```

There are no parameters.

When the CALIBRATE command is issued it creates a file named CALIBRAT.DAT on the disk. Once a system has been set up and calibrated with the CALIBRATE command, the CALIBRATE_F command can be used. *As long as the relative robot to vision system positions have NOT changed and the units of measure have not been changed.*

CAPTURE

The CAPTURE command digitizes an image from the camera and stores it in the frame grabber's buffer memory. Since this is an analogue to digital conversion process, it is highly unlikely that any two frames captured (even if they are captured at nearly the same time) will have exactly the same grey level information for each and every pixel in the frame. This means that subsequent operations on such frames such as binarizing and segmenting will also yield slightly different information.

The CAPTURE command needs no parameters. It *always* stores the image in window 1 in window 2.

The general form of the command is:

```
CAPTURE
```

There are no parameters.

COLOR

The COLOR command highlights an object on the vision monitor with a colour specified by red, green, and blue components. The information in colour is always provided by the user. This allows you to easily differentiate between information provided by the vision system and information provided by you. This works in this system because all the vision information is in black and white.

The general form of the command is:

```
COLOR <id>, <red value>, <green value>,
   <blue value>
```

The <id> refers to the object's id number as used to reference parameters with the segment command.

Each of the **red, green and blue parameters** can have a value from 0 to 31 inclusive.

Before an object can be coloured, it must have been segmented. The SEGMENT command automatically sets a variable called OBJECTS, which is the number of objects that were found in the frame (remember holes are also separate objects). A loop can then be used to access all the objects, for example: for K=1 to OBJECTS, where K is the object's id number.

CONVOLVE

The CONVOLVE command performs convolution or edge enhancement on a captured frame. The image can be either binary or not.

A full discussion of the enhancement of images can be found in any good text on computerized vision systems. The discussion here is limited to the discussion of the command as is it is used in RoboTalk.

The general form of the command is:

CONVOLVE <kernel>, <destination>,
<source> [,<directional / magnitude>]

Convolutions enhance the edges of objects in a frame. The **kernel parameter** specifies the kind of edge enhancement to be used.

Normally a frame would simply be binarized to distinguish between foreground and background, and then the SEGMENT command, which requires a binary image, would be used. Before this is done, a convolution can be used to perform some grey level processing (if speed is not critical). This process will highlight the edge of an object. Then the BINARIZE and SEGMENT commands can be used to treat the edge of the object as an object. This gives a capability to the system which is beyond that which a purely binary system would have. The kernel parameter can indicate a kernel that has been custom made by the user, or default values can be used. A description of the defaults is provided below.

The **destination parameter** is a window number which can be either a display window number or a storage window number.

The **source parameter** is a window number which can be either a display window number or a storage window number. The destination window must be at least as large as the source window. If one window is a display window and the other is a storage window, their pixel boundaries must either exactly coincide or not overlap at all. See the WINDOW command for a description of display and storage windows.

There are two types of kernels, directional and non-directional. A non-directional kernel is a $k \times k$ grid of pixel weights, where k is the kernel size. The grid is used for each pixel in the source window. The surrounding pixels are multiplied by the corresponding weight values and these products are added together. The total result is then put in the destination pixel.

The difference between a directional and a non-directional kernel is that a directional kernel actually consists of two grids, for which two totals will be calculated. The two grids will be the same size but may contain different values. Two different operations can then be done with these two totals. The arc-tangent of one total divided by another gives a **measure of the direction of an edge** near the source pixel, and so this operation is called a directional operation with a directional kernel. The square root of the sum of the squares of the two totals gives a **measure of the steepness of the edge** near the source pixel, and this operation is called a magnitude operation with a directional kernel. So the last parameter is only valid for directional kernels. For this parameter, an 0 (or the omission of the parameter) indicates a **magnitude operation** with a directional kernel, and 1 indicates a **directional operation** with a directional kernel.

All parameters to this command are integer expressions.

CURSOR

The CURSOR command displays a cross hair cursor on the vision monitor and the X and Y world co-ordinates of the cursor on the computer monitor. The user can move the cursor with the arrow keys on the numeric keypad. The shift arrow keys stretch and shrink the cursor. The minus key decreases the stride and the plus key increases the stride. The camera must have been calibrated before the CURSOR command is issued.

The general form of the command is:

CURSOR [<window>]

The **window parameter** is used to clip the cursor to a window that may be smaller than the display. It is an integer expression.

DILATE

The DILATE command performs dilation on a captured and binarized window. Dilation in combination with erosion can be used for closing small holes that may be caused by noise within an image. Dilation expands or spreads pixels out according to a pattern specified in the kernel.

The general form of the command is:

DILATE <kernel>, <destination>, <source>

All parameters for this command are integer expressions.

The **kernel parameter** is the number of a kernel previously defined. It must not be a directional kernel. The DILATE command uses a kernel slightly differently from the way the CONVOLVE command uses it. For the DILATE command, the kernel is considered as a grid of Boolean values, that is, 0 or non-zero values. The grid is masked over the source pixel and its surrounding pixels, and for each non-zero grid entry, if the centre or source pixel is 0 (black) then the pixel corresponding to that grid entry is also set to 0. If that grid entry is 0, then the corresponding pixel is not changed. In this way, black (usually foreground) pixels are dilated according to a pattern specified in the kernel.

The **destination parameter** is a window number which can be either a display window number or a storage window number.

The **source parameter** is a window number which can be either a display window number or a storage window number, but it must not overlap the destination window.

See the WINDOW command for a more detailed explanation of windows.

DISPLAY

The DISPLAY command outputs the contents of the display memory to the monitor. This is similar to the LIVE command which directs the video camera's output to the monitor. The DISPLAY command directs the monitor to show the contents of the frame grabber's memory.

The general form of the command is:

DISPLAY

Issue the DISPLAY command whenever you want to display the contents of the frame grabber board memory. This command moves window 2 to window 1 and thus makes it visible. Window 2 contains whatever was on the LIVE display when CAPTURE was last issued. So DISPLAY lets you go back from LIVE to the last image that was captured.

DRAW_LINE

The DRAW_LINE command draws a line in the display memory from a point whose co-ordinates are $x1, y1$ to a point whose co-ordinates are $x2, y2$.

The general form of the command is:

DRAW_LINE <x1>, <y1>, <x2>, <y2>

If the parameters are integer expressions, the end points are interpreted as pixels. If the parameters are floating expressions, the end points are interpreted as millimetres or inches depending on the units of measure set in the CONFIG menu.

ERASE_LINE

The ERASE_LINE command erases a line drawn with DRAW_LINE in the display memory from a point whose co-ordinates are *x*1,*y*1 to a point whose co-ordinates are *x*2,*y*2.

The general form of the command is:

ERASE_LINE <x1>, <y1>, <x2>, <y2>

If the parameters are integer expressions, the end points are interpreted as pixels. If the parameters are floating expressions, the end points are interpreted as millimetres or inches depending on the units of measure set in the CONFIG menu.

ERODE

The ERODE command performs erosion on a captured and binarized window. Erosion in combination with dilation can be used for eliminating small notches that may be caused by noise in an image. Erosion contracts or shrinks pixels according to a pattern specified in the kernel.

The general form of the command is:

ERODE <kernel>, <destination>, <source>

All parameters to this command are integer expressions.

The **kernel parameter** is the number of a kernel previously defined. It must not be a directional kernel. The ERODE command uses a kernel slightly differently from the way the CONVOLVE command uses it. For the ERODE command, the kernel is considered as a grid of Boolean values, that is, 0 or non-zero values. The grid is masked over the source pixel and its surrounding pixels, and for each non-zero grid entry, if the centre or source pixel is 31 (white) then the pixel corresponding to that grid entry is also set to 31. If that grid entry is 0, then the corresponding pixel is not changed. In this way, white (usually background) pixels are dilated, and black (usually foreground) pixels are eroded according to a pattern specified in the kernel.

The **destination parameter** is a window number which can be either a display window number or a storage window number.

The **source parameter** is a window number which can be either a display window number or a storage window number, but it must not overlap the destination window.

See the WINDOW command for a more detailed explanation of windows.

GETINTSECT

The GETINTSECT command gets the number of intersections or pixel transitions from an intersect line that was set up with the SETINTSECT command. See the SETINTSECT command and the GET_INTERSECTS command for a more complete description of intersect lines.

The general form of the command is:

GETINTSECT <line number>, <variable name>
[,<x>, <y>, <u>, <v>]

Line number is an integer expression and refers to an intersect line set up as above.

Variable name refers to an integer or integer array variable where the number of intersects along the line is to be put.

As an example, suppose you had a solid object in the middle of the screen. You binarize the image and then set up an intersect line with the SETINTSECT command:

```
SETINTSECT 1    set up the line to cross the object
GETINTSECT 1,K
TYPE K
```

will cause the number of transitions, in this case 2, to be typed. This command works on grey level images, but every change in grey level produces a transition, so there will be many transitions. These commands GETINTSECT and SETINTSECT are analogous to the GET_INTERSECTS command, except that lines can be set up by hand instead of with numbers.

The **last four parameters** are optional. They can be either all integer variable names or all floating variable names (preceded by an @). Integer array elements can be used in place of integer variable names. If they are all integer variables or integer array elements then the pixel values of the first two transitions will be put in them, with the first transition first. If they are all floating point variables then the coordinates in millimetres or inches of the first two transitions will be put in them, with the first transition first. If there are no transitions and these parameters are included, the variables will be indeterminate.

GET_INTERSECTS

The GET_INTERSECTS command gets the number of pixel transitions along a line in display memory. The frame or window does not have to have been binarized, but if it is not there may be too many pixel transitions for the information to be useful.

The general form of the command is:

```
GET_INTERSECTS <x1>, <y1>, <x2>, <y2>,
  <variable name>
    [, <x>, <y>, <u>, <v>]
```

The line is defined as in the DRAW_LINE command, where if the end points are given as integer expressions they are considered as pixels, or if the end points are given as floating expressions they are considered as millimetres or inches. The number of transitions is put in the integer or integer array variable that is given by variable name. A transition is detected if the pixel value changes from one pixel to the next along the line.

The **last four parameters** are optional. They can be either all integer variable names or all floating variable names (preceded by an @). Integer array elements can be used in place of integer variable names. If they are all integer variables or integer array elements then the pixel values of the first two transitions will be put in them, with the first transition first. If they are all floating point variables then the coordinates in millimetres or inches of the first two transitions will be put in them, with the first transition first. If there are no transitions and these parameters are included, the variables will be indeterminate.

GETK

The GETK command inputs a kernel definition and assigns it to the number specified in the kernel parameter.

The general form of the command is:

```
GETK <kernel> [,<filename>]
```

If the **filename parameter** is given, the **kernel** is read from a file written previously with the SAVEK command. The filename parameter must be a string variable or a quote. If the filename parameter is not given, the user is asked to type in a kernel, and it is assigned the number given in the first parameter, which is an integer expression. Default numbers assigned by the system (these numbers *cannot* be reassigned) are:

1 Sobel magnitude
2 Sobel directional
3 Roberts magnitude
4 Roberts directional

These are defined as follows:
Sobel:

dx =	–1	0	1
	–2	0	2
	–1	0	1

dy =	1	2	1
	0	0	0
	–1	–2	–1

Roberts:

dx =	–1	0
	0	1

dy =	0	1
	–1	0

Try defining your own kernel and using it with the CONVOLVE command. A good one to try would be the Laplacian, which is non-directional:

1	4	1
4	–20	4
1	4	1

GETW

The GETW command retrieves a window's contents from a file.

The general form of the command is:

GETW <window>, <filename> [, <storage>]

The filename does not have to have an extension but an extension of .win will be used as the default. The **filename** must be a string variable or a quote.

The **window parameter** is an integer expression that defines where the file's contents will go. If that window number has not already been assigned, it will be assigned bounds identical to those with which the file was written. If the window had been set up previously, it must be big enough to hold the window in the file.

The **storage parameter** is only necessary if the window had not been defined, and it is 0 if the file is to be written to display memory, or 1 if the file is to be written to storage memory.

HISTOGRAM

After a CAPTURE, the HISTOGRAM command collects information on the total number of pixels with each of the 32 grey levels. The results are put into the integer array h[0..31], or histogram[0..31].

The general form of the command is:

HISTOGRAM [<window>] [, <bargraph>]

The **window parameter**, which is an integer expression, defines the sub-window on the display which will be used in collecting the histogram information. The window parameter must be a display window and not a storage window. The default window is 1, which is the entire display.

The **bargraph parameter** is an integer parameter which specifies whether a bargraph of the histogram is to be displayed on the PC's monitor. If it is 1 the bargraph will be displayed, and if it is 0 (the default) it will not be displayed. The histogram[0..31] array, along with the lut[0..31] or look up table array, are set up when the VISINIT command is issued.

LABEL

The LABEL command displays the contents of the third parameter on the vision monitor.

The general form of the command is:

```
LABEL <x>, <y>, <string/quote/int/float
  variable> [, <erase>][, <size>]
```

The third parameter is displayed at a point whose co-ordinates are given by *x* and *y*. The first two parameters, if they are integer expressions, are interpreted as pixels, or if they are floating expressions they are interpreted as millimetres or inches, depending on the current units specified in CONFIG.

The variable or value written to the monitor can be a quote, or the value of a string variable, integer expression, or floating expression.

The **erase parameter**, if included and not 0, will cause whatever had been drawn with a previous and identical label command to be erased.

The **size parameter** defines how large the displayed text will be, and can have a value from 1 to 4, with the default being 2.

LEARN

The LEARN command saves identification information in memory for a frame of objects.

The general form of the command is:

```
LEARN
```

The user is prompted to type in the name of each object in the frame. Each object will be labelled on the screen with a number by the system. The user types in that object's name.

Up to 35 objects can be learned in a frame. These objects are used as templates against which other objects will be matched with the match command.

One frame of learned objects can be kept in memory at one time and the number that can be written and recalled from disk is limited only by available file space.

The commands to read and write this template information to disk are the REMEMBER and RECALL commands.

LIVE

This selects the live mode of the frame grabber board so that input from the camera is displayed directly on the vision monitor.

The general form of the command is:

```
LIVE
```

MATCH

The MATCH command matches an object to the object template information stored in memory by the LEARN or RECALL commands.

The general form of the command is:

```
MATCH <id> [, <weight1>][, <weight2>]...[,
  <weightK>]
[, <"characteristic-1,...characteristic-K">]
```

The **id parameter** is an integer expression which identifies the object to be matched, and it is a number between 1 and the system variable OBJECTS inclusive.

The subsequent parameters are optional, and if they are omitted the default mode of matching objects is used.

The **weight parameters** refer to the corresponding characteristics in the last parameter, which is a string. Each characteristic is assigned a weight according to its order in the string. For example:

```
MATCH K,2,3,"area,perimeter"
```

would indicate that object K is to be matched to the template objects and its perimeter is to be considered 1.5 times as important relative to its area in the matching process. The weight parameters are integer expressions. Their value does not affect their order, only the corresponding characteristic in the string affects their order.

The result of the match is that the name of the object among the template objects which is found to be the nearest match to the object given in the match command is copied into that object's namefield. So for the example above, object K may not have a name prior to the above MATCH command being issued. After that MATCH command K\rquote s.name might be "square" if it matched an object in the template objects with a name of "square" in the nearest neighbour sense.

Proper lighting is very important as the MATCH command is very sensitive.

The valid characteristics that can be listed in the characteristic string are:

MOMENTS (invariant moments)
AREA (area excluding holes)
PERIMETER (length along outside perimeter)
MAJORAXIS (length along major axis)
MINORAXIS (length along minor axis)
COMPACTNESS (4*PI*area/perimeter^2)
CIRCULARITY (4*area/(PI*majoraxis^2))
ELONGATEDNESS1 (abbreviated by e1, area/minoraxis^2)
ELONGATEDNESS2 (abbreviated by e2, majoraxis/minoraxis)
POROSITY (area of holes/area of object)
HOLES (number of holes)

The above characteristics can be abbreviated by the first two letters of the characteristic name: i.e. co for compactness. If the weights are not included, they default to 1. The string can include any of the above fields in any order. The default method of matching takes into account each characteristic and considers the distances together, as in a vector distance, instead of separately as in the weighting scheme described above.

PIXMATH

The PIXMATH command performs various pixel operations on windows.

The general form of the command is:

PIXMATH <operation>, <destination>, <source>

The operation, which must be a string variable or a quote, can be one of the following: AND, OR, NOT, XOR, ADD, SUB, MUL, DIV, MIN, MAX, MOV, LUT, SWITCH.

The source and destination can be the same or can overlap, except in the case of the SWITCH command, where overlapping windows cannot be switched.

For DIV and SUB, which are not commutative, the order is destination = source of destination.

The MOV operation simply moves the window.

The LUT operation moves the window while translating each pixel with the LUT[0..31] array. This array can be set directly one value at a time or with the SETLUT command.

The destination window must be at least as big as the source window.

The destination and source window parameters are integer expressions.

RECALL

The RECALL command retrieves a frame of learned objects from a disk file.

The general form of the command is:

RECALL <filename>

The file to be retrieved is specified in filename, which is a string variable or a quoted filename.

See the MATCH command for an example of its use. The filename can be specified with or without an .obs extension. If it is not specified it will be provided.

REMEMBER

The REMEMBER command writes a frame of learned objects to a disk file.

The general form of the command is:

REMEMBER <filename>

The file is saved under **filename**, which is a string variable or a quoted filename.

The LEARN command must previously have been issued.

The filename can be specified with or without an .obs extension, which will be provided if it is not specified.

See the MATCH command for an example of the use of the REMEMBER command.

SAVEK

The SAVEK command saves a kernel to disk.

The general form of the command is:

SAVEK <kernel>, <filename>

Kernel is an integer expression kernel.

The **filename parameter** must be a string variable or quote. It does not have to have an extension. The file created will have the extension .ker.

A kernel can be retrieved from disk with the GETK command.

SAVEW

The SAVEW command saves the specified window's contents to a file.

The general form of the command is:

SAVEW <window>, <filename>

The **window parameter** is an integer expression that specifies the window. The window number can be either a display or a storage window.

The **filename parameter** is a string variable or quote that specifies the file where the window will be stored. The file will have the extension .win but this does not have to be provided.

See the WINDOW command for a more detailed discussion and description of windows.

SEGMENT

The SEGMENT command makes a list of the objects in a frame, along with their characteristics.

Before you can use SEGMENT, the system must be calibrated. After calibration the vision system must be in the capture mode and the frame must have been binarized.

The general form of the command is:

SEGMENT [<window>][, <weedcount>]

The **window parameter** must be a display window number. The default is 1 which is the entire display frame.

The **weedcount parameter** is the minimum number of pixels that must be in an object or a hole for it to count as such. The default is 2.

The object's characteristics can be referred to subsequently in any statement with:

OBJECT.CHARACTERISTIC

where OBJECT is an integer variable with the value of 1 up to OBJECTS, where OBJECTS is the returned number of objects. The same characteristics accessible for each object are also accessible for that object's holes. For example, to access the characteristics of the holes in object i, you would use i.holes.j.characteristic, where j is the hole number. A characteristic is one of the following:

AREA: The area of the object in world units. A decimal variable.

ANGLE: Orientation angle, from –90 to 90 degrees, where 0 is horizontal (along positive X axis) and 90 is positive vertical (along positive Y axis). A decimal variable.

BORDERPIX: The number of pixels in the perimeter of the object. An integer value.

CENTERX: X centroid in world co-ordinates. A decimal variable.

CENTERY: Y centroid in world co-ordinates. A decimal variable.

CIRCULARITY: Defined as (4\'b9 * area) / majoraxis. A decimal variable.

COMPACTNESS: Defined as (4\'b9 * area) / perimeter. A decimal variable.

ELONGATEDNESS1: Defined as area / minoraxis. A decimal variable.

ELONGATEDNESS2: Defined as majoraxis / minoraxis. A decimal variable.

HOLES: Number of holes(objects) within this object. An integer variable.

MAJORAXIS: Distance in world co-ordinates along the major axis. A decimal variable.

MAXX: The largest X co-ordinate of the object in world co-ordinates. A decimal variable.

MAXY: The largest Y co-ordinate of the object in world co-ordinates. A decimal variable.

MINORAXIS: Distance in world co-ordinates along the minor axis. A decimal variable.

MINX: The lowest X co-ordinate of the object in world co-ordinates. A decimal variable.

MINY: The lowest Y co-ordinate of the object in world co-ordinates. A decimal variable.

NAME: A character variable of up to 15 characters, which identifies the object's shape. This is initialized with the MATCH command. A string variable.

PERIMETER: The distance in world units around the object. A decimal variable.

PIXELS: The number of pixels in the object. An integer variable.

POROSITY: Defined as (area of all holes) / area. A decimal variable.

The following is an example of how to use the segment command:

```
      CAPTURE      capture image
      BINARIZE     binarize with adaptive threshold
      SEGMENT      make object list, OBJECTS vari-
                     able is set
      FOR I=1 TO OBJECTS
          IF I.HOLES = 1 THEN GOTO 100
          GOTO 200
100       I.NAME = "WIDGET"    every object with a
                     hole is a widget
          GOTO 300
200       I.NAME = "THINGAMAJIG" otherwise it's
                     a thingamajig
300       IF I.ANGLE < 0 THEN GOTO 400 check
                     angle
          PRINT I.NAME," IS OUT OF KILTER"
400  NEXT
```

As another example, say you wanted to know the distance between the holes in all objects that have two holes:

```
     FOR I = 1 TO OBJECTS
     IF I.HOLES = 2 THEN GOTO 100
     GOTO 200
100  J = 1
     K = 2
     @D = ((I.HOLE.J.CENTERX -
                  I.HOLE.K.CENTERX) ^ 2 +
                  (I.HOLE.J.CENTERY -
                  I.HOLE.K.CENTERY) ^ 2) ^ 0.5
200  continue
```

SETINTSECT

The SETINTSECT command allows a user to set up an intersect line with the arrow keys. See the GET_INTERSECTS command for a more detailed description of intersect lines.

The general form of the command is:

```
SETINTSECT <lineno> [, <x>, <y>, <u>,
  <v>][, <window>]
```

Lineno is an integer or integer expression from 1 to 20 inclusive, which specifies an intersect line that can be referred to later. When this command is issued, the user is prompted to set an intersect line with the arrow keys on the numeric key pad. The arrow keys shift the intersect line, and the <shift> arrow keys spin or shrink the line. The <+> key will increase the increment with which the line is moved (the stride), and the <-> key will decrease it. Once the line is set up, it can be referred to in subsequent GETINTSECT commands.

The **x, y, u and v parameters** are integer or integer array variables in which the ending points of the line in pixels are returned.

The **window parameter** specifies the window to which the intersect line will be clipped. It must not be a storage window.

SETLUT

The SETLUT command displays the contents of the look up table and then prompts the user to type in the 32 values of the look up table.

The general form of the command is:

```
SETLUT
```

The look up table is an array accessible through RoboTalk as L[0..31] or LUT[0..31]. When used with the PIXMATH command, this will serve as a translate table for pixel values.

VISINIT

Initializes the vision system and sets the camera in live mode.

The general form of the command is:

```
VISINIT
```

The histogram array HISTOGRAM[0..31], along with the look up table array LUT[0..31], are set up when the VISINIT command is issued. See HISTOGRAM instruction.

This command must be executed in each program before any other vision command is given.

It must be given in the DO mode before any other vision command is used in the DO mode.

WINDOW

The WINDOW command sets up a window in the display memory or in the storage memory. These are the two memory areas in the system.

The **display memory** is on the frame grabber board and it is where the image is stored when a capture command is issued. The capture and display commands display this area.

The **storage memory** is a part of the memory in the PC, and it is used by the PIXMATH, CONVOLVE, DILATE, ERODE, or GETW commands to move areas from the display memory to or from the storage memory.

A window is a subregion of either the display memory or the storage memory.

The general form of the command is:

```
WINDOW <window> [, <winminx>,
  <winminy>, <winmaxx>, <winmaxy>]
  [, <storage>]
```

The first parameter is an integer expression that gives a number to the window. The rest of the parameters are optional. If they are not given, the user can set up a window in the display memory with the arrow keys on the numeric keypad. The arrow keys move the window's centre, and the <shift>arrow keys shrink or expand the window.The <+> key increases the stride and the <-> key decreases the stride.

If the parameters after the window parameter are given, then the next four are the pixel boundaries that the window will have. They will be integer expressions. The last parameter specifies whether this window will exist in storage or display memory. It is an integer expression, and if it is 0 the window is in display memory. If it is 1 the window is in storage memory. Two windows are defaults: the entire display memory is window 1. The entire storage memory is window 2. They each have window boundaries of x,y = 0, 0 for the lower left corner and x,y = 199, 255 for the upper right corner. Windows 3 to 50 can be defined by the user.

CHAPTER ELEVEN

Selecting a suitable robot design for building

In this chapter I will show you how I selected a robot design that can be built by the average tinkerer with relative ease and at a reasonable cost. The design I selected had to have interesting possibility for experimentation and help to introduce the builder to the general concepts associated with robotics.

There are a number of important items that have to be considered carefully when deciding to build anything as complicated as a robot. The ones that I considered the most important for this particular project to be successful were as follows:

(1) The cost of the total project had to be kept as reasonable as possible so that the largest number of people could afford to build it.
(2) Anyone with average building skills had to be able to build the robot.
(3) The tools needed to build the robot had to be inexpensive and readily available.
(4) The components needed had to be inexpensive and readily available.
(5) The finished robot had to be able to run from an inexpensive computer with no need for any unusual or expensive computer peripherals.
(6) The robot had to be able to be easily programmed by someone not familiar with sophisticated programming techniques but willing to put in the time to learn how.
(7) The robot had to be complicated enough to make this an interesting and educational project.

I decided not to implement feedback from the general environment of the robot back to the computer because this adds too much cost and complication to a rudimentary project designed to be an "introduction to robotics". If you like, you can make these additions to the robot that you build. Printed circuit boards called add-on cards that allow you to interact with the environment of the computer/robot are available for almost all computers. These cards let you detect both digital and analogue signals and all the information you need to use each card is easy to understand and implement. It will be easier for you to use digital information only (on/off signals) in the early stages of your experimentation.

As we discussed in the first half of the book, any robot is essentially a number of motors and linkages that are controlled by a computer. This being the case, the selection of the motors becomes a prime consideration because we need a large number of them for all but the most rudimentary devices. If we select the wrong motors, the expense will become prohibitive and the interconnection between the motors and the computer will become too difficult for the novice to undertake.

The motors we select must have a way that allows us to position their output shafts to a specifiable location under computer control. In industrial robots like the ones one would find on the shop floor, this is done with a dedicated microprocessor that run each motor. Each motor has an (incremental) encoder attached to it for feedback. Using optical encoders is expensive and would be very difficult for the average tinkerer to implement. For this reason I decided to avoid using optical encoders altogether. This means that our solution has to have some sort of absolute position indicator that gives us the position of the shaft that we are controlling. Although not the most accurate indicator, a variable resistor or potentiometer is the most inexpensive way to encode the position of a shaft. This technique will be accurate enough for the uses we have in mind and will adequately serve our needs.

An inexpensive motor-resistor package with a built-in feedback system, gearbox and amplifiers is used by model aircraft hobbyists for controlling the control surfaces of radio controlled model aircraft. I decided to use these servos to provide the muscles for the robot – they cost about $12.00 (£8.00) each (1997 US retail) and contain all the circuitry that we need to position them automatically with a computer. These motors respond to the length of an electrical pulse and position themselves in accordance with the length of this pulse. To do this these servo motor packages must have a feedback system built into them. This feedback is self-contained in the servo and error signals from it are not available to us at the host computer. This means that we cannot make any decisions based on these error signals. Once we send out the pulse, the servo works to assume the position commanded and we assume that it did so successfully. This is not ideal but in our case it is satisfactory and, most important, affordable.

The controllers for these motors use small single chip computers called microcontrollers as their control component. Each controller can control 8 motors and more than one microcontroller can be used on one device (we will use only one). The integrated circuit used as the brains of the controller has all the components of a computer on it. A fully fledged controller can be made by adding just a few components and then programming the chip. Small (about 40mm × 40mm, 1.5in. × 1.5in.) printed circuit boards with all the work already done i.e. all pre-programmed and ready to use, are available off-the-shelf. A detailed description of how these motors and controllers are to be used is provided in Appendix 3. We will use one of these controllers as the interface between our desktop host computer and the eight servo motors on the robot.

As stated above, each of these motor control microcontrollers can control up to 8 of these servo motors. Eight is a convenient number when working with computers because 8 bits make up a byte, computers work with bytes of information, and the contents of a byte in memory can be easily displayed or impressed on 8 lines. Each line provides the signal pulse to control one of the motors. The signal is a repeating pulse between one and two milliseconds long (0.001 to 0.002 seconds) on each line. The pulse length on each line can be controlled independently from the pulse length of any other line and once the pulse length is set the microcontroller maintains it until it is changed. The pulse is repeated continuously.

When making our design decisions, there seems to be no good reason not to use the full 8 motor capability of the microcontroller. Each

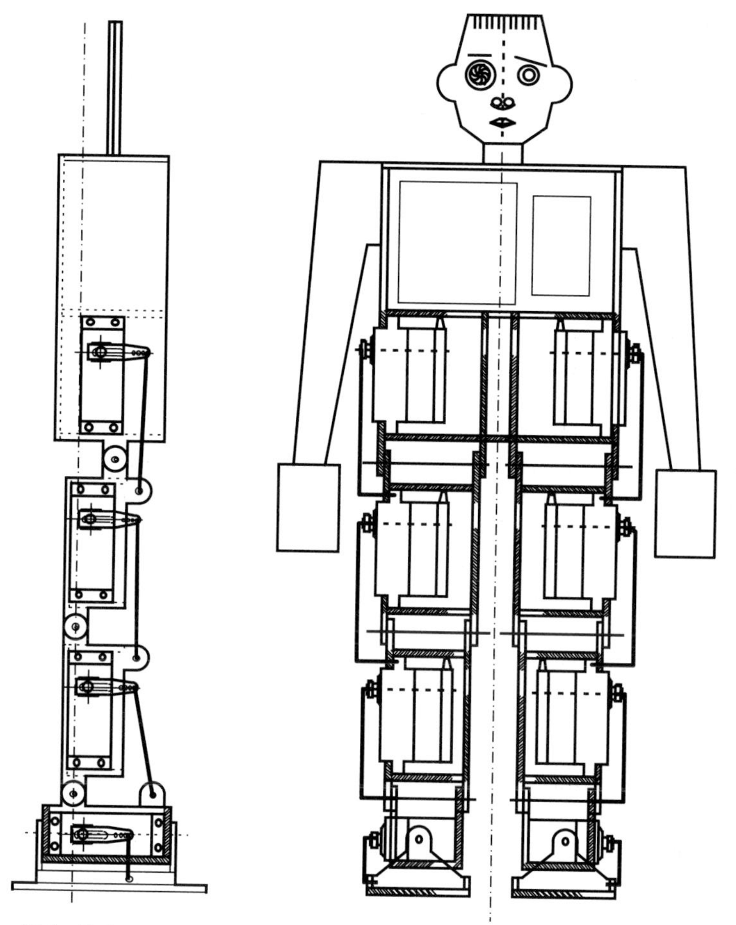

Figure 11.1 Robot side and front elevation. This is the (reduced) original drawing of the robot.

motor adds only the cost of the motor itself. We will already have the microcontroller, the batteries (or power supplies), the wires and the computer.

Thus the most efficient design would use one controller and 8 or less servo motors. Since one can never have enough motors on a robot we will use all 8 motors in the design that we come up with. With 8 motors, some fairly interesting robots can be created. In this book I will describe the construction of a two-legged, humanoid, walking robot in some detail.

Of course you are also encouraged to build your own designs from the ideas and techniques described in the book. All the hardware needed to build a walking robot can be used again and again to build many other designs. It would be possible to experiment with many designs, with minimal additional expense, by simply re-using the components.

The biped walker that I decided to design for the project as the hands-on introduction to the subject uses the 8 servos to control the two legs of the robot. Four servos are dedicated to each leg. Biped walking is a very interesting and complicated phenomenon and can be investigated in some serious though preliminary detail with the robot described. Interestingly, the 8 servos used, necessitate a walk that is not quite as natural or elegant as you might expect.

One of the goals of the selection process was to pick a process that you might already be familiar with. It cannot be too trivial and it cannot be too complicated – something in between is best. Fortunately, biped walking fills the requirement rather well. Before one can address any task, a considerable familiarity has to be gained with the problems associated with that task. This being the case, we have to pick the task carefully. We are all completely familiar with walking, in that it is a task we perform every day, even though we hardly ever think about what we are doing. Not ever thinking about it is what makes it an interesting task to duplicate with a robot because although we know *how* to walk, we do not *know* or *understand* how we walk. Now we will have to think about it, break walking down into its most basic components and analyse each component in detail. The most basic concepts will then have to be carefully filtered out and implemented on the robot. What we do with a very powerful computer (our brains) and hundreds of muscles with exquisite feedback will now have to be done with a small desktop computer, only 4 primitive muscles in each leg and no feedback at all!

Of course walking is not the only thing the robot can do. It can bend eight individual joints in a thousand ways or more. It can stand on one leg. It can shift its balance back and forth between the two legs. It can stand on one leg and wave the other leg around. It could do a rudimentary dance. It can turn. It can be an interesting puppet. The only limit is your imagination!

Consider standing on one leg and moving the other leg through all its motions. This is not as easy to do as it first appears because you have to take the shift in the centre of gravity of the system into account as the free leg is moved. In robots this means that a mathematical representation of the centre of gravity of the robot has to be developed and then implemented in the operating system. We need to know how the various positions of the legs change the centre of gravity of the robot. The centre of gravity has to remain above the footprint touching the ground at all times or the robot will fall over. This means that any move that potentially moves the centre of gravity to a forbidden area is itself forbidden unless the fall is from one foot to the other as a part of the walking process that we are so interested in. In our case walking will be a process of falling from one foot to the other again and again! The moves we implement will have to be slow enough to allow us to ignore the dynamic and inertial aspects of the walk.

There is considerable formal, scientific interest in the walking process. Walking with any number of legs is under investigation at a number of universities in countries all over the world. Multi-legged locomotion is of interest for traversing rough terrains. It also lends itself to adaptive control algorithms and so is used to learn about the design of these algorithms. These algorithms are segments of programs that learn from experience and modify themselves to be more efficient as they are used. Learning how to write programs that will learn from experience is an important segment of current robotic software development efforts.

With a little thought we can probably come to accept the idea that biped walking is the most sophisticated form of locomotion because that is the form of locomotion used by the most highly evolved animals on earth. The technique provides efficient locomotion at any speed of up to about 20 mph (30 kph) for a 160kg (200lb) vehicle. At slower speeds, almost all but the most difficult terrains can be traversed and there is no difficulty in going around obstacles and obstructions. With proper programming, quite exquisite, gymnastic exercises can be undertaken. At high speeds the vehicle actually leaves the ground for a portion of each movement cycle.

There is some considerable evidence that four-legged walking is more stable and that a four-legged scheme is actually necessary at higher speeds. Evolution too seems to support this hypothesis.

Software is the essence of robotics. The more serious investigators among you will want to experiment with language design and implementation for robots. To allow this the selected task has to be able to be implemented with a fairly straightforward language. Here again walking is an activity that is amenable to lending itself to the design of a relatively simple language to control it. A truly powerful language for the control of a walking robot would probably have to be powerful enough to allow the choreography of ballet dancers, ballet being the ultimate challenge in locomotion design. A much simpler language will allow us to control our robot but it would be very instructive to spend a few hours thinking seriously about how you might go about specifying a dance sequence. In a dance language, the movement of all parts of the body would have to be able to be specified with respect to time and space.

The size of the robot that I designed was determined by the size of the servo motors that were to be used. The servo motors were selected strictly on the basis of cost. I picked the most inexpensive units in the radio control hobbyist's catalogue.

The smallest component of the robot that needs to have a servo motor placed in it is the robot's foot, so I started at the feet and worked my way up from there. I decided to use plywood construction throughout to make it easy for just about anyone to make the parts that were needed. A piece of plywood, a fretsaw and some glue applied with a little elbow grease will build a usable robot.

CHAPTER TWELVE

Skills, tools, time and materials

In this chapter I will provide you with an overview of the resources that you will need to make and operate the walking robot which will allow you to determine if you have the tools needed to do the job before you start. (This is more detailed than it needs to be to encourage those of you who have never done anything like this before now.)

The intention of the design is to allow an experimenter with a minimal amount of skill and a minimum number of tools to build the robot and to keep the cost as low as possible. Even so, some minimal familiarity with hand tools is desirable and there is some expense associated with buying the servo motors and controller that are needed. This is not to suggest that it would not be useful to have more than the minimal number of tools to do the work, only that it can be done with a few common hand tools.

If you have ever built a model aeroplane and still have the tools that you used, you probably already have all the tools that you will need. The only material that needs fabrication is 3mm (1/8in.) plywood. This can be cut with a motorized jigsaw or a manually operated fretsaw and sanded to the final shapes needed with a hobby sander or by hand.

You will save time and energy if you have the following tools on hand before you start. I have indicated the use of each tool, so that you can substitute some other tool that you might have on hand that can do the job just as well.

- Coping saw or fretsaw to cut and shape the plywood. (I used a motorized unit made by Ryobi but the work can all be done by hand.)
- Dremel Moto Tool and accessories for drilling and sanding the plywood. Not a must but very handy to have for all sort of hobby uses. (I used one along with the Dremel belt/disk sander – also optional.)
- Drills, 1/16", 5/64", 3/32", 7/64" and 1/8" to drill holes for linkages etc.
- Soft pencil to mark up your work.
- 6-inch metal ruler to use as a guide to cut wood and for taking measurements.
- Xacto knife with a couple of number 11 blades for general trim work.
- Xacto plastic clamps or something similar to hold glued parts together while the glue sets. A 2-inch G clamp is also very handy.

- Needle-nose pliers with an integral wire cutter to cut the threaded servo rods.
- 4-inch file to smooth servo rod ends after cutting and for filing the plywood parts in tight spots when needed.
- A small hobbyist vice for holding parts and assemblies as needed in any project.
- A soldering iron and 6 inches of rosin core solder may be needed depending on how you decide to do your wiring (or perhaps you could borrow one).

Materials needed

The following parts and supplies are needed for the walking robot. These are harder to substitute for because other design changes will be needed in the robot itself if changes are made in these parts.

- One 8 servo controller to be the interface between the computer and the eight servos (see Appendix 3).
- One adapter board to connect the controller to the power supply and to all the servos. This is built in on some controllers and separate on others. Order it with your controller after you know what type of servo connectors you have. Futaba J connectors are recommended.
- 8 model aircraft R/C servos. The most inexpensive units you can buy will suffice. You may be able to borrow units for the duration of your project. All must have the same J connectors (see above).
- 16 complete ball end connectors for the servo rods at the servo ends and the robot ends. 24 inches of all threaded servo rod to suite the ball end connectors.
- One 7.2 volt DC rechargeable NiCad battery to power the servo motors like the ones used by the R/C model aircraft enthusiasts. (The batteries can be replaced with power supplies.) A charger for the batteries is needed. A 6 volt lantern battery can also be used.
- One 9 volt DC battery for logic power to the controller.
- Plywood. 2 square feet of 3mm (⅛in.) 5 ply model aircraft plywood. Solid wood can be used if you like but is harder to make into the thin sections that are needed. It is easier to use the 3mm (⅛in.) material. Plastic sheeting could also be used but is considerably heavier (not a good idea.)
- Sandpaper – one sheet of 120 grit (one sheet of 180 grit, optional).
- Wire for the communication cable and the power cables. Multi-stranded 22 swg wire is best. A soft wire that will follow the robot is desired. The power used is less than 2 amps at 7.2 volts. You need about 20 feet of wire to make one 4 wire by 5 foot strand.
- An end connector with pigtails for a 9 volt battery if not already provided with the controller. A connector for the communication port on your computer, to suit.
- A cable connector to connect the power cables to the battery connector. We have to be able to disconnect to charge the batteries (not a must but very convenient).
- 1 small switch for the controller power.
- 1 small switch for the motor power.
- Glue. Elmers or carpenter's glue (works better than model aircraft cement). A small bottle or tube will suffice.

Space needed

The kitchen table or an office desk will be all the space you need to build the robot and to program it. Since you will be using glue, some precautions to make sure you do not get the glue on surface you want to protect will be necessary. Newspapers or waxed kitchen paper will serve.

The entire project and all the tools will fit in a large cardboard box between work sessions.

Since the work can be messy, an area that can be cleaned up with ease is recommended. Special caution is given for the dust created during the sanding process. All sanding is best done in the garage or outdoors.

Time needed

Depending on your skills and the speed with which you work, the robot can be built in about 30 hours with ease. There is no limit to the time you can spend programming and playing with the robot. Hopefully you will spend months programming it, will enjoy every moment and in the process will learn more about robots and programming with every minute that you spend.

Computer needed

You must have a small personal computer to run the robot. There is no alternative for this piece of equipment. The discussion is again written for the uninitiated.

The IBM-PC, or what is now called the Wintel (Windows-Intel), computer is now pretty much the standard the world over and much of the following discussion is about these computers. However, an old Apple IIe, a Macintosh such as I use, a BBC educational computer or any other computer could be used with ease and will work fine. (All these provide the BASIC language although any language can be used.)

Ideally it will be your own computer but if you can borrow one for an extended period of time it would serve. You will spend a lot of time trying out all sorts of algorithms to make the robot walk and that is the fun part. Having to take the computer back to its owner (every evening?) will detract considerably from your efforts and the pleasure that you derive from the project.

The computer you use does not have to be the latest 200 megahertz Pentium computer made by the most expensive supplier, nor will you need a lot of memory, hard disk space or a high resolution monitor. In fact an old 8086 processor-based computer with a floppy drive or two will do. However it should be stated that a hard disk drive is a real convenience on a computer and if you can purchase a computer that has one, you will not regret your decision to do so. Even a very small hard drive (40 Mb) will be a considerable asset. (In the US such computers can be bought for well under $100.00 at a hobbyist meet if you ask around.)

Here are the minimum requirements for the computer you need to run the robotic legs.

- It must have a serial output port that can send out information in the RS-232 format. This is the kind of port that run modems and printers from computers. COM1 and COM2 on the IBM-PC are ports that meet this specification. Both the printer port and the modem port on the Apple Macintosh can be used to run the robot. The port has to run with the following protocol because that is the protocol of the controller that we will be using.

  8 data bits
  odd parity
  9600 baud
  1 stop bit

  This is a very standard protocol, very similar to the protocol used by almost every printer and modem on the market. The values themselves are programmable from the computer if they have to be changed. To the computer the robot will look like a printer that we are running from it but instead of printing characters on paper, our controller will interpret the commands as signals that it will use to move the eight servo motors to the positions specified.

- It is a real advantage to have a friend who is somewhat familiar with computers (particularly your specific computer). There are things that one needs to be able to ask about even when one has the best instructions in the world on hand and someone who understands what you are talking about will make your life easier. If not, your local computer store will be able to help you. All the information that you will need is fairly fundamental, you will not be asking difficult or time-consuming questions and it is my experience that they will be fascinated by your robot project and delighted to help (the owner of the hobby store I frequent has already read most of this book!).
- The computer must be able to run the BASIC computer language and the BASIC must be available for it from a current source so that you can get support if you need it. You must get the documentation (the manuals) for the software when you get the software. Repeat: MUST. However BASIC is not a must – any language will work – but it is the easiest language to use if you are new to this and it is the language I will use in the book.
- The computer must have a monitor to display the information it generates.
- It must have a standard keyboard for input to the computer.
- It must have a disk drive to allow information storage, and for information input and output. If you can get even a small (an old 40 Mb unit will do) hard drive it will be a real convenience. You will still need a floppy drive to transport programs between computers. The 3.5" floppies are more universally acceptable than the older 5.25" units because that is what a newer computer would write to. You need to be able to get information to and from these newer computers because the person helping you will want to look at the work you have been doing and in all probability he or she will have a newer computer.
- A printer is a real convenience but *not a must.* A printer lets you list your programs and a printout is much easier to edit with pen or pencil. The printer can have a serial or a parallel interface. The newer printers use a serial interface.
- A newer computer is always desirable but is not essential for the project that we are working on. The make and model of computer you get is not important though the world has now pretty much settled on the IBM-PC or Wintel computers and the discussions in these pages are suitable for these computers. I used an older Apple Macintosh. (Wintel = Windows – Intel, i.e. IBM-PC compatibles.).
- If you intend to do other work with your computer and intend to own a computer in the future, (a great idea) you may want to consider a newer used computer as a good value.

Computer software needed

You need a way to send information from the computer to the controller of the robot. For this you will need software that is used to write programs as opposed to software for word processing or accounting.

I am going to recommend that you use BASIC if you have never done any programming. The examples I give will be in BASIC. All the work we need to get done can be done with the simplest commands in BASIC. In fact we could do it all with just the PRINT command but we will want to do more than that as our sophistication increases. The more you learn, you more you will want to do.

Almost all languages support a PRINT command of some sort to allow information that has been generated, by the program that you write, to be printed on paper.

You do not need a very sophisticated version of BASIC – an older version will be fine. You should insist on the manuals so that you can look up exactly how the various commands are to be used. It is a rule with computers that without the manuals you have nothing. This is the information age and the information is in the manuals. Need I say that if you do not read the manuals (many times) you also get less for your money than you could have!

The software that you get has to be guaranteed to work on the computer that you have. This is important because software is very computer specific. However almost every computer is provided with BASIC as the one language that comes with the computer whether you want it or not so this should not be a problem.

BASIC made by Microsoft is completely acceptable. I used their QuickBASIC for the Macintosh. IBM-PC QuickBASIC is almost identical. (Repeat: get the manuals!)

PASCAL is a similar language to BASIC that can be used in a pinch but is usually more powerful and therefore harder to learn and use.

Languages like FORTRAN are optimized for doing calculations (FORmula TRANslation) and therefore do not serve the needs of robotic hobbyists well. Earlier versions of FORTRAN did not even support a PRINT command. Not recommended.

If you have a friend who is willing to help you with a language that he or she is very familiar with you can use that language (but stick with BASIC).

Computer skills needed

You do not need to be a computer science engineer to do the work needed to make the robot walk but it would be helpful if you have an understanding of what a computer is and how it is used. If you own a computer and have played with programming it, you probably already have the skill and the interest needed. Any introductory book on programming will give you the information that you need.

You should be able to understand terms like subroutine, loop and application program so that you can follow the instruction in the programming section. If you can understand the chapter on designing a computer language you will be able to program the robot. It is not necessary to write a language to run the robot. It can be done from PRINT commands alone. Designing segments of the language or even a complete language will give you the hands-on experience you need to really understand how all this works in the real world.

I give examples that you can follow throughout.

CHAPTER THIRTEEN

Making the walking robot

This chapter provides the instructions and illustrations needed to build the walking robot. Detailed drawings for building the robot, with both SI and imperial dimensions, are provided in Appendix 5.

As in any design there are certain critical components that determine how a machine will be built so that these components can be incorporated properly into the machine. In our particular case the critical components are the 8 servo motors that provide the muscles for the legs. The design is based on using the most inexpensive of the servo motors that are used by radio control (R/C) hobbyists to control model aircraft control surfaces, engines and landing gear.

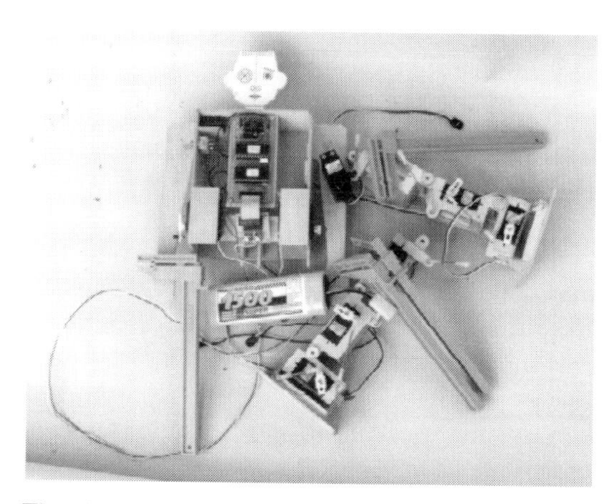

The robot components ready for final assembly. Xacto plastic clamps are very handy for clamping plywood parts together – I used 4 on the project.

The servo motors that I selected were not the fastest or the most powerful, or the smallest or the lightest – they were the most inexpensive units on the market. We need eight of them so any savings are multiplied by eight. In the USA these servo motors are available for about $12.00 (1997) each and sometimes for less (about $10.00 each) if a sale is in progress. As such these eight motors and their controller (about $50.00) form the most expensive parts used in the project. If you already own some servos or if you can borrow some for the duration of the project, you can save yourself some money. All the servos do not have to be identical but it would be helpful if they were in matched pairs to allow the legs to be made identical. (They do not have to be identical pairs either but then the challenge of walking gets a little tougher.)

If you cannot obtain exactly the same servo motors as I have used, you will have to modify certain dimensions slightly to make sure that the servos fit in the legs. The modifications are minor and if you follow these instructions there should be no problem. There is nothing magical about the dimensions I used. What I was trying to do is keep the robot as short and as bottom heavy as possible to ensure maximum stability. You should be able to do this with the dimensions of your servos without complications.

The robot components are designed to be as small as possible and still contain the eight servo motors. The most critical location is the servo motor that controls the nutation (twist) of the foot in that this is the smallest part of the robot that has to accommodate a servo. This is also the joint that needs to be as backlash free as possible because small loose movements at this joint translate into big problems when tipping from side to side and when walking. The next most critical joint is the ankle.

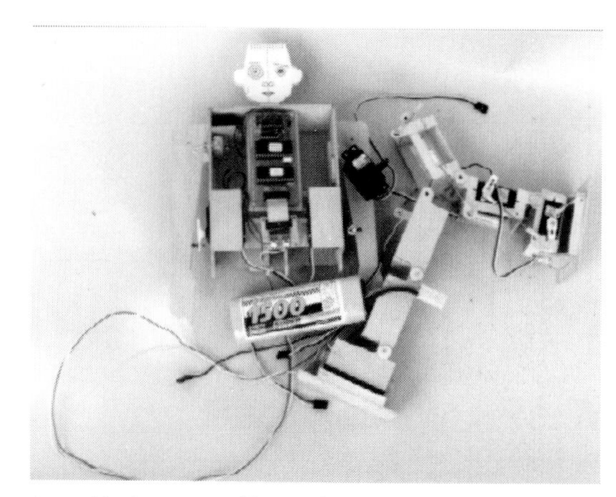

Assemble the torso and legs as the main assemblies. The main components of the robot ready for final assembly.

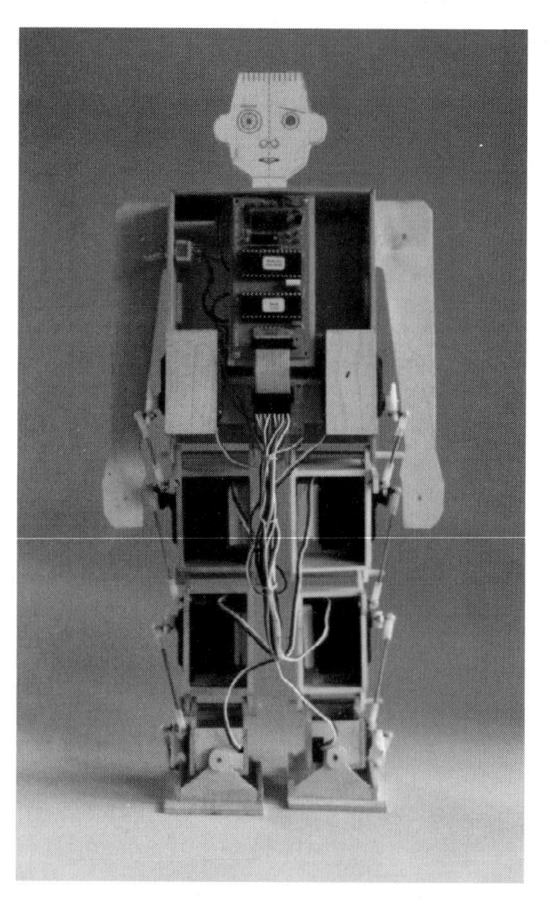

The front of the completed robot.

The servos that you buy should be provided with J connectors as made by the Futaba Corporation. This is a standard connector in the model aircraft radio control trade. The pins that the controller manufacturers provide are designed to accept connectors that match this pattern. **Confirm this on the controller that you purchase before you buy the servos and vice versa**. It is better if they match.

Make all components in matched sets of twos and fours because it is desirable that the legs be as close to identical as possible. Start at the feet and build up to the body of the robot. None of the dimensions are critical, but you will find that it is much easier to work to drawings because that saves a lot of calculation and reworking. If you are not working to the drawings, change only those dimensions that you must to accommodate your servos.

Keep in mind that the two legs of the robot are *mirror images* of one another so that as you

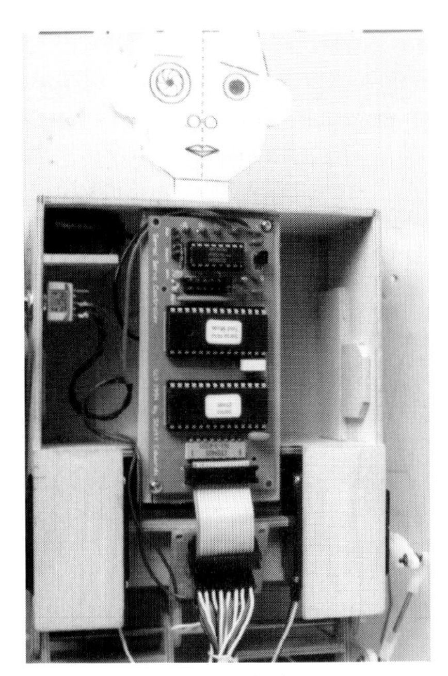
The front of the completed robot torso.

make pairs (or quads) of parts, they are to be made identical and then assembled as mirror images of one another. Since we will be using 3mm (⅛in.) dowel bearings it is possible to drill

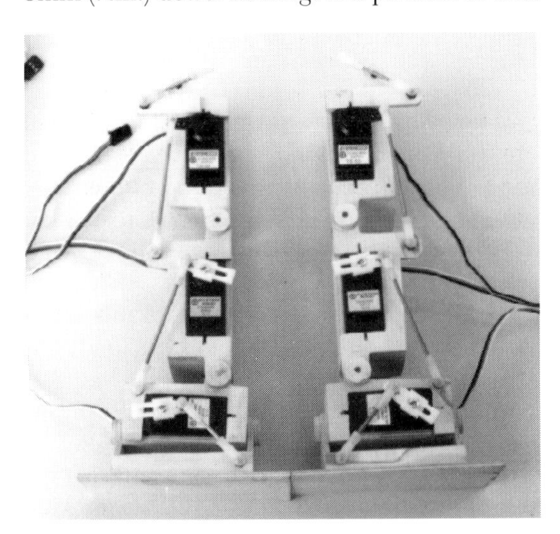
The legs are mirror images of each other. The servos also have to run backwards from each other to perform similar duties. Six of the eight servos are mounted in the legs.

3mm holes in the bearing locations and then cut and sand each set at one time. The joint holes should be drilled before you start sanding the parts and all identical pieces should be pinned

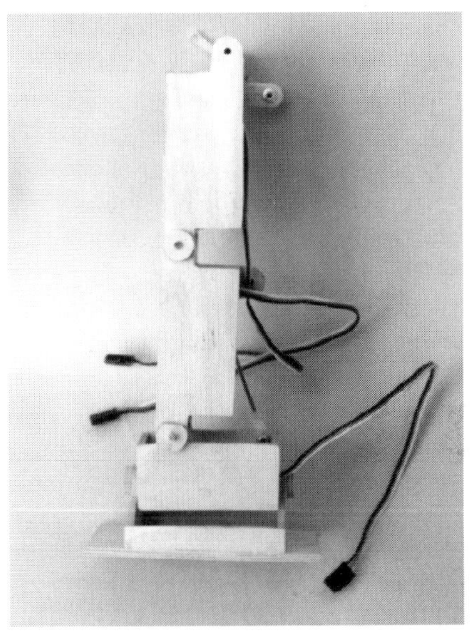
View of the inner construction of the left leg.

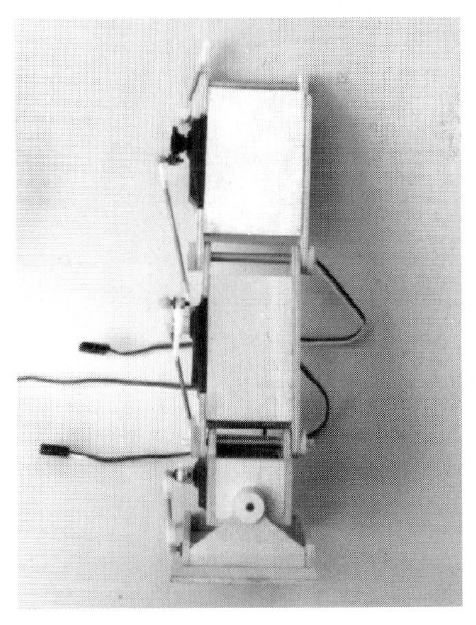
The back view of the left leg. Note how the actuation rods angle.

together with small 3mm dowels. Sand them a set at one time to make sure that they come out identical.

Clamp all the identical side parts for each segment together and drill straight 3mm (⅛in.) holes in them. Then use two ⅛ inch wood or steel dowels to hold the parts in register as you sand. This will make sure that the parts come out identical. A 12mm (½in.) diameter washer with a 3mm (⅛in.) hole in it, made of steel or brass, can be used as a guide to sand all the rounded ends so they all come out perfect. Use it with the dowel.

Holes can be spotted accurately by drilling a 3mm hole in the anvil of a G clamp and marking the spot to be drilled with a cross with a pencil. Clamp the part with the hole exactly on the cross and then drill through for a perfectly centred hole ever time. The photo shows how the clamp is modified.

The foot assembly consists of the top of the foot that contains the servo, and the base of the foot that is twisted by the servo motor. This allows the robot to lean left and right on either foot. Make the boxes for the servo motors first. The boxes should be made so that the servos fit snugly in the open boxes – there is no advantage in having any extra space. We want it as compact as possible and we want **as short a robot as possible** (see drawings). Glue on the sides of the box after the wrap of the box has been glued, snug to the servo. This makes it easier to sand it all down to finished surfaces. It will be helpful to drill the holes for the servo mounting bolts and the various pivots before you glue the box sides on but this is not essential – the servo can be made tight in the box with spacers (without fasteners).

Sand the outsides of the box smooth before you start building the soles of the feet. In that way you can build the new components right to the sanded outside dimensions of the foot components and get a perfectly snug fit.

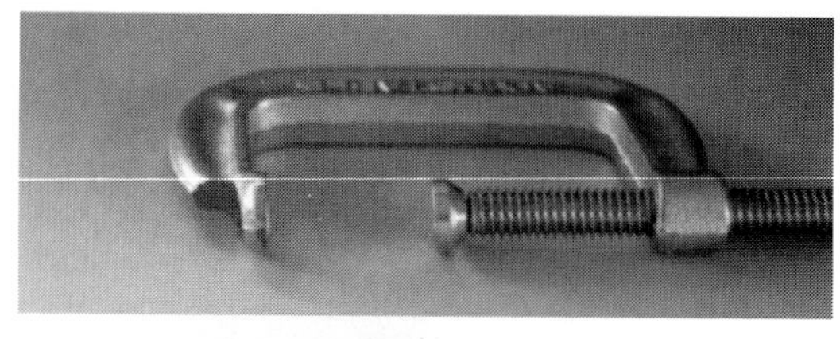

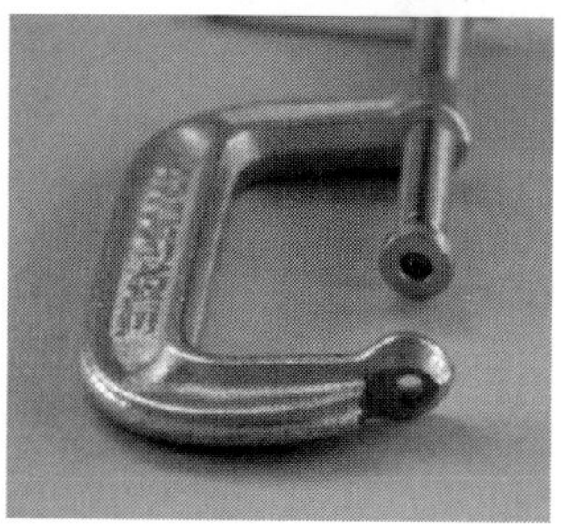

Clamp modification.

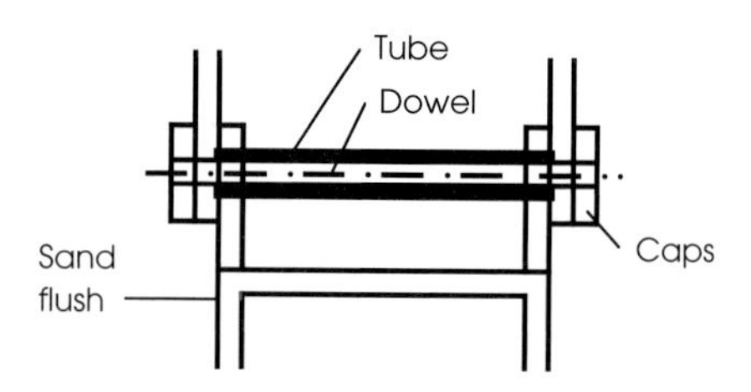

Figure 13.1 Using a brass tube as a bearing. The tube is glued to the inner frame and the dowel is free to move in the tube.

The bearings on which the various joints of the robot operate can be made in a number of ways. The less free play you have in the bearings, the easier it will be to control the robot. The simplest way of making the bearings is as follows.

Drill a hole at the pivot locations that is the size of the rod or dowel (3mm or ⅛in.) that you are going to use. The plywood will give way just enough to give you a nice fit. I used this technique for the original robot. I then found some brass tubing that was exactly ⅛ inch ID (5⁄32 in. OD) so I modified the joints to use a brass tube around the dowel. The tubing is epoxied to the internal plates and the dowel is glued to the caps only, of the outer plates, as shown in Figure

13.1. These caps are made of 12mm (½in.) diameter plywood rounds, 3mm (⅛in.) thick with a 3mm hole in them for the dowel. Sand off the caps off to disassemble the joint and replace the dowel and the caps to remake the joint.

The bearings need to be flush to the sides of the plywood at the top of each servo holding segment. Consult the drawings as you proceed. If you get a little glue in the bearing tube during assembly it can be removed after it sets with the 3mm drill (that was used to make the dowel holes). Be careful not to get the dowel shaft glued into the bearings.

In all cases, ball joint ends used by the radio controlled aircraft community should be used on both the servo end and the leg end of each of the control rods. These ball ends will accept threaded rod and these threads provide a very fine adjustment for the length of the control wire (tendon). Using ball ends means that the control rods do not have to be bent to route them accurately as they would have to if we were to use clevises. Study the photographs.

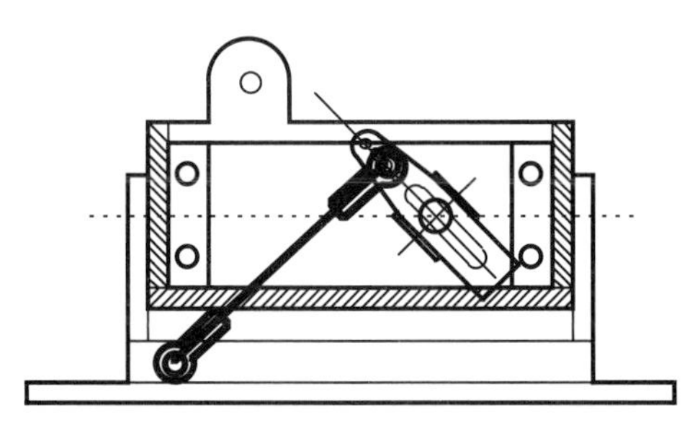

Figure 13.2 Side view of the foot. Keep the lever arm on the servo side as short as possible for the finest control possible. The lever arm on the other is essentially beyond our control. The servo is shown in its middle position.

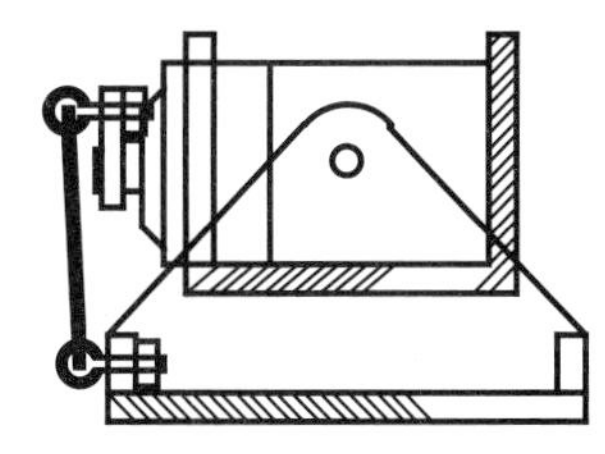

Figure 13.3 Front view of the foot nutation mechanism. There are no hidden lines so you can see everything. Also study the photographs of these parts.

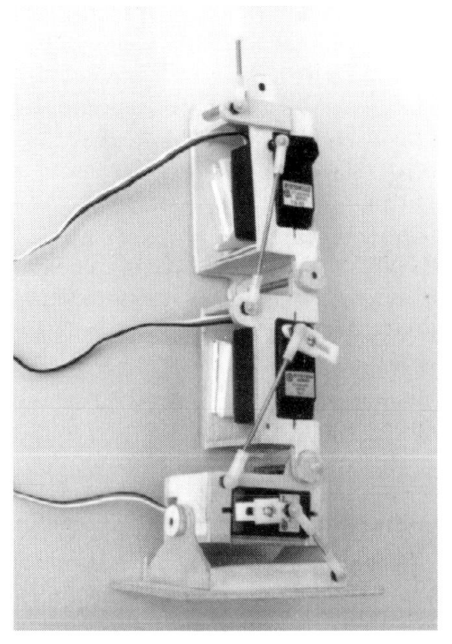

View of the left leg. Note the use of ball ends on all servo actuation rods at both ends. Pins are bolted in at the servo end and at the leg end on both sides.

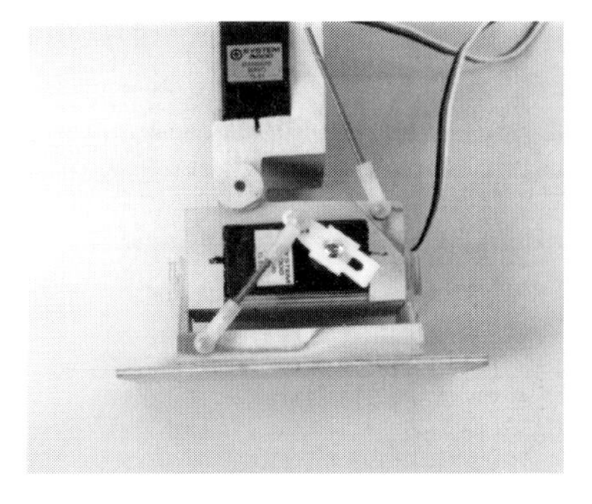

Detail of the foot nutating mechanism (right foot). The servo is in mid position in this view. Note that the servo arm is at right angles to the actuation rod. Limits are placed in the software to prevent over-actuation of the foot.

The trick to making a good strong joint is to create a joint that fits well and has a thin continuous layer of glue in it. It is not a good idea to fill the pores of the wood with fine wood dust because open pores help the glue to get into the wood and this makes a better glued joint. An unsanded joint will make a better glued joint if you make sure that the joint is well fitted before you apply the glue. Make the outside parts oversized and then sand the parts to size after they are glued together. This will give you the best finished parts. Use a coarse paper to get parts to size when fitting them together. Coarse sanding will not fill the pores with fine wood dust the way fine sandpaper will. Hand sand the finished parts prior to painting to kill the edges and get a better appearance.

Most of the photographs in the book show unpainted components to allow you to see the components in greater detail.

Once the two casings for the foot servos have been built, build the soles of the feet. These should be a firm, but shake free, fit on the feet. The servo should be able to move the foot without binding. On this one joint, the range of motion needed is quite limited because even a tiny motion of the foot will tip the robot considerably. Make the servo lever as short as possible and the foot lever as long as possible. The motion should be shake free so that the robot does not teeter on its foot. What is needed is a small amount of very backlash free motion so that the control can be positive as well as responsive.

You might want to consider making the soles of the feet oversized in the beginning and then cut them back later. This will make for a more stable robot while you develop the skill to control it.

As each section of the legs is built, make sure that each component can move through its entire range without binding. Each joint is independent of all other joints so no complicated fitting procedures are needed. You should try to get the movement you need around the middle 90 degrees of motion of the servo. Adjust rod lengths and crank lengths accordingly.

After the feet have been completed, build the calf sections and then the thigh sections of the legs. These are similar to one another and are straightforward. Since these parts are wider than the foot section, there is now more space

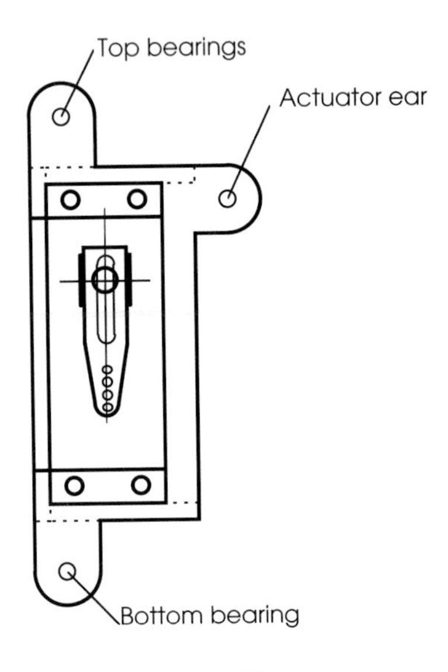

Figure 13.4 Side view of the calf.

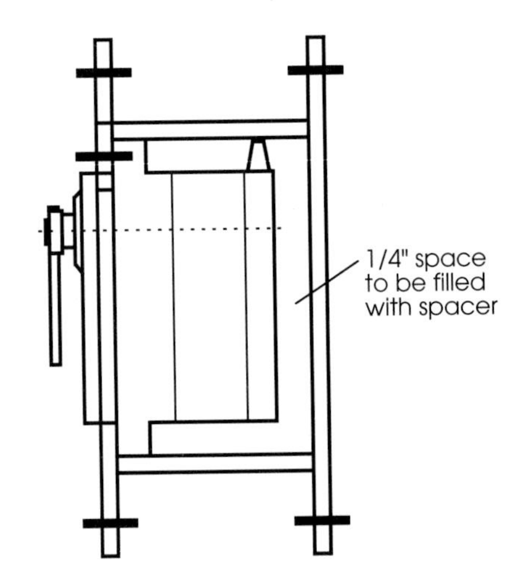

Figure 13.5 Front view of the calf.

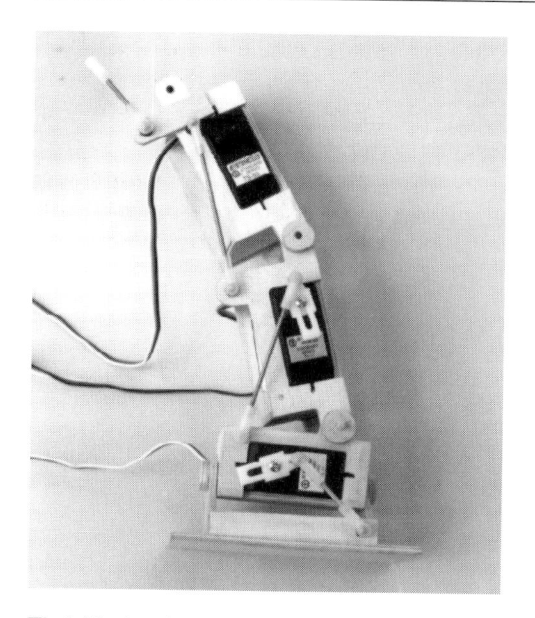

The left leg bent back. Motion is limited by using the actuation arms on the servos at their shortest adjustment. This can be increased later.

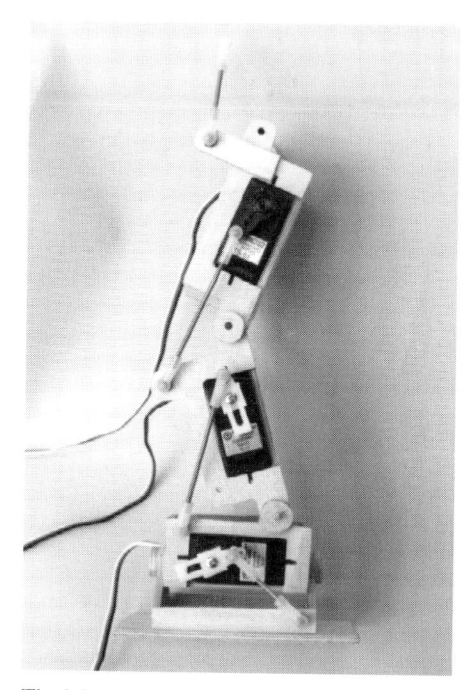

The left leg showing bend at knee joint while the hip stays above the ankle.

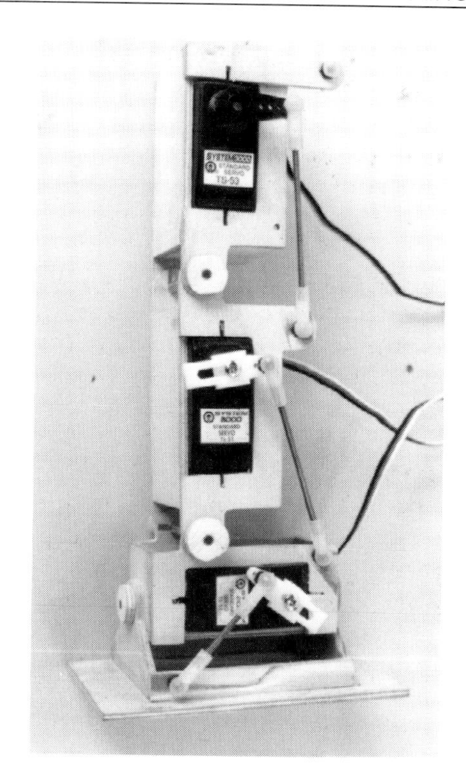

The right leg of the robot as seen from the right. Note that the lengths of the servo arms are adjustable. Keep them short to start with and then adjust them as needed by the software that you develop.

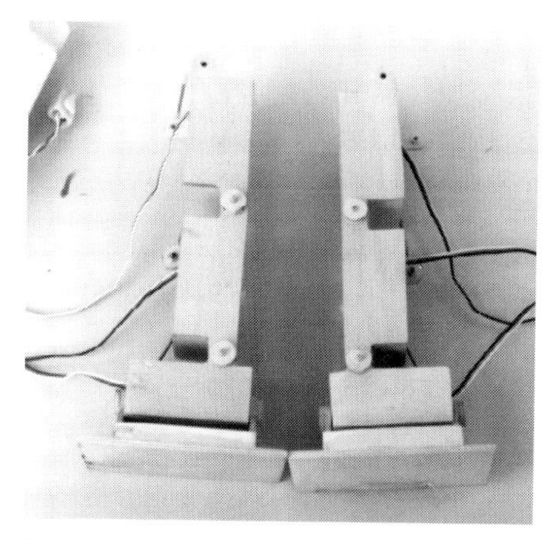

Inner sides of the legs. All linkages are on the outside for ease of adjustment and removal. Note the bearing reinforcements at each joint.

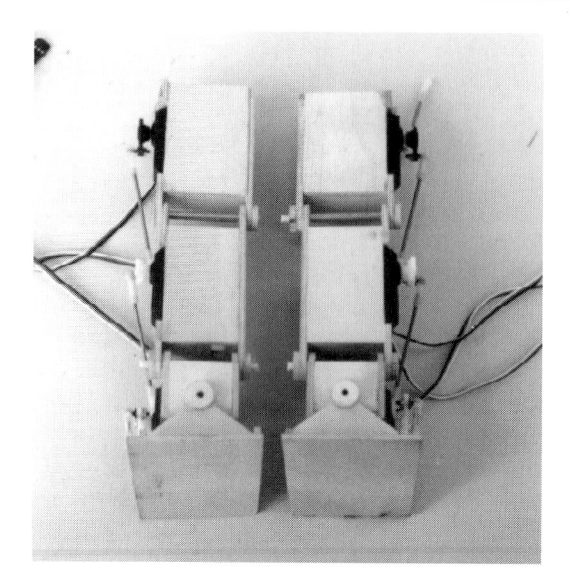

Back view of the legs. Note that the soles of the feet are extended to the outside to provide greater stability for the robot. These can be made smaller when you become more skilled at controlling the robot.

for the servo motors. Each section should be exactly two plywood thicknesses wider than the one below it. Build (two and four plywood parts thick) spacer wedges as shown in the photographs to hold the servo in the section. This will allow you to install and remove the servo motors, from these sections, without difficulty though this facility will not be available in the foot section. The servo motors should be installed in the various sections as the work proceeds.

Do not forget to provide the openings that allow the wiring for the servos to be routed up to the servo controller in the robot body if you want to route them in this way. These openings need to be large enough to allow the connectors at the end of the wires to pass through them. The servos that are the farthest away from the controller will have to have extension cables attached to them if their cables are not long enough. Be sure to make the openings large enough for these extension connectors. Check the cable length when you buy the servos. You can save money by selecting servos with long enough cables – standard lengths were long enough on my robot.

The body of the biped needs to have special attention paid to it. The sections should be fabricated and installed as shown on the drawings

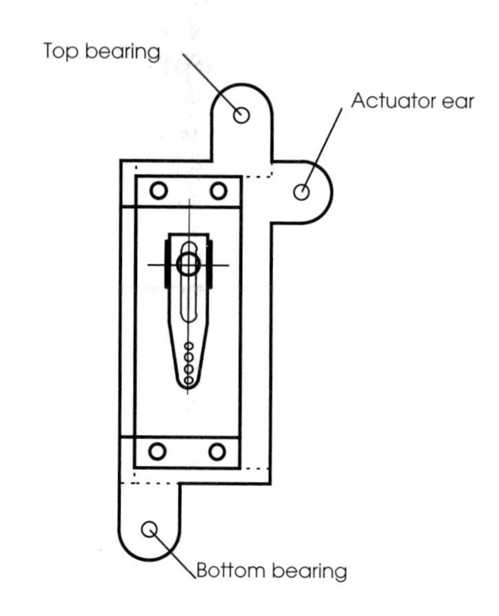

Figure 13.6 Side view of the thigh.

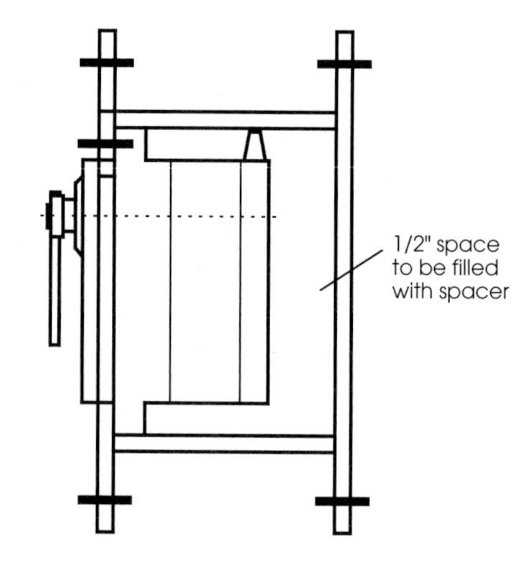

Figure 13.7 Front view of the thigh.

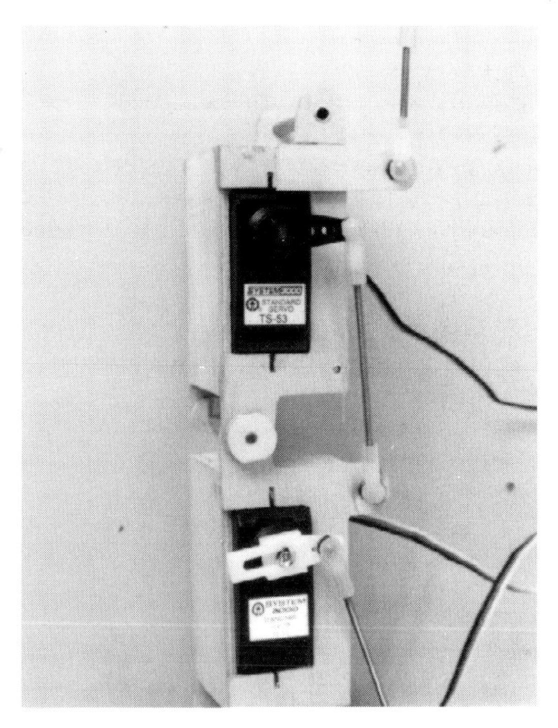

Detail of the right thigh. The notches in the plywood are for structural gussets on the servos that keep the servos from sitting flush in the box. The notches make space for the gussets.

to give the unit the strength that it needs. However, the dimensions should match the controller that you buy. (The controller I used was made in 1994 and the new units are much smaller than it.) The controller should be installed so that all the servo wires can reach the connectors if at all possible. Work the dimensions out to fit your particular controller before you start on the fabrication of the body. Study the photos of the body to see what I had to do.

The sections that have the inner bearings for the hips in them should be made long as shown so that there is a lot of glue surface holding them in place. Tie these into the cross pieces as shown to make sure that they have the lateral support that they need. The plate that the controller mounts to can come down to these as long as you clear the mounting for the two servo motors. Line all four elements up with a 3mm (⅛in.) dowel while the glue sets to make sure everything is perfectly in line.

It is in our interest to have the centre of gravity of the robot as low as possible to make the robot as stable as possible. For this reason, the head and arms have been made as light units and the body is relatively small. The centre of gravity can also be helped by installing the controller itself as low as possible and by installing the battery for the motors off the robot. The prototype shows a battery cradle on the back of the robot – this is for use while in the suspension harness only, then there are only two wires to the

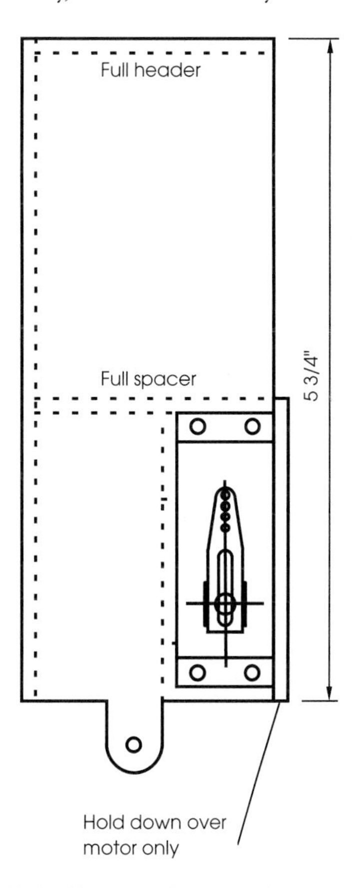

Figure 13.8 Side view of the robot body. This shows the prototype arrangement. See the drawings in Appendix 5 for the improved arrangement.

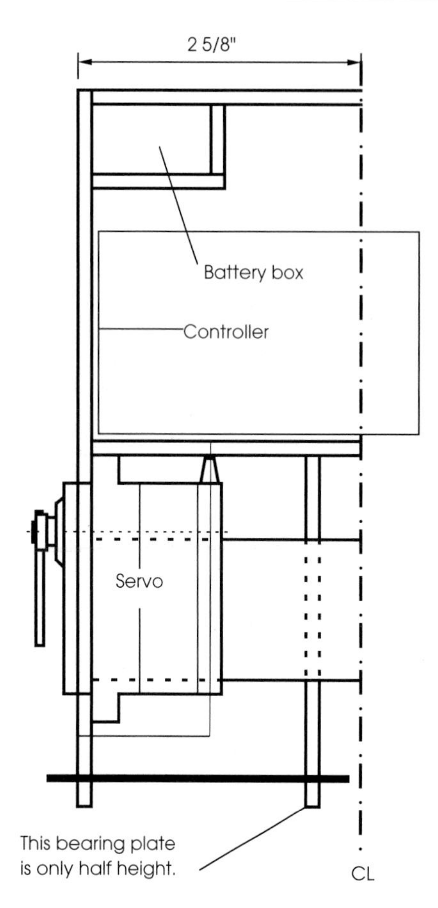

Figure 13.9 Front view of the robot body. Only half the body is shown in this view.

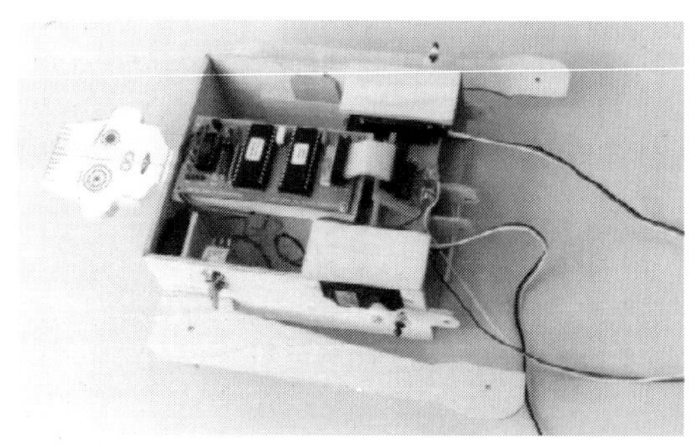

The robot torso without legs. Note how the hip joints are constructed and how the plates carry up into the torso so that they can be tied into the other plates. Also note the location of two switches for the batteries.

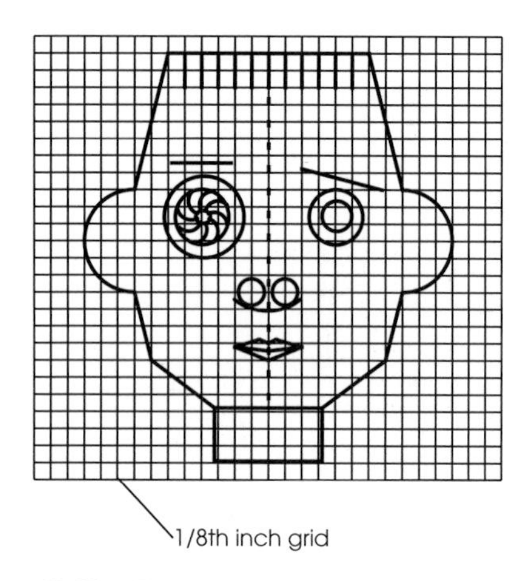

Figure 13.10 Front view of the robot head.

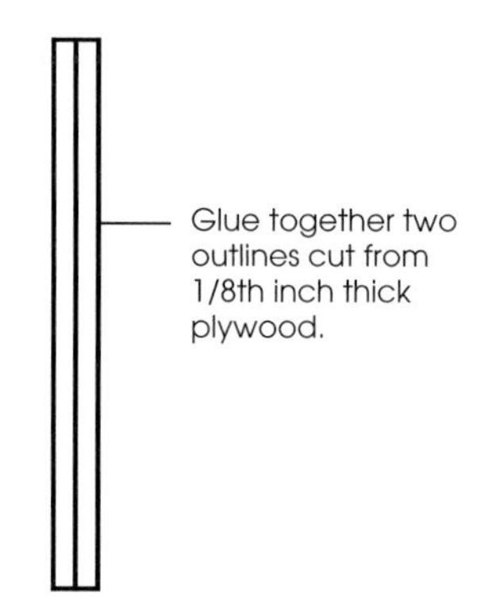

Figure 13.11 Side view of the head.

robot (the communication wires). When walking, the battery should be taken off the robot and placed on the table to lower the body weight. Servos should be installed as low in the leg segment as possible if you make changes. If you build as shown there will be not much choice about this but you should feel free to experiment and hopefully make a better robot than I did.

Installing the controller

The controller is mounted in the robot chest on a plywood plate (see photos). This holds the con-

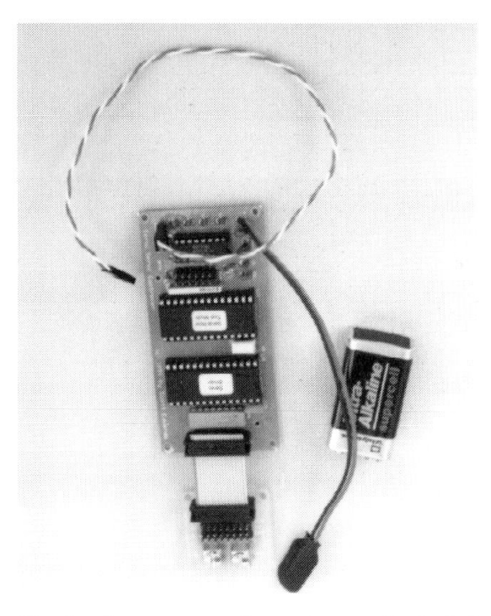

The 8 axis servo controller and controller logic battery. This controller is made by Scott Edwards and was assembled in 1994. The new controllers use the same instruction set but are about 25 per cent of the size of this unit. Note the extension to the connector for the 8 motors. You have to order this separately from the controller.

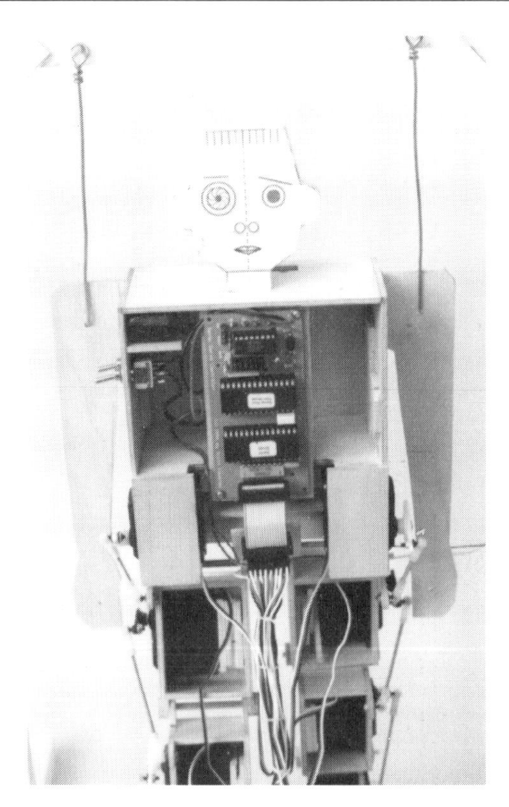

Installation of the controller (1994 version). Note the battery box for the 9 volt battery at the upper right shoulder of the robot.

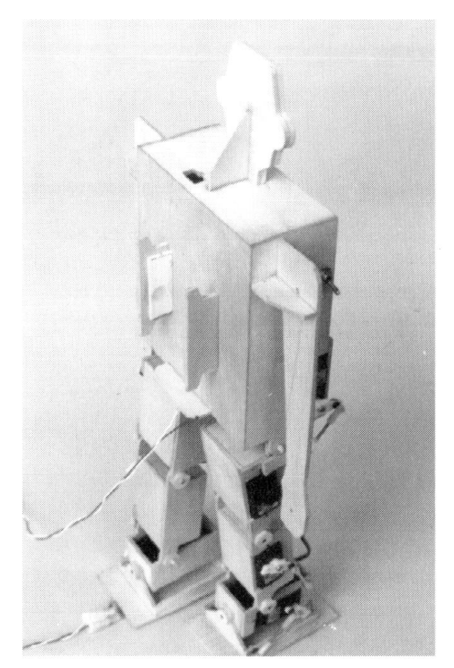

Rear quarter view of the completed robot.

troller in place vertically and allows the small PC board that the servo connections are made to be mounted low so that all servo cables can reach it. The controller is an expensive component and the design that you settle on should allow it to be removed with ease for re-use on your next project.

Installing the 9 volt controller battery

Build a small two-sided box for the battery to allow you to slide a new battery into position with ease as shown in the drawings. The box should be a snug fit on the battery. The vertical member needs to be shorter than the battery so that the cable can find its way past the battery while staying within the body box.

The power supply for the motors

The power supply for the motors can be either a battery or a small power supply. A six volt, direct current power source is desired. A number of small DC sources that plug into household current with a line transformer are now on the market for use with the myriad of electronic items in everyday use. One of these can be used as our power supply. Two amps should be enough at 6 volts. The best power source is two rechargeable battery packs as used by R/C modellers (you also have to buy a charger for them). Use one for power and the other as a standby. Initially I decided to piggyback the battery pack onto the robot so that I would not have to have the two power wires trailing the robot. This makes the robot a bit too top heavy (and adds to the walking challenge!).

The batteries I used are 7.2 volt 1.2 amp hour rechargeable NiCad units. These batteries are readily available from your hobby shop and can be recharged with an inexpensive charger also available from the hobby shop. If you have two batteries (one is adequate), as I have, you can have one on charge while you use the other. (One is adequate for fairly long sessions and you can recharge it fairly rapidly.)

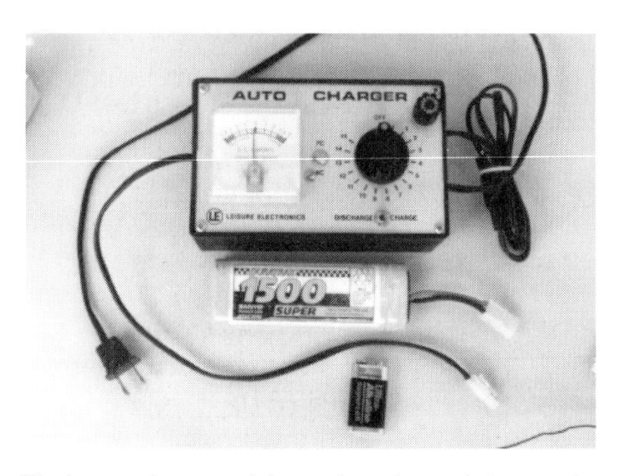

The battery charger and the two batteries needed to run the robot. The charger and NiCad battery are supplied by the radio control hobby trade. The small battery is a standard 9 volt battery.

The umbilical cord

The cord from the computer to the robot has to have two wires for communications. You also need two wires for the motor power lines. In either case the 9 volt battery for the controller logic power should be on board the robot. This is the best way to handle the minimal needs of the controller logic. Although you can use the same battery for the controller and the motors that is not a good idea because when the batteries get weak they start to interfere with the proper operation of the controller. When running motors it is imperative that the controller should not exhibit unpredictable behaviour.

For the connection to the computer, the two communication wires from the robot controller have to go to two pins on the serial port on the computer. Follow the directions provided with your controller.

The controller shown in the photographs is an early version (1994) of the Scott Edwards controller. The new controllers have been modified to reflect the latest availability and miniaturisation of electronic components and are much smaller. Electronic items are constantly under improvement so check the information that you get with your particular controller to make sure that the pin outs are connected properly. In any case we are interested in the transmitted signal and the ground wire. Other wires at the computer end have to be connected to certain other wires at the computer end to indicate that the signals are ready for receiving, sending, processing etc. (The complete manual for the Scott Edwards Electronics controller is included in Appendix 3 by permission of Scott Edwards.)

An LED on the controller lets you know when a communication signal is being received. If you have a problem with communicating with the controller, it will almost certainly have something to do with the timing or wiring between the robot controller and the COM port. There is nothing much to go wrong at the controller end because the controller does not check to see if things are ready or not. It is guaranteed to be fast enough to receive and process everything you send it as long as it is timed right and in the right format. If we send out information faster than the motors can execute it, that is our problem. We will be careful about that and will take care of the problem in the software. I will show you how to add the delays needed.

Timing problems can be addressed by trying the various protocols that can be used. Since there are only a few combinations to try, this is not as tedious as it might seem at first sight. Use 9600 baud, 8 data bits, odd parity and 1 stop bit to start. However you must first check with your specific controller instructions to make sure.

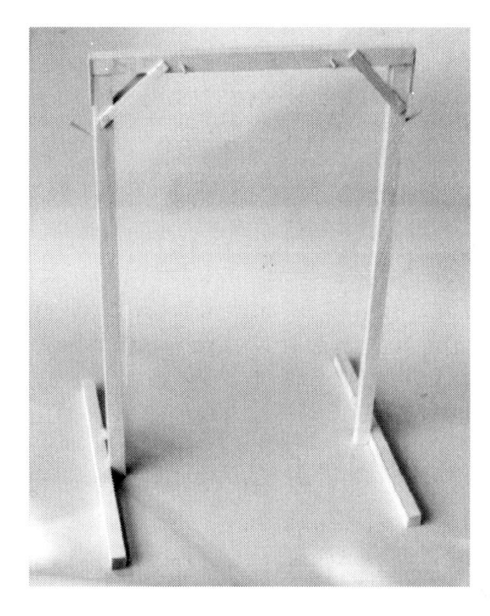

Front view of the suspension frame. Note the plywood bracing at the upper left and right on the outside. This is necessary to hold the top down on columns.

A suspension framework

Build the suspension frame after you finish the robot so that it accommodates what you built and fits on the space that you intend to work on.

It is well worth making a framework from which you can suspend the robot while you are experimenting with how to program it. I did not do this to start with and had to break down and build one after getting tired of having to hold the robot so it would not fall over every time I wanted to try out a new program routine. Since there will be is a lot of this to do, the sooner you build the frame, the happier you will be!

Build a very simple frame out of ¾ inch square pine braced with ⅛ inch by ½ inch plywood strips (½ inch square and ⅝ inch square wood could also have been used). What I have shown can be built in about 20 minutes in the wood shop. Glue and clamp all joints and braces. Do not use nails or staples because small sections of wood tend to split if that is done.

The robot is suspended in the framework with bare, soft copper wire (12 or 14 swg) or string using the dowels that are at the shoulders of the robot. Also refer to other photographs in

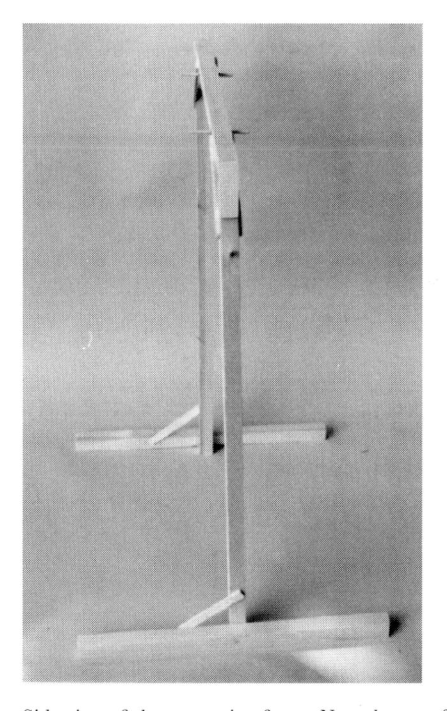

Side view of the suspension frame. Note the use of dowels to allow rubber bands to secure the robot suspension wires. All construction is wood and glue – no nails are used.

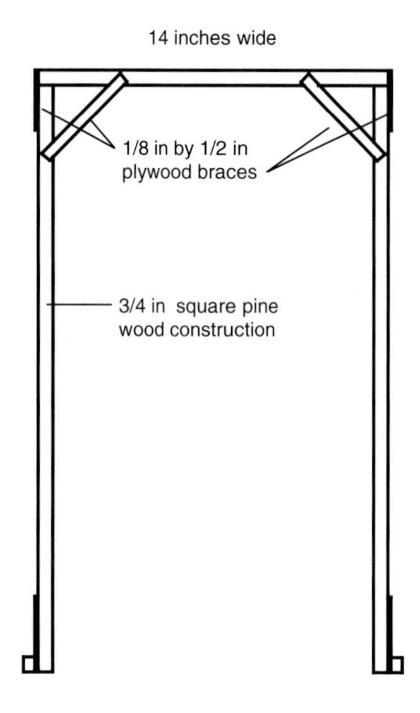

Figure 13.12 Front view of the suspension frame.

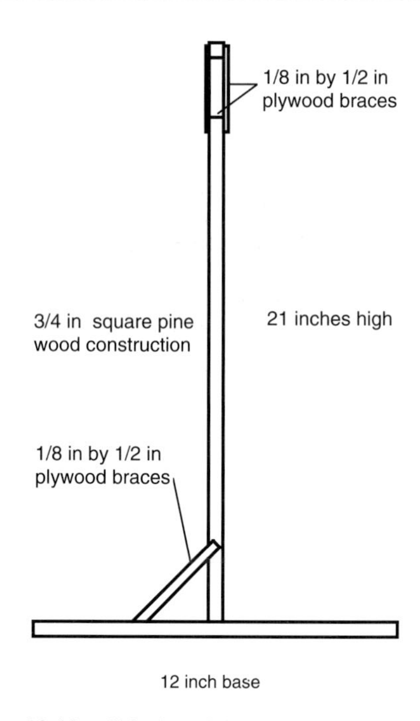

Figure 13.13 Side view of the suspension frame.

this chapter to see how the suspension frame is used. Wire works better than string because it is stiffer and constrains the robot nicely.

Suspended in the frame is also the easiest way to transport the robot from place to place by hand or on the car seat. It is also the best way to store the robot.

Switches and turn on sequence

Provide two switches for the electrical power to the robot. One switch should be in the power line to the controller and the other switch should be in the power line for the servo motors.

When you turn on the robot use the following procedure. Turn on the controller first. Send it data to position all the servos, then turn on the servo power. The servos will go to the programmed locations. This is one way to keep the servos from assuming centred positions on start up. If you always position the servos before shut down, they will always be under your control. (The new Scott Edwards controller sends out a centring signal (127) to all motors on start up.)

CHAPTER FOURTEEN

RoboWalk – a language for a walking robot

RoboWalk is a very simple and rudimentary language designed to allow interested experimenters to investigate the mechanics of machines that walk with a biped humanoid mechanism. This is essentially a software experience. Designing this language is intended to be a learning experience.

Now that we have a robot, we are ready to run it from a computer. In this chapter I will discuss the design of a language to control a walking robot. We already have an understanding of what a robot language looks like (Chapter 9) so we are ready to understand how the robot handles its language. In the computer world, things are done in a number of ways that are not intuitively obvious to the uninitiated. The basic concept that you need to understand is that a lot of time is spent doing nothing by most computers. By this we mean that they may actually be processing information only 5 per cent of the time. In other words most computers are actually processing information for less than 30 minutes in an average 8-hour day – the rest of the time they are on idle. This idle time can be put to good use when we are running robots and this is done in any sophisticated program. I will discuss what is done and how it is done so that you can emulate this in the programs you write if you like (after you gain some expertise).

Let us look at the programming process in some detail.

Imagine that you are about to write a new program. You type in a line of code. The computer accepts the code a keystroke at a time and displays it on the screen so that you can see what you typed. At the same time the code is stored in the memory of the computer. It will be stored on disk as a disk file when we get done with the programming. This is simple enough and does not take a lot of time. The spare time between keystrokes could be used to check what we just typed in for errors. We will come back to this later.

When you run the program, the computer looks at each line of code to make sure there are no mistakes in the code. It then parses (breaks it up into its various components) each line of code and interprets what the line of code means so that the robot can do whatever the line of code tells it to do. A lot of this work can be done while we are typing the program in. We will come back to this too later.

The robot is a state machine. There are a fixed number of states that the machine can be in and it can move from one state to the other in only a given number of ways. All other paths are illegal. A viable program is a set of instructions that move the machine from one state to the other along a path that does not violate any of the rules that the machine is to obey. If we were to list a large number of states one after the other, it would form a viable program and the program could be used do useful work. Although this would be adequate, this is a very time consuming, inefficient and cumbersome way to write a program.

In order to increase the speed and efficiency of programming, higher level languages have been developed. In these languages, instead of telling a motor to move to a couple of thousand consecutive positions one move at a time with velocity and timing information for each position, we just tell the motor to move thus:

Move motor A 3000 counts (positive counts are indicated)

or Move A 3000

The controller interprets the instruction as follows:

- Start the motor
- Accelerate to a given or pre-specified velocity
- Run the motor at the given velocity
- Work out when to start decelerating the motor
- Slow the motor down
- Stop the motor at the exact point where it is supposed to stop

The velocities and accelerations are usually defined in other parts of the program. Usually the machine contains a table of parameters that determines how the machine is to behave. For the above example (for the control of motors) there will most likely be some table or parameters that define the following:

- Maximum acceleration under any condition no matter what
- Maximum acceleration for the machine as set up
- Maximum acceleration as a function of the velocity
- Maximum velocity under any condition no matter what
- Maximum velocity as a function of the length of the move
- Maximum permitted position move position
- Maximum permitted negative move position
- Home position for the axis (this is a reference position)

There are other parameters that might further modify positional parameters. For example, we may not want the leg to move too fast if it is extended all the way out. There might be a multiplier function that is based on the leg extension angle to make sure that this does not happen.

The point to understand is that there is a lot of computation that has to be undertaken in real time before a robot can make a move, so much so that the movement of the robot might seem sluggish for some purposes. The computational bottleneck can be avoided by processing a lot of the information that will be needed before the move is ever started.

All the error checking that makes sure that the lines of code are correct before they are processed can be undertaken as the information is entered. This can be done as each keystroke is actually entered or at the end of each line – both techniques are used. Checking at each keystroke is usually not necessary so the line is usually checked as soon as the carriage return key press indicates that the line is complete. The computer then checks the line and if there is an error, the error is annunciated and the line of code can be corrected. This technique makes sure that the system does not have to take the time to check the program a line at a time as it is executing the program. A considerable amount of time can be saved in a program written in a sophisticated language because in a powerful language it can take a lot of work to determine if a line of code is correct.

Although the line may make sense syntactically, it might still not make sense as far as an actual move is concerned. We might be asking the robot to move its gripper through itself. This too can be addressed ahead of time in a well thought-out and well-written software package. Here again most of the work is being done in the background while the program is being written. Things are starting to become a little bit complicated now because we now have to set up a mathematical model of the robot and make sure that each line of code is not doing anything impossible. The added complication that needs appreciation is that when we edit a program, every move made after the edited line can be affected drastically. So each edit means that the rest of the program may have to be re-processed to make sure that no "impossible to execute" moves were created. Usually all the following incremental moves will be affected by an edit. The absolute moves are unaffected though access to an absolute move might become a problem after an edit. (Example: what was not an obstacle along a path might have become an obstacle.)

To all this we have to add the dimensions of the environment that the robot is working in and make sure that it does not violate any rules as might be related to the environmental constraints created by the presence of other machines and of operators etc.

We also need to appreciate that there are situations where not everything can be worked out up front because there can be a lot of IF...THEN... conditions that can make the work needed to work out everything in advance beyond the scope of the average controller. This is one of the reasons why we may have to step the robot through the program a couple of times before we start to run the system under automatic control.

There are software packages that allow the engineers to see what the robot will do on a computer screen simulation before the actual run takes place. These are made necessary by the fact that the tasks being undertaken can be very complicated as indicated in the following real world example.

There are five robots that paint all the cars that go through the paint line at the General Motors plant at Wentsville near St. Louis in Missouri, USA. This plant makes Buicks and Cadillacs of all body styles. Each robot has two arms, one with the paint gun at the end of it and one that allows the robot to open the doors on the cars to paint the insides. Each paint head has a number of paint nozzles to dispense various colours of paint that are needed. All the robots are in one room on this one paint line. Three robots are on one side, two on the other, each side's robots on a common set of tracks. *If any one of the robots breaks down, the other robots take over its work seamlessly* and the line keeps moving while the necessary repairs are undertaken. (The painting is done electrostatically, and the paint booth is surprisingly clean.)

As you can well imagine, the software needed to do this is not trivial. Imagine the changes needed as various models of cars move through this one paint booth without a hitch. The plant makes Buicks and Cadillacs of all body styles and of all colours on this one line. There are close to 3000 cars in the pipeline, meaning that about 3000 cars have to be made and painted before the first finished one comes out of the plant. The robots had better keep on painting!

In Chapter 9 we learned what a rudimentary language to run a robot arm consists of and in Chapter 10 we learned about the rudimentary commands that form a robotic vision system. In this chapter we will investigate the design of a robotic language by actually describing, discussing the designing a very simple language to control our walking mechanism. **You do not actually have to design a language in order to run the robot you have built**. This chapter shows you how to design and implement a language **if you want to**. A lot of what robots are is the software that runs them so understanding the software aspects of the machine is important to a comprehensive introduction to robotics.

Lest we get too carried away, which is always easy enough in any software project, let us agree that the goal here is to design a very rudimentary robotic language that will allow the robotic legs that we have made to execute a semblance of a humanoid walk. No matter the quality of the walk at this stage, if the legs walk we will have done our job and will have learned many things about robotics and robotic languages along the way. The rest is experience, practice, research and refinement (and of course a lot of time and energy).

The walk we design will, intentionally, be very slow and ponderous to eliminate the effects of dynamic motion. At the rate at which we can communicate with the robot it will not be possible to respond fast enough to any dynamic changes taking place in a fast moving robot. Additionally, we have no sensors on board the robot to tell us what is actually happening at the robot in real time and in any case we are not receiving any information from the robot. If we had this information it would allow us to make decisions we need to make as soon as possible but unfortunately this is beyond the scope of this project. We will be communicating at 9600 baud or about 960 characters a second which is very little information indeed when trying to control eight motors in real time. A real situation might need about a million characters a second (and more if vision was involved).

The language that we speak is the primary vehicle that allows us to communicate with one another. There are also gestures, smiles, frowns and other complications like volume and inflection (and even accent) that are too complicated for this discussion. As a part of the use of language we need to comprehend that we cannot discuss those things for which there are no words. In order to discuss those things for which there are no words, we have to first invent and then define the words in an unambiguous way. This is specially true of robotics which is a new discipline for we have not yet had the time to coin all the words that we need. Consider trying to discuss electronics today without the words transistor and electron, both words that have only relatively recently entered the human vocabulary. Now take a few moments to consider how important these two words are to us today.

As the language with the largest vocabulary, English is the most dynamic and useful language in the world and as such it is the ideal language for controlling a robot (or anything else for that matter). We use it every day to control and direct millions of human beings who can be considered to be very sophisticated organic robots. Unfortunately there are a number of problems with using everyday English when it comes to controlling robots.

(1) The entire language is much too large to be used with even a supercomputer or two (or ten), much less a desktop personal computer. In other words it would take a huge amount of memory and a very powerful computer to accommodate the entire language and its many interpretations. The software effort needed to use all this information effectively in a robotic context would be a very long and difficult undertaking. At the present time the ability for us to do all this is still some considerable distance in the future. Even when we can interpret language with machines, the interpretation will have to be fast enough for robotic purposes and that is even further in the future.

(2) The meanings of words in any evolved language are context sensitive (and even ambiguous) i.e. the meaning of the word is af-

fected by the way in which, where and when the word is used. Although this makes for great poetry, it is a disaster when controlling robots. In robotics, at the present state of development, a word must have one, and only one, very specific, rigid meaning.

(3) We do not need, and cannot effectively use, the entire language. Most of the words in the language are not useful in a robotic context (again we are discussing the basic level that we are interested in). For reasons of economy the language that any robot uses has to be as small as possible for the tasks at hand.

(4) No one subset of the language will serve every robot in every instance. Each family of robots needs to have its own language. The language will reflect the use to which the robot is to be put and this is the most economical way to do it. Note that human language is influenced in the same way. The words needed by an Eskimo to describe his work and environment are quite different from those needed by a tropical forest dweller for his or someone in Tokyo for hers.

In the specific case we have before us, our interest is in designing a language to control two-legged walking by a simple robot with eight servo motors on it. In this project we have no interest in welding and closing grippers and the like, so all the words that have to do with these and similar activities are not needed in our language. We do not need words to control the ninth servo either because in this particular universe there is no such thing. Our task is quite compartmental and clearly defined.

Walking is a particularly interesting activity to design a language for because we are all completely familiar with the activity. The ideas and commands needed for the activity are not contaminated with what most other robots do. This allows us to be both specific and original in our thinking and allows our effort to be more compartmentalized in that we do not have to think about anything else when designing this language and this in turn enhances our learning experience by not distracting us.

Since there tends to be no realistic limit to the number of words that can be implemented in a language let us agree that we will limit our discussion to the implementation of about a dozen or two of the most important words. We can always add more words later on as we get more comfortable with the ideas and techniques involved.

The information that the computer will send to the robot controller will consist entirely of zeros and ones. They may be represented as two frequencies or two timed signals or may use a number of other techniques but basically it is thousands upon thousands of zeros and ones. So in a way the language we will use already exists, it is just that this is too hard for humans to understand and edit commands in this language. This is not unlike Morse code which consists of dots and dashes separated by relatively fixed spaces. Imagine transmitting and understanding Morse code thousands of times faster than is done with a Morse key.

The first level of higher language consists of turning the zeros and ones into letters of the alphabet. A combination of eight zeros or ones can represent 256 different characters. The computer industry has agreed on a standard way of representing these codes. It is called ASCII text. Since there are only 26 letters of the alphabet and 10 numbers, the rest of the 256 combinations are used for lower case, international notations, punctuation and headings etc. (ASCII defines only the first 128 codes). A sample listing to show you how this is implemented as the 128 codes is provided in Appendix 2.

Having defined an alphabet, we can move onto putting the letters together into words and the words into a language. A language allows us to manipulate the zeros and ones in a way that allows us to get useful information out of the raw data that we put in. The information appears on the screen for human consumption and can be sent out of the computer on wires for use by other machines. The primary way in which the human communicates with the computer is through the keyboard by pressing the keys. The primary way in which the computer communicates with the human being is through the computer screen. One reads what is on the screen to understand what the computer is saying.

Let us now get back to the design of our specific language and so to the next level of complexity for us. The words that we select for our language will have to do with the following activity:

> They will implement the control of eight motors – NOTHING ELSE IS REQUIRED.

That is all we have to do because that is all there is on the robot. However this does not make it trivial and a lot of interesting ideas lie ahead.

The eight basic movements (each one controlled by one servo motor) that the robot we have built can execute are as follows:

- Nutate (twist)the foot for either foot
- Bend the foot for either foot at the ankle
- Bend the knee for either leg
- Bend the hip joint for either leg

Each of the above movements is controlled independently by one of the eight servo motors on the robot. If we could specify a number to represent the movement or position for each motor, these commands would be enough for complete control. Just like the zeros and ones give complete control, this is all that is truly needed or possible. However this level of control is still too cumbersome so we have to create still higher level commands. The commands that we decide on have to combine the above eight commands to make it easier for us to specify and thus control the movements of the robot. We want to move in the direction of making the language more or less conversational and English-like in its nature. The more like English it is, the easier it will be for us to use it. The computer does not really care what the language that we use looks like. All it knows is that there are a lot of zeros and ones to process and that it can do with facility.

The first new idea we need to consider is the concept of speed control, meaning that we need to be able to make the movement of each servo at a controllable rate. We are already constrained at the fast end in that the servos used will run only so fast. All other speeds have to be slower than that fastest speed. The servos that we are using can be positioned to 256 different positions within about a 180-degree movement of the output shaft. Of this 180-degree movement we will use about 90 degrees. We cannot control the speed at which the servos move from one position to the other, but we can break each move up into smaller moves and control the delay between subsequent moves to get the control we need.

If the servo is at position 0 and we tell it to go to position 255 it will do so in about 0.5 seconds on most model aircraft servos like those we are using. However if we tell it to move to position 1 and then pause for 0.1 seconds and then to move to position 2 and to pause another 0.1 seconds and on ... to position 255, it will take the servo a little over 25 seconds to make the same move. It can be argued that this is really 255 small, jerky moves, and of course it is, but for our purposes it will be good enough.

So we need to add a speed command or more appropriately a "time to make the move" command that can be used to slow the servos down. You should think about the implications of this command. There is a very distinct difference between the speed of a move and time taken to make a move. The major advantage to us will be that when we make compound moves (i.e. moves with more than one motor moving) the time taken by all the motors to make the move will be the same because some motors can now be moved more slowly than others. This will be a major control convenience and simplification for us.

With the above in mind, we can define a move for the two legs as a **timed compound move** with a command which looks something like this:

MOVE 1.5, 0, 25, -107, 31, 0, 0, 0, 0

This is an incremental move command i.e. the move is an increment from the present position. This command would be interpreted to mean that the legs were to be moved as follows:

- The first number specifies the duration of the move. This move is to take 1.5 seconds to complete and in this move ...
- The left foot nutation servo would remain unmoved (the first zero)
- The left ankle would move positively 25 counts from its present position
- The left knee would move negatively 107 counts from its present position
- The left waist joint for the left leg would move 25 counts from its present position
- The right foot nutation would be "no move"
- The right ankle movement would be "no move"
- The right knee movement would be "no move"
- And the right waist joint would not be moved

In the above example, the move has been simplified by moving the left leg only. This may not actually be the case very often but is used here as an example to keep it simple.

We need to address all eight motors simultaneously because the task before us is complicated enough to require such simultaneous motion. This makes it a bit cumbersome when we have to move only one motor but in our application these cases will be rare.

If we had a robot that needed to move a couple of motors together a lot of the time we would implement commands that would do just that. For example, this might be the case for the head of a robot or the eyes in a talking head (an interesting robot idea and 'do-able' with the hardware we have at hand).

Now let us go back and start at the beginning. Before we start a move sequence, we will want to have a standing position that the robot can be sent to with relative ease. The command for doing so can be called whatever we like but it is easier if we pick English-like commands that are intuitive and easy to remember. Let us use

STAND

to keep it conversational.

Whenever the system receives this command, it will assume a position where the robot stands straight up. Our intention is that all our move sequence will start from this one known position.

Since we do not know what position of each motor makes the legs stand exactly straight up in the way we want them to, we also need to define the default STAND position. The position is indeterminate because there will always be some difference in the lengths of linkages and the centre position of the servos that need to be adjusted for. This is how we make that adjustment. It could, of course, also be done mechanically but it is easier and more flexible if done in software (and more importantly this is how it should be done in any computer-controlled machine).

For this adjustment we will use the SETSTAND command. The command will be implemented to be used in the following way:

SETSTAND 0, 34, 50, -12, 0, 32, 55, -14

SETSTAND is always to be followed by eight signed numbers.

The first four numbers define the position

adjustments for the left leg and the next four define the position adjustments for the right leg servo motors. Note that the two sets of numbers are similar. This would normally be the case because both legs are similar and the slight variations take into account the differences in the lengths of the linkages etc. as mentioned above.

The numbers could specify the position from one end of motion for each motor or be error corrections from the middle or neutral position of the servos. It would be at our discretion to design a system that best suited our needs. Our intention would be such that if we forgot the SETSTAND command, things would not get completely out of hand. For this reason, the theoretical positions would be put in the parameter table of the program and the adjustments would be defined in the SETSTAND command. Then if we forget to send SETSTAND, the stand of the robot will be off by only the corrections needed. In a sophisticated program, the software would be designed so that the SETSTAND command would have to be seen before a STAND command in every program or an error would be annunciated. (The STAND command in turn would have to precede any moves and so on ... it gets complicated fast!)

SETSTAND and STAND would normally be the first two commands in any program. Before these two commands were executed, the robot legs would of necessity have to be assumed to be in a random position.

Next let us define two easy commands. These will allow us to

START

walking and

STOP

walking.

START will be needed at the beginning of a program and also to restart the walk if we need to stop a robot in the middle of a program for some reason. For simplicity sake, in our language, START will assume that the robot is standing still whenever this command is received. Having commands like START and STOP allow you to perform the many housekeeping functions that are always needed before and after every move sequence.

STOP will take the legs from whatever position they are in and bring them to a controlled STAND position without the robot falling over. This is more complicated than it seems at first sight because we do not know the position of the robot when the command is executed. The path, or the algorithm for the path, that is needed from every possible position to the standing position is not obvious.

Shifting the weight to one leg or the other

Next we will start walking so let us address shifting the weight of the entire robot from the standing position to either foot. In this position it would be possible to move the weightless foot forward in anticipation of taking a step. We are slowly moving towards being able to take a step.

Let us call these commands

SHIFTLEFT

meaning shift all the weight of the machine to the left foot and

SHIFTRIGHT.

The hip joint on a human being is movable in just about every direction. In our case we can move the leg back and forth only, so shifting the weight will need a slightly different technique. We will have to bend one knee or push off with the other foot to shift the weight while at the same time nutating the first foot to take up the weight transfer. So effectively we will shorten one leg and lengthen the other to shift the weight.

Once the weight has been shifted to one foot, we can move the other leg back and forth in the air. As the leg moves back and forth we have to tilt back and forth on the supporting foot/ankle or waist to take into account the change in the centre of gravity.

Next let us assume a continuous walk. This is motion consisting of many steps. We need to decide exactly what we think a step consists of. We need to decide when it starts, when it stops and what its discrete, dissectible components are so that we can define the components and then execute them as a part of each step. Essentially what we have do is to move a leg forward and shift the weight to it. That would make one step. Next we can put steps together to form a walk.

Let us call the action of moving the free left foot forward and transferring the load to it STEP. Since the load may have to be transferred to one leg or the other, we need to be able to specify the leg also. We can do this by adding either LEFT or RIGHT to the command so that the commands now become

```
STEPLEFT
```

and

```
STEPRIGHT.
```

A simple walk routine could consist of a sequence of commands as listed below:

```
     SETSTAND
     STAND
200  SHIFTLEFT
     STEPRIGHT
     SHIFTRIGHT
     STEPLEFT
     GOTO 200
     END
```

We have now defined the software commands to walk in a straight line. Almost a straight line would be a more appropriate description because we have no way of guaranteeing that each leg will behave identically to the other or that the surface we are walking on will be perfectly uniform or that the cables will not be tugging on the robot! There will be conditions that will make the walk slightly off a straight line path no matter what our intent. Murphy's law will be tugging at our robot at all times.

We now need to add the ability to make a turn. During a turn we would continue to walk but either the left or the right step would be shortened to make the turn. We will want to use a variable that specifies how many steps the turn is to consist of and a variable that specifies how far the legs are going to turn. We will determine what the range for these variables is after we have actually built the robot and can experiment with it. We do not have enough information (in the form of experience) to do this with just theoretical knowledge.

The commands for turning will be

```
TURNLEFT 90,16
```

meaning turn left 90 degrees in 16 steps and

```
TURNRIGHT D, N
```

in which we are to turn right and variables are shown instead of numbers.

The language we have designed consists of the following words at this stage, listed alphabetically:

```
MOVE
SETSTAND
SHIFTLEFT
SHIFTRIGHT
STAND
START
```

STEPLEFT
STEPRIGHT
STOP
TURNLEFT
TURNRIGHT

Since we could have controlled the legs completely with just the MOVE command the utility of the higher level language is in that it is easier to use and understand and thus to modify a program that has been written in it. As you can see, a program consisting of a few thousand zeros and ones or even a list of 100 MOVE commands would be much harder to read and edit than a program written in a language employing just the above set of words.

Although we could implement an editor as a part of our program, there is no particular robotic learning in writing an editor and so instead I will suggest that we either use a common word processor in "plain text" mode for writing our programs or embed them in the BASIC program. In the early stages of software development computers could run only one program at a time so one had to completely shut down an editor before one could load the robot operating system software and vice versa. As a convenience the editor had to be made a part of the operating system of the robot. Now we can run each program in its own window so this is not a major inconvenience and will save us a lot of time.

Because of the way we are writing our programs *we* will have to check the program to ensure it is free of errors or our operating system will have to be designed to check the program for this before it can run a program.

Next let us add a command that helps with debugging

RESET.

RESET is a useful command when you are developing a language. It does not affect the robot itself – it is used to set all the variables in the software program to a known value. The values may be zero but would not have to be. In a well debugged language this command would not be necessary and we may want to eliminate this command later on in our development but for now it is convenient to have a command that allows us to get to a known start-up condition for the software. Knowing exactly where you started from allows you to debug the software with greater ease.

The command is convenient because when we are writing software, and especially if we are new to this discipline, there is a possibility that we will use a variable inadvertently and change its value without realizing it. Then when we use the variable again we will get strange results. As a matter of fact this is a very common programming bug or error.

Other commands, further developments

Other commands can be added as your expertise in the discipline increases – your imagination is the only limit. Here are some ideas that you might want to consider.

- Turning in place
- Walking backward
- Walking with bent knees
- Speeding up the walk
- Incremental and absolute moves for motors
- Special moves for less than 8 motors

Some questions:

- Is it possible to walk using less than 8 servos?
- What did you discover about walking that surprised you?
- If you had two controllers and 8 more servos, what would you do?
- What other walking related words cannot be implemented on the robot?

Motor positions

Since there is no feedback from the robot, you have to keep track of where each of the servos are at all times. Once positioned, the servos stay where they are. The controller card handles this automatically with the width of the pulses that it generates. The fact that there is no feedback from the robot is not as critical as it might seem because the robot hardware can be simulated in software as a part of the control algorithm. Also since the robot moves relatively slowly, the need for real time feedback is minimized.

Weight and inertia

It would be interesting to use the weight and the centre of gravity of each leg component and maybe inertial inputs to calculate the movements needed to execute a faster walk. Initially, inertia can probably be ignored if we start off with slower movements however as the speed is increased, inertia will become more important.

CHAPTER FIFTEEN

Programming

This chapter is written more for the beginner than for the trained software engineer. If you are familiar with programming, you can read the manual for the controller and go from there. Scan this chapter for general information.

When I got to this part, I was on the verge of neglecting important duties and you are hereby warned of the dangers that you are about to enter into.

I am not going to discuss the BASIC language itself because you will get much more for the time you spend if you read the manuals that you received with your computer and its software. If all this is completely new to you, a beginner's book on Microsoft QuickBASIC will be helpful as will a friend familiar with simple programming. We will not be doing anything really complicated and I will use less than 20 of the 200 or so commands in BASIC. My goal is to keep it as simple as possible (you are to add the complications). I will be using Microsoft QuickBASIC (version 1.0e) for the Macintosh but all BASICs are very similar, especially so for the few commands that I am going to use. (All the programs discussed have been tested on my system and they all work! I used a very slow 9 year-old 16 MHz Apple Macintosh IIX so speed is not an important factor here.)

You do not have to do it the way I did it – in fact it will be much better if you do it in your own way because you will learn more if you muddle it through and get your brain really working with the programming. What I am showing you is one of the many ways through the forest I have got you into. The way is not simple if you have never done anything like this before but I will show you a way that is easy to follow. What you will want to do should be elegant, fast and interesting so our goals are not identical and you need to understand this. Running eight motors is not exactly simple, but if we do it a step at a time in an orderly way, we will gain an understanding that will lead to the solutions we need to run a robot. Take your time. You must understand each and every line of code in that this is not unlike a geometry proof and no steps can be missed. You must understand every line of code before you go on to the next step.

Although you, of course, are going to be familiar with what is being done and will find it challenging and interesting, friends who do not understand what is being done by the software will find the movements of the robot fascinating if not magical.

Before reading any further, scan this entire chapter to get a good look at what we are about to do.

There is a lot of new information in this chapter and if you are new to programming this is going to be somewhat overwhelming. Go slowly, follow some of the examples in the software manuals so you can see how this is done and things will start to fall into place after a while. This is where it helps to have someone who is willing to sit next to you quietly and answer your questions. I have tried to make the programming as simple to follow as possible. This makes it somewhat cumbersome but that is how we need to do it at this stage.

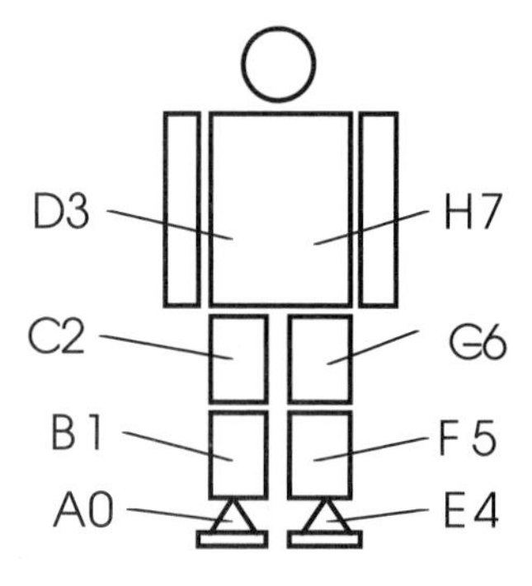

Figure 15.1 Variable and motor designations on the robot. These are used for all the programs discussed.

A 3mm (⅛in.) hole for a shoulder harness is shown in each shoulder of the robot. Run a wire or a string through these two holes and suspend the robot above the table, in its harness stand, next to your computer during your development work. A robot that spends half its time falling over can get to be a bit of a frustration. This harness can also be used to limit the severity of the falls by allowing only a little slack in the string when you first start walking. Once you get

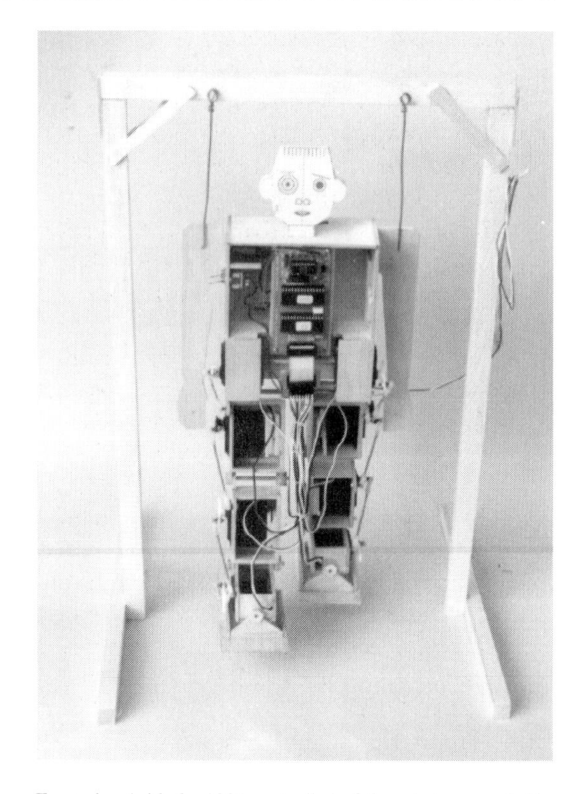

Front view (with the 1994 controller) of the robot suspended in the programming and transportation frame. The cradle is 53cm (21 in.) high and 33mm (13 in.) wide. The robot is 45cm (18 in.) high.

all the moves and algorithms worked out in the air, you can set the robot on the table and run your programs to see how well you did.

There is no way to provide canned programs that will work with every language and every computer likely to be used to run the robot and besides, canned programs are rather boring and will not introduce you to much of anything. Instead what I will do is show you how to write the programs to do it your way. Actually making it work in your way with programs you have written is the educational part of this because it is the actual interaction of the brain with your hands and the experimental apparatus that leads to an exciting learning process (that sticks).

Some notes on biped walking

True two-legged, humanoid walking is quite a bit more complicated than we tend to think it is. Thus the dearth of true biped, weight shifting, walking robots in the toy market. We are about to discover this for ourselves and to be surprised by what we will find. This is not trivial but you do not have to be a rocket scientist either (the way we are going to do it).

The process starts with the robot standing balanced on both feet. The following steps are:

(1) Push down with the right foot and nutate the left foot to shift the weight completely to the left foot. The robot is now standing on its left foot and it is now possible to lift the right foot up.

(2) Move the right foot forward and at the same time lean forward and to the right with the left foot. It is best to keep the right foot low and develop a shuffling walk with short steps first. You will have fewer falls this way. The above will make the robot fall onto the right foot. Adjust the right foot to lie flat on the floor The robot should now again be resting on both feet.

(3) Push forward with the left toe to transfer the weight forward and to the right foot. It may be necessary to bend the right knee or create a similar effect as you do this.

(4) When all the weight has been transferred to the right foot, the left foot can be picked up and moved forward. As the left foot is brought forward it will be necessary to adjust the right foot to take up the weight change.

(5) Continue moving the left foot forward and on to the next step.

It may be necessary to bend at the waist as the walk is made more and more human. A decent gait is quite complicated. Turns are even more so and consist of short steps on one side and longer ones on the other. You can control which foot slips in the turn by arranging the weight on the feet appropriately. (I am avoiding telling you more on purpose to make you think about it – a puzzle with the solution attached is intellectual grand theft!)

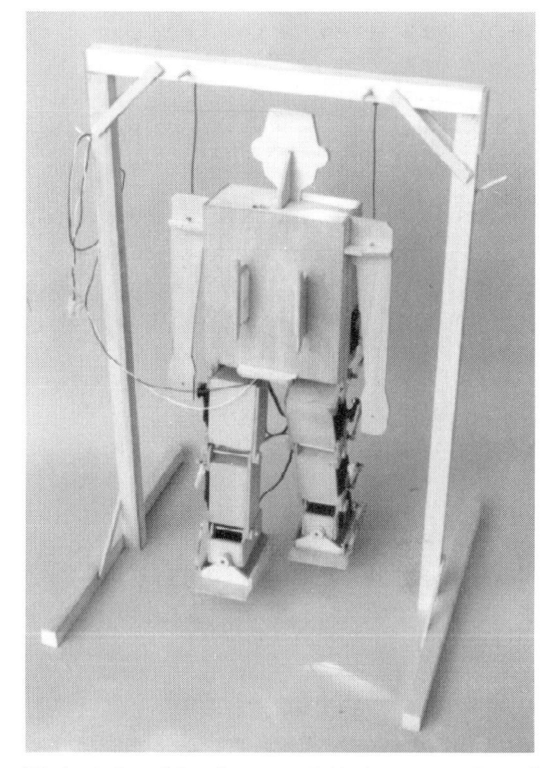

The back view of the robot suspended in the programming and transportation frame. The battery support brackets are shown but although this is a convenient location for the battery with the robot in the harness the arrangement is too top heavy for walking. Place the battery on the table when walking.

Since the joint movements are not linear, you can create look up tables that will give you linear motion if you feel that this is necessary (do it later if you must). In a look up table, each command corresponds to another command in the look up table. Instead of making a move to A you make a move to the number in position A of the table. Since we can have 255 moves for each motor, the table for a motor has to have 255 locations in it. The values are programmed into a table as a part of the code or read in from

DATA statements. You do not need a table in the initial experiments. Keep it simple until you feel comfortable with it.

I will describe two different ways to program the robot. One is a very simple and straightforward but a lower level way of doing it, and the other is a more sophisticated method in which I will show you how you could write a simple language interpreter and your imagination, drive and the time you have will be the only limits to what you can achieve.

Read the section on how the controller is commanded in Appendix 3 to have its command structure fairly well in mind *before* you read the following.

I will show you how to write programs to do the following. This is a progression.

- Control one motor, with 3 simple keystroke commands
- Control one motor and have speed control, more sophisticated
- Control two motors at one time
- Co-ordinate the motion of two motors
- Write a program to manipulate all the motors with the keyboard so that you can see what motor counts are needed at each joint to design your walking moves
- Show you how a sequence is taught and played back
- Show you how to write a simple language interpreter
- Give you some ideas for what to do next in your experiments

Let us creep up on the solutions a little bit at a time.

Controlling one motor

Let us start by controlling one motor and understanding some of the most fundamental techniques that are to be used.

Hook up the controller as shown in Figure 15.2. The program reflects a motor connected to port 0, the first port. At this stage you do not need to be hooked up to a robot although it will

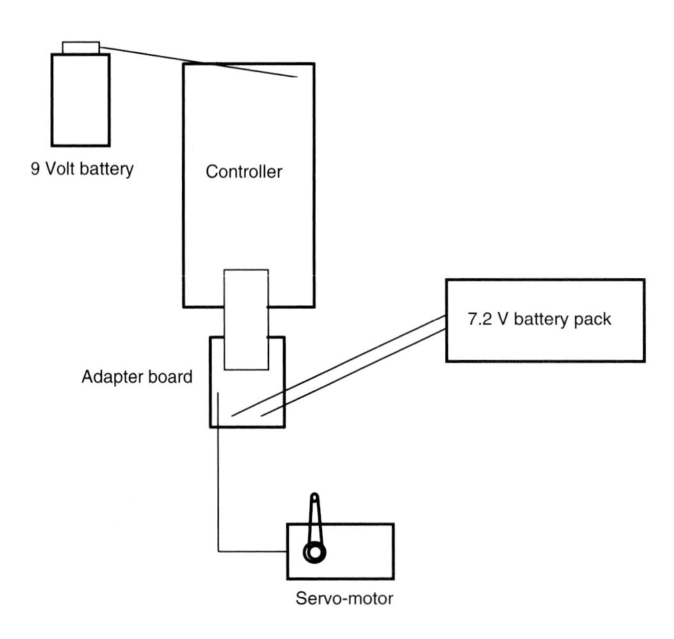

Figure 15.2 Controller hook up for one motor. You do not need a robot connected for the early experiments.

not hurt if you are working with the robot if you go slowly. However, it is better to have a bare motor and controller so that you do not have to worry about bending anything up at this stage. (This comes under "the heading of stress management" for the model engineer!)

All program listings are available on disk (see Appendix 4.)

Let us list the program so that we can refer to it:

```
REM     THIS IS PROGRAM NUMBER 100
REM     PROGRAM TO CONTROL ONE MOTOR
REM     FROM THE KEYBOARD WITH "R", "A" AND
          "Z" KEYS

OPEN "COM1: 9600,N,8,1" FOR OUTPUT AS #1

A.MID.POS=127
A.MIN.POS=67
A.MAX.POS=187
MTR.STP=5

50  A=A.MID.POS
    PRINT #1, "A0";A

100 PRINT A
    A$=""
150 A$=INKEY$
    A$=UCASE$(A$)
200 IF A$="" THEN GOTO 150

IF A$="R" THEN GOTO 50
IF A$="A" THEN
    A=A+MTR.STP
    IF A>A.MAX.POS THEN A=A.MAX.POS
        PRINT #1, "A0";A
    END IF

IF A$="Z" THEN
    A=A-MTR.STP
    IF A<A.MIN.POS THEN A=A.MIN.POS
        PRINT #1, "A0";A
    END IF
GOTO 100
END
```

Let us go over the program.

We can ignore the REMark lines.

First we have to establish communications with the controller. This is done with the first line as follows:

```
OPEN "COM1: 9600,N,8,1" FOR OUTPUT AS #1
```

This is the line that will have to be modified to match the software in your computer.

We are opening

> COM1 at 9600 baud using
> No parity,
> 8 data bits and
> 1 stop bit.

This will be referred to as port #1 in our program. (BASIC lets you to send data to a number of numbered ports in the same program). If you do not specify a number the output goes to the screen.

On the servo motors that we are using we need to define the following variables in our program to be able to properly control the motor. These values can be more easily changed if they are defined as variables. Since these values will be referred to again and again in the program, we will not have to go to each location where they are mentioned to change them if we define them as variables.

- Starting position of the motor – "A" motor's middle position
- Minimum value permitted for the motor – "A" motor's minimum position
- Maximum value permitted for the motor – "A" motor's maximum position
- Amount the motor should move in each step – Motor step

The section of the program that defines these is:

```
A.MID.POS=127
A.MIN.POS=107
A.MAX.POS=187
MTR.STP=1
```

Next we set the "A" motor to its middle position and tell the controller to move it to that position with the PRINT command. "A" is the motor position.

```
50      A=A.MID.POS
        PRINT #1, "A0";A
```

The next command prints the value "A on the screen so that we can see where the motor is (PRINT is used without the #1 to print to the screen).

```
100     PRINT A
```

The next section of the program is a loop that looks at the keyboard to see what key you have pressed. The first line clears the variable as a housekeeping measure. As long as you do not press a key the system stays in this loop.

```
A$=""
150 A$=INKEY$
A$=UCASE$(A$)
200 IF A$="" THEN GOTO 150
```

Each key press letter is converted to uppercase in the third line above.

As soon as you press a key, the system drops down to the next line. This code make a decision on three keys only: "R", "A" and "Z". "R" is used to reset the motor to the middle position and it does so in one fast move! A slower move can be implemented in your more sophisticated version of the software.

The "A" and the "Z" move the motor back and forth. The counts are displayed on the screen as the motor moves (in increments of MTR.STP).

All other keys are ignored. The code for "R" the reset function is as follows:

```
IF A$="R" THEN GOTO 50
```

This sends the program to the beginning code where the initial values are reset and then executed.

For the "A" key the code is

```
IF A$="A" THEN
    A=A+MTR.STP
    IF A>A.MAX.POS THEN A=A.MAX.POS
    PRINT #1, "A0";A
END IF
```

We add MTR.STP to the motor count and then make sure that the upper limit of travel has not been exceeded before we run the motor.

For the "Z" key the code is similar except we are now decrementing the counts and checking for the minimum allowable position.

```
IF A$="Z" THEN
    A=A-MTR.STP
    IF A<A.MIN.POS THEN A=A.MIN.POS
        PRINT #1, "A0";A
    END IF
GOTO 100
```

You can expand this program to control all the 8 motors from the keyboard using the "A S D F G H J and K" keys for moving the motors in one direction and the "Z X C V B N M and comma" keys for moving the motors in the other direction. This gives you a control panel on your keyboard on the two lower rows of keys. Other additions are limited only by your imagination.

A slightly modified program that does just this is listed later in this chapter.

One motor with speed control

Some servos are fast enough to travel the full 180-degree range of the output shaft in about 0.50 seconds. This is way too fast for our purposes so we need to develop a way to slow the motors down. We do this by making the motor move one step in each command and adding a delay between commands. If we want a slower speed we increase the length of the delay. If we want faster operation we increase the number of steps taken in each move. This is not the smoothest way to do it but it is good enough for our purposes. We must keep costs down and this is the best that we can do with the hardware we have. Since the delays are created with software loops and the time taken to execute one of these loops depends on the speed of your computer, you will have to experiment with the program to see what size constants you need in your programs to make them work properly.

```
REM     THIS IS PROGRAM NUMBER 200
REM     PROGRAM TO CONTROL ONE MOTOR
REM     ADDS SPEED CONTROL

OPEN "COM1: 9600,N,8,1" FOR OUTPUT AS #1

A.MID.POS=127
A.MIN.POS=67
A.MAX.POS=187
MTR.STP=2

50  A=A.MIN.POS
    PRINT #1, "A0";A

100 FOR X=A.MIN.POS TO A.MAX.POS STEP
                MTR.STP
    PRINT #1, "A0";X
    GOSUB DELAY
    NEXT X

FOR X=A.MAX.POS TO A.MIN.POS STEP -MTR.STP
PRINT #1, "A0";X
GOSUB DELAY
NEXT X

GOTO 100

DELAY:
FOR Y=1 TO 500
NEXT Y
RETURN

END
```

The constant in the delay loop has to be large enough to allow the motor to make its move before the next command is sent to it. After that, increasing the constant starts to slow the motor down. If commands come too fast one upon the other the motor can get confused.

The fact that all the communications take a certain amount of time is a complication in all motor control schemes and can be overcome by anticipation in more sophisticated programs. As you can well imagine, faster computers and faster communication protocols would be a great help (but these are not available to us in this particular case).

In the above program we are moving the motor in a large number of small jerky movements but we will see this as a slow smooth move that is suitable for our particular purposes.

This demonstrates how a servo is slowed down. The same technique has to be used on all the servos and needless to say other features can be added as you get better at programming.

In the programs that we develop, the idea is to keep the robot balanced at all times so that the loads on the servos are minimal. This is not a brute force exercise and, in any case, these servos are not strong enough to raise heavy loads.

Working with the robot

The next program works with the robot. It moves motors slowly under program control. This program will shift the weight of the robot from leg to leg if the parameters are adjusted properly for your particular robot. It uses only the two motors that nutate the feet. On my robot these are connected to ports 0 and 4. This is the beginning of walking. We can consider this to be walking in place!

```
REM    THIS IS PROGRAM NUMBER 300
REM    THIS PROGRAM SHOWS YOU HOW TO
REM    MOVE MOTORS SLOWLY TO SHOW HOW
REM    THIS IS DONE THE ROBOT BALANCE
REM    CHANGES FROM FOOT TO FOOT.
REM    ADJUST NUMBERS FOR COMPLETE LIFT
REM    OFF FROM EACH FOOT

OPEN "COM1: 9600,N,8,1" FOR OUTPUT AS #1

A.MAX=185 :REM INCR THIS INCREASES TILT OUT
          RT FOOT
A.MIN=117 :REM DECR THIS INCREASES TILT IN
          RT FOOT
E.MAX=137 :REM INCR THIS INCREASES TILT OUT
          LF FOOT
E.MIN=60 :REM DECR THIS INCREASES TILT IN LF
          FOOT

PSE.CONST=200
STP=1

PRINT #1, "A0";A.MIN
PRINT #1, "A1127";"A2127";"A3127"
PRINT #1, "A4";E.MIN
PRINT #1, "A5127";"A6127";"A7127"

100 REM
    FOR X=A.MIN TO A.MAX STEP STP
    PRINT #1, "A0";X
    GOSUB DO.PAUSE
    NEXT X

    GOSUB DO.PAUSE

    FOR X=A.MAX TO A.MIN STEP -STP*4
    PRINT #1, "A0";X
    GOSUB DO.PAUSE
    NEXT X

    FOR X=E.MAX TO E.MIN STEP -STP
    PRINT #1, "A4";X
    GOSUB DO.PAUSE
    NEXT X

    GOSUB DO.PAUSE

    FOR X=E.MIN TO E.MAX STEP STP*4
    PRINT #1, "A4";X
    GOSUB DO.PAUSE
    NEXT X

    GOTO 100

DO.PAUSE:
    FOR P=1 TO PSE.CONST
    NEXT P
RETURN
END
```

If we were to add a slight shuffle to the movements made, we would have our most rudimentary walk.

Controlling two motors at one time

Now that we can control the speed of a motor we can proceed to the next level of sophistification which is the control of two motors. First we will control them by just making them move and then we will add co-ordination.

Motors rarely start or stop simultaneously. What looks like simultaneous motion is really very rapid sequential turn on. In what we are

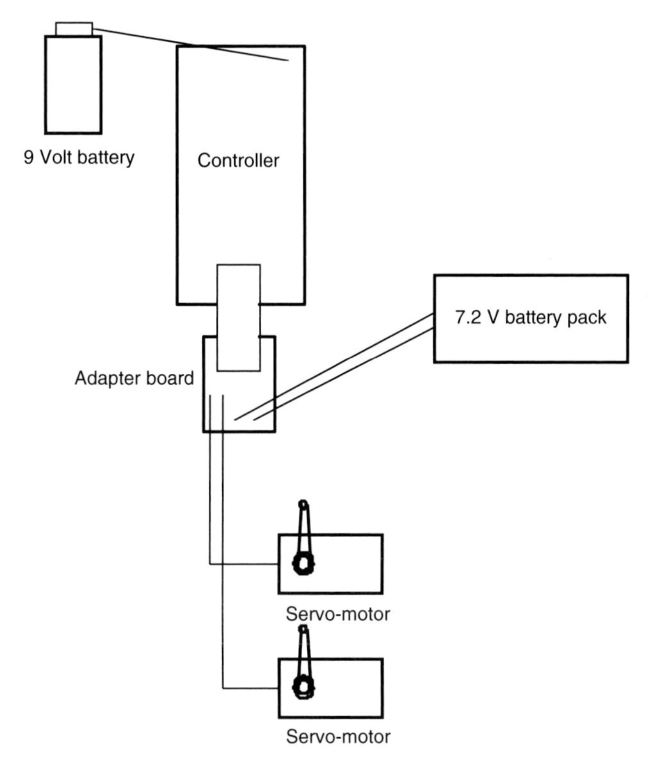

Figure 15.3 Two motors connected to the system.

about to do only the start will seem simultaneous. The stop will depend on the length of the moves specified.

As you did with the one motor, co

```
REM    THIS IS PROGRAM NUMBER 400
REM    PROGRAM TO CONTROL TWO MOTORS
REM    NO SPEED CONTROL

OPEN "COM1: 9600,N,8,1" FOR OUTPUT AS #1
A=127: B=127: C=127: D=127
E=127: F=127: G=127: H=127

PRINT "Reset all motors"
PRINT #1, "A0";A:FOR X=1 TO 1000:NEXT X
PRINT #1, "A1";B:FOR X=1 TO 1000:NEXT X
PRINT #1, "A2";C:FOR X=1 TO 1000:NEXT X
PRINT #1, "A3";D:FOR X=1 TO 1000:NEXT X
PRINT #1, "A4";E:FOR X=1 TO 1000:NEXT X
PRINT #1, "A5";F:FOR X=1 TO 1000:NEXT X
PRINT #1, "A6";G:FOR X=1 TO 1000:NEXT X
PRINT #1, "A7";H:FOR X=1 TO 1000:NEXT X

A.MIN.POS=64
A.MAX.POS=190
B.MIN.POS=40
B.MAX.POS=210

100 PRINT #1, "A0";A.MIN.POS
PRINT #1, "A1";B.MIN.POS
GOSUB DELAY

PRINT #1, "A0";A.MAX.POS
PRINT #1, "A1";B.MAX.POS
```

```
GOSUB DELAY

GOTO 100

DELAY:
FOR Y=1 TO 4000
NEXT Y
RETURN
```

The constant in the delay loop has to be large enough to allow the motor with the longest move to make its move completely before the next command is sent to it. Note that a delay is required after each move set.

Notice that one motor stops well before the other one. This would tend to make our moves seem amateurish. In the next program we overcome this by adding the code necessary to start and stop each of the two motors at almost the same time.

Co-ordinating the motions of two motors

In this program we co-ordinate the motion of the motors so that they both start and stop at the same time. This program could be modified to make the robot totter back and forth on its ankles slowly by adjusting the movement limits and the speed of the servos. In this case both motors would move the same amount but in my example they will move different amounts. I will leave any improvements you might want up to you.

We will have one motor move its full range of motion and the other move about half its range. The numbers are easy enough to change if you want to experiment with them (change the DATA statement). We will read the variables in from a DATA statement in order to introduce this new concept into our learning experience. DATA statements can usually appear anywhere in a BASIC program.

In the generalized case the first thing we have to do is to find out which of the motors has the longest move to make. All other motors keep time with the motion of this motor. Next let us take the example where one motor moves 254 positions and one moves 127 positions. If we break this move up into 254 segments the slower motor has to move $^{127}/_{254}$ of a move during each segment. Since we will be working with integers, the divisions will drop the remainder and we will get a working system. We have the added complication that the 254 counts may need moving in say a second and a half so delays have to be added between each move to slow the entire process down. The delays will depend on the speed of the computer you are using. Although communications at 9600 baud is the same for all computers, the calculations that are made between transmissions and other executions vary with the speed of the computer that you are using. You will need to run some experiments to determine how to construct the delays you need for your particular computer.

There is one added complication. Each transmission takes a certain amount of time and this has to be taken into account when you make your delay calculations.

Now let us take a look at what the minimal code for the co-ordinate move looks like. This program nutates the two feet, one twice as far as the other.

```
REM     THIS IS PROGRAM NUMBER 500
REM     PROGRAM TO CONTROL TWO MOTORS
REM     SIMULTANEOUS STARTING AND
REM     STOPPING NUTATES BOTH FEET
REM     BACK AND FORTH

OPEN "COM1: 9600,N,8,1" FOR OUTPUT AS #1

P.COUNT=1
A=127: B=127: C=127: D=127
E=127: F=127: G=127: H=127
MTR.STP=5
```

```
PRINT #1, "A0";A:FOR X=1 TO 1000:NEXT X
PRINT #1, "A1";B:FOR X=1 TO 1000:NEXT X
PRINT #1, "A2";C:FOR X=1 TO 1000:NEXT X
PRINT #1, "A3";D:FOR X=1 TO 1000:NEXT X
PRINT #1, "A4";E:FOR X=1 TO 1000:NEXT X
PRINT #1, "A5";F:FOR X=1 TO 1000:NEXT X
PRINT #1, "A6";G:FOR X=1 TO 1000:NEXT X
PRINT #1, "A7";H:FOR X=1 TO 1000:NEXT X
PRINT "Reset all motors"

RESTORE
PRINT "Reading data"
READ A.MIN, A.MAX, E.MIN, E.MAX
PRINT A.MIN; A.MAX; E.MIN; E.MAX
PRINT "Read"

PRINT #1, "A0"; A.MIN
PRINT #1, "A4"; E.MIN

X=ABS(A.MAX-A.MIN)
IF  X<ABS(E.MAX-E.MIN)  THEN  X=ABS(E.MAX-
                E.MIN)

100 REM START OF COORDINATED MOVE

FOR M= 1 TO X STEP 1
PRINT #1, "A0"; A.MIN + M* (ABS(A.MAX-A.MIN)/X)
PRINT #1, "A4";E.MIN + M* (ABS(E.MAX-E.MIN)/X)
NEXT M

REM REVERSE OF COORDINATED MOVE
FOR M= X TO 1 STEP -1
PRINT #1, "A0"; A.MIN + M* (ABS(A.MAX-A.MIN)/X)
PRINT #1, "A4";E.MIN + M* (ABS(E.MAX-E.MIN)/X)
NEXT M

GOTO 100
DATA 64, 195, 96,162

END
```

Writing a program to manipulate all 8 motors with the keyboard so that you can see what motor counts are needed at each joint to design your walking moves.

This is the utility program that you will use to move each of the motors one at a time so that you can see what the position on the robot needs to be as you design your walking sequences. It is not possible to make any progress by guessing where each joint needs to be. This programs lets you move each motor one step at a time from the keyboard and at the same time displays the counts on the screen so that you can see where each joint actually is. You should write a program similar to this one on your own because this is a very useful exercise in co-ordinating key presses with things that happen outside the computer.

First this program opens the COM port.

Then it sets all motor counts to 127, the middle position and then moves each of the motors to this position. This is the starting point. This position can be modified by changing the constants.

The program looks at the keyboard to see which key is pressed and responds to that key by moving the appropriate motor one count up or down. The program checks for maximum and minimum position for each motor to make sure that you do not wrap the robot up on itself.

Note that the 127 starting point for each motor and the minimum and maximum position for each motor can be changed to better suit your particular robot.

Study this program and understand it. This is a very important program for beginners to understand as it demonstrates a number of important concepts, all of them critical to amateur experimentation.

```
REM    THIS IS PROGRAM 600
REM    THIS PROGRAM ALLOWS YOU TO MOVE
REM    ONE MOTOR AT A TIME FROM
```

```
REM     THE KEYBOARD TO DISCOVER HOW
REM     MANY COUNTS YOU NEED TO MAKE THE
REM     VARIOUS MOVES THAT YOU HAVE TO
REM     MAKE TO MAKE A PROPER WALKING
REM     GAIT. THIS IS A UTILITY PROGRAM
REM     KEYS 1,2,3 CHANGE THE STEP SIZE TO
REM     1,5,10

OPEN "COM1: 9600,N,8,1" FOR OUTPUT AS #1

50  REM SET MOTORS TO THEIR MID POINTS
    A=127: B=127: C=127: D=127
    E=127: F=127: G=127: H=127
    MTR.STP=5

PRINT #1, "A0";A:GOSUB PAUSE
PRINT #1, "A1";B:GOSUB PAUSE
PRINT #1, "A2";C:GOSUB PAUSE
PRINT #1, "A3";D:GOSUB PAUSE
PRINT #1, "A4";E:GOSUB PAUSE
PRINT #1, "A5";F:GOSUB PAUSE
PRINT #1, "A6";G:GOSUB PAUSE
PRINT #1, "A7";H:GOSUB PAUSE
PRINT "Reset"

100 PRINT A; B; C; D; E; F; G; H
110 A$=INKEY$
    GOSUB PAUSE
    IF A$="" THEN GOTO 110
    A$=UCASE$(A$)

SELECT CASE A$

CASE "R"
    GOTO 50

CASE "A"
    A=A+MTR.STP
    IF A>187 THEN A=187:GOTO 110
    PRINT #1, "A0";A: GOTO 100

CASE "Z"
    A=A-MTR.STP
    IF A<87 THEN A=87:GOTO 110
    PRINT #1, "A0";A: GOTO 100

CASE "S"
    B=B-MTR.STP
    IF B<7 THEN B=7:GOTO 110
    PRINT #1, "A1";B: GOTO 100

CASE "X"
    B=B+MTR.STP
    IF B>177 THEN B=177:GOTO 110
    PRINT #1, "A1";B: GOTO 100

CASE "D"
    C=C+MTR.STP
    IF C>255 THEN C=255:GOTO 110
    PRINT #1, "A2";C:GOTO 100
CASE "C"
    C=C-MTR.STP
    IF C< 1 THEN C=1:GOTO 110
    PRINT #1, "A2";C:GOTO 100
CASE "F"
    D=D-MTR.STP
    IF D<1 THEN D=1:GOTO 110
    PRINT #1, "A3";D:GOTO 100
CASE "V"
    D=D+MTR.STP
    IF D>255 THEN D=255:GOTO 110
    PRINT #1, "A3";D:GOTO 100

CASE "G"
    E=E+MTR.STP
    IF E>255 THEN E=255:GOTO 110
    PRINT #1, "A4";E:GOTO 100
CASE "B"
    E=E-MTR.STP
    IF E<71 THEN E=71:GOTO 110
    PRINT #1, "A4";E:GOTO 100
CASE "H"
    F=F-MTR.STP
    IF F<1 THEN F=1:GOTO 110
    PRINT #1, "A5";F:GOTO 100
CASE "N"
    F=F+MTR.STP
    IF F>255 THEN F=255:GOTO 110
```

```
    PRINT #1, "A5";F:GOTO 100

CASE "J"
    G=G+MTR.STP
    IF G>255 THEN G=255:GOTO 110
    PRINT #1, "A6";G:GOTO 100
CASE "M"
    G=G-MTR.STP
    IF G<1 THEN G=1:GOTO 110
    PRINT #1, "A6";G:GOTO 100
CASE "K"
    H=H-MTR.STP
    IF H<1 THEN H=1:GOTO 110
    PRINT #1, "A7";H:GOTO 100
CASE ","
    H=H+MTR.STP
    IF H>255 THEN H=255:GOTO 110
    PRINT #1, "A7";H:GOTO 100

CASE "1"
    MTR.STP=1:PRINT "STEP CHANGED TO=1"
CASE "2"
    MTR.STP=5:PRINT "STEP CHANGED TO=5"
CASE "3"
    MTR.STP=10:PRINT "STEP CHANGED TO=10"

CASE ELSE
BEEP

END SELECT
GOTO 110

END

PAUSE:
FOR P=1 TO 100
NEXT P
RETURN
```

In the above program the "R" key clears the screen and resets the robot to its starting position (all 127s) whenever pressed.

- Keys "A, S, D, F, G, H, J and K" move the motors in one direction.
- Keys "Z, X, C, V, B, N, M, and ," move the motors in the other.

The variable MTR.STP determines how far each motor moves with each key press. Five is a good number to start with, ten and fifteen give much faster experimentation, and one gives very fine control. Do not hold the keys down for any length of time ... the input buffer on the computer will overflow and the robot will keep moving even after you have let the key go. Since we do not have feedback from the motors this cannot be avoided. The pause loop in the input routine mitigates this a bit by slowing down the input key presses.

The limits that the counters are compared to can be set so that the motors do not get out of their motion range. For example the foot nutation counts should be limited to the maximum movement that can be made before the robot falls over.

This program shows you how a sequence is taught, remembered and then played back

Imagine that you wanted to teach your robot a simple sequence that needed to be repeated on command as often as needed. How does one go about doing this if one does not have access to a higher level language for controlling the robot?

I will show you how to teach a "one motor" move sequence of up to 25 moves. You will then have to work out how to extend this program first to two motors and then to all eight motors. It is not that hard to do once you see how. The two motor sequence can be used to do the foot to foot weight transfer.

The technique consists of moving a motor with a couple of the keyboard keys (as we have already done) and accepting the move by pressing "Y" when we are satisfied with the motor position. Acceptance consists of storing the data in a table as the number of counts that the motor moved. We then move to the next move and accept that position as the data for that location and so on until we get to the last move that we need to make.

We can request playback at any time by pressing "P". On playback we go back to a section of the program where we recall the moves one at a time and move the motor to the specified locations one at a time. As always delays have to be added to make sure that moves do not run into one anther.

Here is the code for a one motor sequencer.

```
REM     THIS IS PROGRAM NUMBER 700
REM     PROGRAM TO CONTROL ONE MOTOR
REM     FROM THE KEYBOARD WITH
REM     FOLLOWING THE KEYS
REM     "R" TO RESET THE SYSTEM
REM     "A" AND "Z" TO MOVE MOTOR UP-DOWN
REM     "Y" FOR ACCEPT A MOVE AND STORE IT
REM     "P" FOR PLAYING BACK THE MOVES
REM     LIMITED TO 25 MOVES OF RIGHT KNEE
REM     ALL OTHERS MOTORS PARKED AT 127
REM     COUNTS

OPEN "COM1: 9600,N,8,1" FOR OUTPUT AS #1
DIM M(25)
A=127: B=127: C=127: D=127
E=127: F=127: G=127: H=127

PRINT #1, "A0";A
PRINT #1, "A1";B
PRINT #1, "A2";C
PRINT #1, "A3";D
PRINT #1, "A4";E
PRINT #1, "A5";F
PRINT #1, "A6";G
PRINT #1, "A7";H

MTR.MID.POS=127
MTR.MIN.POS=0
MTR.MAX.POS=254
MTR.STP=10

50  CLS
    PRINT "COUNTERS RESET"
    A=MTR.MID.POS
    N=1: M(N)=A
    PRINT #1, "A2";A

100 PRINT A

150 A$=""\par A$=INKEY$
    A$=UCASE$(A$)

200 IF A$="" THEN GOTO 150
    IF A$="R" THEN GOTO 50
    IF A$="Y" THEN GOTO 500
    IF A$="P" THEN GOTO 600

SELECT CASE A$
CASE "A"
    A=A+MTR.STP
    IF A>MTR.MAX.POS THEN
            A=MTR.MAX.POS:GOTO 150
    PRINT #1, "A2";A

CASE "Z"
    A=A-MTR.STP
    IF A<MTR.MIN.POS THEN
            A=MTR.MIN.POS:GOTO 150
    PRINT #1, "A2";A
CASE ELSE
END SELECT
GOTO 100

500 REM Y
    M(N)=A
    PRINT "STORED";A;" IN LOCATION ";N
    N=N+1
    IF N>25 THEN STOP
    GOTO 100

600 REM P
    CLS
    PRINT "PLAY MODE"
    PRINT #1, "A2";MTR.MID.POS
    OLD.POS=MTR.MID.POS
```

```
FOR X=1 TO N-1
    Q=1*SGN(M(X)-OLD.POS)
    PRINT "MOVING TO POSITION";X"
        =";M(X)
    IF Q=0 THEN Q=1
        FOR Z=OLD.POS TO M(X) STEP 1*Q
            PRINT #1, "A2";Z
            FOR P=1 TO 50
        NEXT P
    NEXT Z
    OLD.POS=M(X)
NEXT X
PRINT "DONE"
PRINT "Press P again to repeat sequence"
GOTO 150

END
```

Writing a simple, language interpreter

This is more complicated than is necessary for the interests of some of you, however there are some people who will get hooked and may want to do more sophisticated work. My goal in this is only to show you how this can be done. If you get really interested in this you have some serious reading, learning and programming to do.

A better way of controlling the robot consists of implementing a rudimentary higher level language as discussed in Chapter 14 and described next.

At this stage of the game you need to review your BASIC programming manuals so that you have a better feel for all the commands that are available to you and how they are to be used. I will demonstrate the rudiments of a very simple parsing scheme and you can extend this to create as sophisticated a program as you like within the context of using the BASIC language. (To do really serious programming you would use "C" or some other language designed to do such work.) What you can accomplish will also depend on the language that you have designed and going through this exercise will give you some insights into how to design a language that is easier to parse. It all ties together in the end!

The data file that the robot executes can come from a disk file read a line at a time or it can come from DATA statements like we had in the examples above. I will use DATA statements as already shown above for the sake of simplicity and because this allows us to do all our work from within the BASIC environment. This includes the editing of the program as DATA statements. These will constitute our program.

We are working towards using the higher language that we designed for the robot as a part of what we learned in Chapter 14 on language design. Putting it as simply as possible ... each DATA statement in the program contains a keyword and the arguments associated with that particular keyword. The program first reads the keyword and then branches to an area of the program designed to process that particular keyword. If for example the keyword is STAND the program jumps to the section of code that executes the STAND command. Here the program expects that there will be no arguments and brings the robot to a STAND position from whatever position the robot was in – in an orderly manner so that it does not fall over. Once that is done the program returns to the main thread of the program to read the next DATA statement and to continue on from there.

If the program reads a word in a DATA statement and it does not match any of the words in its vocabulary, or the keyword is mis-spelled, it knows that an error has taken place and the program jumps to an area where the program is terminated. An error message is usually annunciated on the screen as a part of the termination process so that the operator knows what happened and can take corrective action. Depending on how the program is designed, rather sophisticated messages and even automatic recovery routines can be implemented. As the programming gets more complicated, more sophisticated error messages and other diagnostic techniques are needed to allow faster debugging.

What is presented is a very simple parsing scheme. Parsing can become quite sophisticated and is one of the more intriguing part of a programmer's art. Designing fast parsing code can be very complicated. When really fast operations are needed we use compilers. A compiler processes the entire program into more rapidly executable code by eliminating all unnecessary and time-consuming processes. Surprisingly a compiled program is usually much longer than an uncompiled program for the same reason that "GO TO LONDON" is shorter than all the instructions that tell you how to get to London. (These longer instructions are however ready to be executed immediately upon reception, i.e. you do not have to go to the book store to purchase a map and puzzle the way to London out etc.)

The parsing code segments are similar to the following:

```
REM     REFERENCE NUMBER 800 XXX
REM     THIS IS NOT A COMPLETE PROGRAM
REM     ONLY A SEGMENT OF ONE THAT PARSES

RESTORE
50  READ KEYWORD$
    IF KEYWORD$="STAND" THEN GOTO 100
    IF KEYWORD$="MOVE" THEN GOTO 200
    IF KEYWORD$="SHIFTLEFT" THEN GOTO 300
    IF KEYWORD$="END" THEN GOTO 400
    IF KEYWORD$="STOP" THEN GOTO 500
    AND SO ON
    AND SO ON

GOTO 900

100 REM PROCESS THE STAND COMMAND HERE
    REM     ALL THE CODE TO DO SO FOLLOWS
    REM     HERE
    REM
    REM
    GOTO 50

200 REM     PROCESS THE MOVE COMMAND
    REM     HERE
    REM     ALL THE CODE TO DO SO FOLLOWS
            HERE
    GOTO 50

300 REM     PROCESS THE SHIFTLEFT
    REM     COMMAND HERE
    REM     ALL THE CODE TO DO SO FOLLOWS
    REM     HERE
    REM
    REM
    GOTO 50

400 REM PROCESS THE END COMMAND HERE
    PRINT "PROGRAM ENDED"
    END

500 PROCESS THE STOP COMMAND
    REM     ALL THE CODE TO DO SO FOLLOWS
    REM     HERE
    REM
    REM
    GOTO 50

900 PRINT "AN ERROR HAS OCCURRED AT ";KEY-
            WORD$

END

NOT TESTED. THIS IS NOT A PROGRAM. NOT SUP-
            POSED TO WORK.
```

The next program implements the following FIVE commands of our robot control language. They are:

SETSTAND
STAND

```
SHIFTLEFT
SHIFTRIGHT
END
```

I have selected five words that would actually form a microlanguage that one could actually write a working program in. I am trying to show you how to do this without giving you so much information that I kill the adventure of working it out. There is a fine line here and there is no rule of thumb as to how to do this for a large and varied readership. However, I think there is enough information here to allow you to take it from here.

Discussion

SHIFTLEFT (and SHIFTRIGHT) has to be able to handle a number of preceding robot positions. It has to determine what the present position of the robot is before deciding how to shift to the left foot i.e. as far as our simple programs are concerned, SHIFTLEFT has to be approached in an orderly manner if the robot is to stay upright. If the weight is on the right foot it is desirable to go directly to SHIFTLEFT to make the step look right. If the robot is in some other position, we have to go to STAND first and then shift to the left foot. In a more sophisticated program it would be desirable to handle more of the possible positions with special routines.

The DATA statements at the end of the program make the robot rock from foot to foot as was done earlier in program 300. Study the similarities. This program also borrows elements from other programs.

The motor position of each motor at the end of each move is stored in the letters A, B, C, D, E, F, G, and H for motors 0 to 7. The motors are designated as shown in Figure 15.1. These are the numbers and letters used in programming the 8 motor moves. You should also read Appendix 3 on the Scott Edwards controller to get the instructions fresh in your mind.

As you review this program, keep in mind that the two legs of the robot are also mirror images as software entities so that where one motor has to go to 127 *plus* 50 to make a certain move, the motor on the other side has to go to 127 *minus* 50 to make the same

This program makes the robot shift its weight to either foot three times and then ends the program. Variables will have to be adjusted/modified here and there (slightly) to match the con-

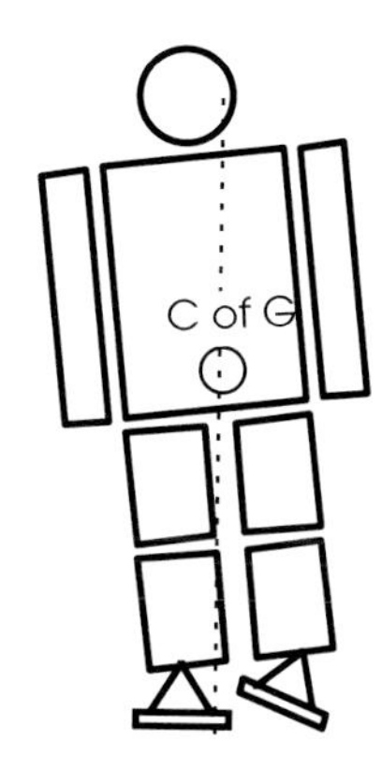

Figure 15.4 Pushing off slowly with the outside of the left foot. the right foot has to be kept flat as this is done. You must work on a perfectly flat surface.

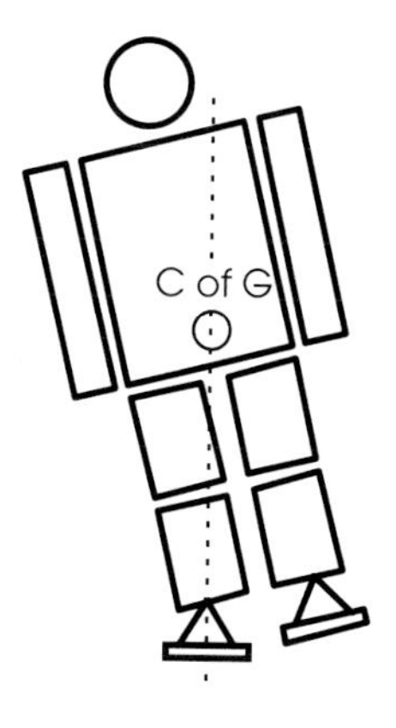

Figure 15.5 The robot standing on its right foot. You have to decide if you want a stable stand or to just barely balance depending on the walk you are designing.

struction of your particular robot.

Once you master the weight shifts you will be ready to add the code for taking the steps and you will soon have a walking robot.

The program listing:

```
REM      THIS IS PROGRAM NUMBER 900
REM      PROGRAM IMPLEMENTS 5 WORDS OUT
REM      OF THE ROBOWALK LANGUAGE

OPEN "COM1: 9600,N,8,1" FOR OUTPUT AS #1

A=127: B=127: C=127: D=127: E=127: F=127:
            G=127: H=127
ADJUST.A=0: ADJUST.B=0: ADJUST.C=0:
            ADJUST.D=0
ADJUST.E=0: ADJUST.F=0: ADJUST.G=0:
            ADJUST.H=0
PAUSE.COUNT=200
STAND.STATUS$="UNSET"
INCR.SIZE=1

A.MIN=60: A.MAX=200
B.MIN=60: B.MAX=200
C.MIN=60: C.MAX=200
D.MIN=60: D.MAX=200
E.MIN=60: E.MAX=200
F.MIN=60: F.MAX=200
G.MIN=60: G.MAX=200
H.MIN=60: H.MAX=200

PRINT #1, "A0";A
PRINT #1, "A1";B
PRINT #1, "A2";C
PRINT #1, "A3";D
PRINT #1, "A4";E
PRINT #1, "A5";F
PRINT #1, "A6";G
PRINT #1, "A7";H

A.SH.LFT=87
E.SH.LFT=87

A.SH.RHT=187
E.SH.RHT=187

RESTORE
100 READ COMMAND$
PRINT COMMAND$
IF COMMAND$="SETSTAND" THEN GOTO 200
IF COMMAND$="STAND" THEN GOTO 300
IF COMMAND$="SHIFTLEFT" THEN GOTO 400
IF COMMAND$="SHIFTRIGHT" THEN GOTO 500
IF COMMAND$="END" THEN GOTO 600
PRINT "ERROR IN WORD";COMMAND$
STOP

200 REM     SETSTAND
A=127+ADJUST.A
B=127+ADJUST.B
C=127+ADJUST.C
D=127+ADJUST.D
E=127+ADJUST.E
F=127+ADJUST.F
G=127+ADJUST.G
H=127+ADJUST.H
STAND.STATUS$="SET"
GOTO 100

300 REM     STAND
IF STAND.STATUS$<>"SET" THEN
    CLS
        PRINT "SETSTAND NOT EXECUTED"
        PRINT "ENDING PROGRAM."
    STOP
    ELSE
END IF
A=127+ADJUST.A
B=127+ADJUST.B
C=127+ADJUST.C
D=127+ADJUST.D
E=127+ADJUST.E
F=127+ADJUST.F
G=127+ADJUST.G
H=127+ADJUST.H
PRINT #1, "A0";A
PRINT #1, "A1";B
PRINT #1, "A2";C
```

```
PRINT #1, "A3";D
PRINT #1, "A4";E
PRINT #1, "A5";F
PRINT #1, "A6";G
PRINT #1, "A7";H
POSITION$="STAND"
GOTO 100

400  REM       SHIFTLEFT
IF POSITION$="STAND" OR
               POSITION$="SHIFTRIGHT" THEN
    X=ABS(A-A.SH.LFT)
    IF X< ABS(E-E.SH.LFT) THEN X=ABS(E-
               E.SH.LFT)
        FOR M=1 TO X
               PRINT #1, "A0";
                      A+INT(M*((A.SH.LFT-A)/X))
               PRINT #1, "A4";E+INT(M*((E.SH.LFT-
                      E)/X))
        NEXT M
    ELSE
END IF
A=A.SH.LFT
E=E.SH.LFT
POSITION$="SHIFTLEFT"
GOTO 100

500  REM       SHIFTRIGHT
IF POSITION$="STAND" OR
               POSITION$="SHIFTLEFT" THEN
    X=ABS(A-A.SH.RHT)
    IF X< ABS(E-E.SH.RHT) THEN X=ABS(E-
               E.SH.RHT)
        FOR M=1 TO X
               PRINT #1, "A0";
                      A+INT(M*(A.SH.RHT-A)/X)
               PRINT #1, "A4"; E+INT(M*(E.SH.RHT-
                      E)/X)
        NEXT M
    END IF
A=A.SH.RHT
E=E.SH.RHT
POSITION$="SHIFTRIGHT"
GOTO 100

600  REM       END
     REM       CLS
     PRINT "LAST INSTRUCTION WAS EXECUTED"
     PRINT "PROGRAM ENDED PROPERLY"
     END

DO.PAUSE:
     FOR P=1 TO PAUSE.COUNT
     NEXT P
RETURN

REM      =====================
REM      THE PROGRAM WE ARE GOING TO RUN
REM      IS IN THE FOLLOWING DATA
REM      STATEMENTS

DATA "SETSTAND"
DATA "STAND"
DATA "SHIFTLEFT"
DATA "SHIFTRIGHT"
DATA "SHIFTLEFT"
DATA "SHIFTRIGHT"
DATA "SHIFTLEFT"
DATA "SHIFTRIGHT"
DATA "STAND"
DATA "END"
STOP
```

In the above program, the position of the motors on the robot after the end of a move are always stored in the variables A thru H.

Each motor has an error value that stores the counts that have to be added to or subtracted from 127 to make the robot stand right. This sets the stand in SETSTAND.

Each motor has a minimum value and a maximum value that it is allowed to assume. It is assumed that any positions beyond these would be inappropriate for any of a number of reasons including joint travel limits, gravity limits and aesthetic limits. Formulas could be designed to set these limits in real time as the robot moved, meaning that the limits would change as the robot assumed different positions. The changes would be a function of the joint angles.

At the end of any move, the status variable POSITION$ is set to the current "position status" so that the software in the next move can determine what the current position of the robot is. It is necessary to know what the current position of the robot is before the next move can be made if the robot is to "not fall over". The implementation of appropriate strategies to do this is the difficult and challenging part of the walking algorithms. Keep these as simple as possible in the beginning.

Since we are actually adding delays between the moves to properly control the servos, these delays could be replaced with calculations and there would be no deterioration in performance. Techniques like these need to be developed to give you the time you need to make the calculations that have to be made without compromising the motion.

You must keep in mind that in the above program there are only 5 commands. There is *nothing else* that has to be or should be considered at this time. When you add to this program, that is another project. It is not a part of what needs to be done here and it is assumed that there is no way of knowing what the changes that you will want to make are going to be.

Some ideas for further experimentation

Here are some ideas for more challenging projects related to what you have done so far.

Determine the centre of gravity of your robot. Suspend a simple, light pendulum exactly 3 inches in front of the robot's C of G on a string and run experiments to determine exactly how far each motor can be moved without tipping the robot over. Make a reference table. Can you convert it into a mathematical expression that can be solved for before each move? It does not have to be an exact expression but it does have to serve its intended purpose.

Weigh each part of the robot and determine its C of G. Use this information to determine a mathematical expression that can be used to keep the robot from falling over under program control. How does this compare with the above technique?

Make the robot bend back and forth as far as possible. What are the problems associated with this?

Once you have mastered walking, see how fast you can make the robot walk. What are the techniques for walking fast? Formalize them. How does one effect a fast start and fast stop without falling? Will leaning forward or leaning back first work?

Extend the language that you designed to add execution speed to the move commands and to modify the length of the stride automatically. What is desired is that you specify the stride in tenths of an inch and the robot makes all compensations to all commands automatically. Implement the instruction STRIDELENGTH, N.

For the more mechanically inclined I suggest making a 4-legged centipede as an exercise. Each leg has two feet on it, one on either side of the centipede for balance. The two feet are connected together and work together. Two motors control each leg – one motor lowers and raises a feet, the other pulls them back and forth. The motion of each of the four sets of feet is identical except for timing. The centipede moves only forwards and backwards. Essentially this is one side of a centipede with 4 legs. The 4 legs on the other side just happen to be connected to and work with the 4 legs on the one side, somewhat like a real centipede. This machine can be built and controlled with the 8 servos and controller that you have at hand. The controller piggybacks onto the centipede. A little wood and glue and you are in business. Does the body of the machine need to be segmented to allow it to undulate? (If I give you a sketch I will have ruined it for you so I will resist). This will not be easy (I too had trouble with it) however you now have eight motors that you can control with a computer and it will be a lot of fun no matter what you decide to build.

Robotics is really all programming (software) and mathematics and mechanisms, the mechanical engineering part. The more you know about programming a robot, the more you know about robots and how they do what they do.

Availability of programs/listings on diskette

If you would like to have all the programs and listings in this book on a diskette, they are available as text files in IBM-PC and Macintosh format on a 3.5 inch diskettes.

A list of what is on the diskettes along with ordering information is provided in Appendix 4.

APPENDIX ONE

A short glossary of robotic terms

Absolute movement Robotic motion where the next point travelled to is calculated as a displacement in motor encoder counts from the hardware home (0,0,0,0,0,0) position.

Argument An argument is a value passed to a function or statement. For example, MOVE 0,123,33,10,100 has arguments of 0,123,33, 10, and 100.

Arm The part of the robot that moves. A five-axis arm is controlled by five motors with a sixth motor for the gripper. A four-axis SCARA (Selective Compliance Articulated Robot Arm) arm is controlled by four motors with a fifth motor for the gripper.

Auxiliary port Ports that may be used to control various external devices like motors and relays where incremental encoder feedback may not be needed. Auxiliary to the robot's basic operation.

Ball nut A special nut designed to be used with a ball screw. It recirculates the ball bearings used in the screw mechanism. See **Ball screw** for a description of the mating component.

Ball screw A screw that uses grooves that accommodate pre-loaded ball bearings for smoother and more accurate movements.

Base The lower part of the robot arm. The part that is usually bolted down to the table. The part of the machine that sits on the floor. The stationary part of a robot.

Baud rate The rate at which data bits are transmitted over a serial interface. The Scott Edwards controller runs at 9600 baud. 9600 baud is about 960 characters per second.

Bit One binary digit. An on/off counter. One eighth of a byte. The smallest piece of information that a computer can manipulate.

Branch To go to a different position in a program unconditionally or based on the outcome of some decision-making process.

Byte Eight bits. A standard piece of information as used in computers.

Code The text to your program. The program that you type into the host computer.

Compiler A program that converts the entire program at one time into code that can be executed much more rapidly than in an interpreter.

Control characters Special characters that are formed by holding down the control key while pressing another key. These characters are not usually visible on the screen.

Controller The device that actually controls the movement of the robot arm.

Co-ordinate An ordered set of numbers that define a point in space. In the XYZ system of co-ordinates, three numbers are needed to define a point in space.

Cursor The small box or underscore that your computer uses to indicate your current position in a line of text.

Direct execution A state in which commands are immediately executed by the software.

Disk file A recording of information on a diskette.

Editor A program, or portion of a program, that is used to create and alter text or other information.

Elbow The joint that corresponds to the human elbow.

Encoded motor Motor that uses an optical or other encoder to count the amount of movement that the motor undertakes.

Encoder The device that allows the system to determine how far a motor has moved at any given time. Any device that turns mechanical information into information that a computer can understand.

End effector The gripper, or hand, of the robot.

Envelope The area that the robot hand can reach to do useful work.

Error message The message printed on the screen of your computer when an error occurs. There are basically two types of error messages. The first is a "syntax error", which means that you typed a command incorrectly. The second is a "run time error", which means that your program caused an error to occur when it was run. Example: dividing by zero would give a run time error on most computers.

Filename The name of a file that resides (is written) on disk.

Fingers The part of the gripper that actually closes, that actually performs the gripping action.

Firmware A program that is permanently fixed and is part of a computer. This is the program that is in the EPROMs of the controller. It can be changed but not with ease, thus the name firmware.

General-purpose computer A computer that is not dedicated to any specific task. An IBM-PC is a general-purpose desktop computer.

Gripper The hand of the robot.

Hardhome A fixed repeatable point from which the robot begins all routines. (See also **Home** and **Softhome**)

Hardware Your computer, the disk drives, the robot and controller. In essence, any object with visible, physical existence.

Home A fixed, repeatable point from which the robot begins all routines. (See also **Hardhome** and **Softhome**)

Home position A known repeatable position to which a machine can be returned under program control or by a command.

Host computer The general-purpose computer used to send information to the robot controller.

Initialize To position the robot in its hardware home position and to reset all motors and other signals to a known condition.

Integer math Arithmetic with no decimals or fractions in it. This means that 10/3 is equal to 3 because the fractional portion is dropped.

Interpret To convert a program to machine language and execute it in a computer, a line at a time.

Interpreter A program that understands one line of code at a time and then executes it.

Intraline editing The special editing commands that are used to change characters within one line of text.

Keystroke One press of a key on a keyboard.

Label A number that precedes a program line and is used as a target by either the GOTO or the GOSUB command to alter and thus control program flow.

Language A set of commands combined with the syntax rules. A way of communicating with a computer so that you can tell it what to do.

Look ahead To look at the next move to see how it will affect the present move. This allows the next move to be combined or blended into the present move for smoother and often faster operation.

Loop In programming, a loop is a fragment of code that will repeat itself until a specific condition is met.

Motor port A connection point for a motor (and usually an attached encoder).

Nested In programming, the term refers to a loop within a loop. The inner loop is said to be "nested" within the outer loop.

Operating system The program that runs the host computer. On the Apple, this is called Apple DOS, on the IBM-PC, it is called PC DOS. DOS usually means Disk (based) Operating System.

Parse To break the various parts of a command into its various components so that it can be understood and executed.

PLC A Programmable Logic Controller. A machine that obeys ladder logic and is often used in conjunction with a robot to control a workcell.

Point A location in space defined by the position of the axes motors on the robot.

Program A group of statements that a robot and controller can execute to perform some specified functions.

RAM RAM stands for Random Access Memory and it is the memory used inside the host computer. The contents of this type of memory can be changed.

Real time Time as it happens instantaneously. Right now.

Relative movement Robotic motion where the next point is determined from the location of the previous point. This differs from **Absolute movement** in which all points are based to the home position.

Robot A mechanical device capable of being programmed to perform a number of variable tasks.

ROM ROM stands for Read Only Memory; memory that is used to store permanent programs inside a computer. The contents of this type of memory are fixed.

Run time events The events that occur while a program is executing.

Servo A mechanism that responds to a changing signal in a specified way.

Shoulder The robot arm joint that is the equivalent of the shoulder joint in a human.

Signal Used to co-ordinate external devices with the robot. The information on the input and output lines is signal information.

Six-axis robot Usually a robot that can position and orient its gripper in any position desired. Six axes are the minimum needed to do this.

Slide base A mechanism that can mount a robot and move it in a straight line along the floor to increase its work envelope.

Softhome A fixed, repeatable point from which the robot begins all routines. (See also **Home** and **Hardhome**)

Software A computer program. The logic that runs on a computer.

Stall A stall occurs when a motor is unable to move. This can be caused by the robot striking an object, or striking itself if the robot folds back upon itself, or the arm being overloaded. A defective motor or electronics can be seen as a motor stall by the system.

State machine A machine that can assume only a fixed number of states.

Straight line move A move that moves the gripper or part tool under consideration in a straight line.

String In programming, a string is a series of characters enclosed in quotation marks. For example, “This is a string”.

Subroutine A portion of a program that can be called from the main part of the program using the GOSUB or similar statement.

Syntax The rules that define how each statement in a programming language is to be used. The format of, or order in which, terms are included in a command.

Teach pendant A hand-held control box used to guide the robot through a series of moves manually. This usually includes the support devices needed to to interact with the pendant itself.

Transform In a robotic context this means: To change between co-ordinate systems.

Variable A named location in memory that is used to hold information.

Wrist The part of the robot that allows various grippers to be mounted to it. Usually a rotatable flange.

APPENDIX TWO

Table of ASCII values

These are based on Microsoft QuickBASIC, the language that we are using in the programming examples.

Of the 256 possible 8 bit codes, the first 128 codes are defined by ASCII. The last 128 codes vary with various systems and are used for foreign language characters etc. The designations are determined by the manufacturer and the font being used.

The first 32 codes are referred to as control codes and (usually) do not cause a character to be printed on the screen or the printer.

Dec	Hex	Char	Explanation
000	00	NUL	Null
001	01	SOH	Start of heading
002	02	STX	Start of transmission
003	03	ETX	End of transmission
004	04	EOT	End of text
005	05	ENQ	Inquiry
006	06	ACK	Acknowledgement
007	07	BEL	Bell
008	08	BS	Back space
009	09	HT	Horizontal tab
010	0A	LF	Line feed
011	0B	VT	Vertical tab
012	0C	FF	Form feed
013	0D	CR	Carriage return
014	0E	SO	Shift out
015	0F	SI	Shift in
016	20	DLE	Data link escape
017	21	DC1	Device control 1
018	22	DC2	Device control 2
019	23	DC3	Device control 3
020	24	DC4	Device control 4
021	25	NAK	Negative acknowledge
022	26	SYN	Synchronous idle
023	27	ETB	End of transmission block
024	28	CAN	Cancel
025	29	EM	End of medium
026	2A	SUB	Substitute
027	2B	ESC	Escape
028	2C	FS	File separator
029	2D	GS	Group separator
030	2E	RS	Record separator
031	2F	US	Unit separator

Dex	Hex	Char	Dex	Hex	Char	Dex	Hex	Char
032	20	Space	064	40	@	096	60	‘
033	21	!	065	41	A	097	61	a
034	22	“	066	42	B	098	62	b
035	23	#	067	43	C	099	63	c

036	24	$	068	44	D	100	64	d	050	32	2	082	52	R	114	72	r
037	25	%	069	45	E	101	65	e	051	33	3	083	53	S	115	73	s
038	26	&	070	46	F	102	66	f	052	34	4	084	54	T	116	74	t
039	27	‘	071	47	G	103	67	g	053	35	5	085	55	U	117	75	u
040	28	(	072	48	H	104	68	h	054	36	6	086	56	V	118	76	v
041	29	)	073	49	I	105	69	i	055	37	7	087	57	W	119	77	w
042	2A	*	074	4A	J	106	6A	j	056	38	8	088	58	X	120	78	x
043	2B	+	075	4B	K	107	6B	k	057	39	9	089	59	Y	121	79	y
044	2C	,	076	4C	L	108	6C	l	058	3A	:	090	5A	Z	122	7A	z
045	2D	-	077	4D	M	109	6D	m	059	3B	;	091	5B	[	123	7B	{
046	2E	.	078	4E	N	110	6E	n	060	3C	<	092	5C	\	124	7C	|
047	2F	/	079	4F	O	111	6F	o	061	3D	>	093	5D	]	125	7D	}
048	30	0	080	50	P	112	70	p	062	3E	=	094	5E	^	126	7E	~
049	31	1	081	51	Q	113	71	q	063	3F	?	095	5F	_	127	7F	Delete

APPENDIX THREE

Scott Edwards controller information

A number of suppliers provide a controller that will allow a computer to control eight servo motors that need a pulse to control each one of them.

These notes provide information about the Scott Edwards controller that I used. Scott has a distributor in Great Britain (Milford Instruments, see Appendix 6 for full address) and this was a major reason for using his controller. The controller I used was purchased late in 1994. The newer controllers are smaller and more sophisticated and their control functions have been expanded. You will need to use the information that you get with your particular controller. These notes are by way of an example.

The computer treats the controller as a printer i.e. it prints characters to it. The controller receives the characters and converts them into eight pulses on eight lines. Once a pulse is entered, the controller repeats the pulse continuously.

The command to set a pulse consists of the following characters:

(1) A letter from A to Z to identify the controller. We will use A throughout since we have only one controller. (Controllers can be daisy chained to control more than eight motors.)
(2) A number from 0 to 7 to identify which of the 8 motors is to be controlled.
(3) A number from 0 to 254 to indicate the length of the pulse. 0=one extreme, 254=other extreme. Total travel is about 180 degrees. (255 has a special use.)

The pulses generated will control the servo lever arm within a swing of either 180 or 90 degrees. The 180-degree controller gives you more flexibility, the 90-degree controller gives you finer control. You have to decide what you want when you order the controller – the robot can use either unit. One does not often use the far ends of motion on the servos but it is nice to know that you can use it if you need to (on some future project) so decide what you want and order accordingly.

Building and using the Mini SSC (Serial Servo Controller) from Scott Edwards Electronics

(Reproduced by kind permission of Scott Edwards Electronics)

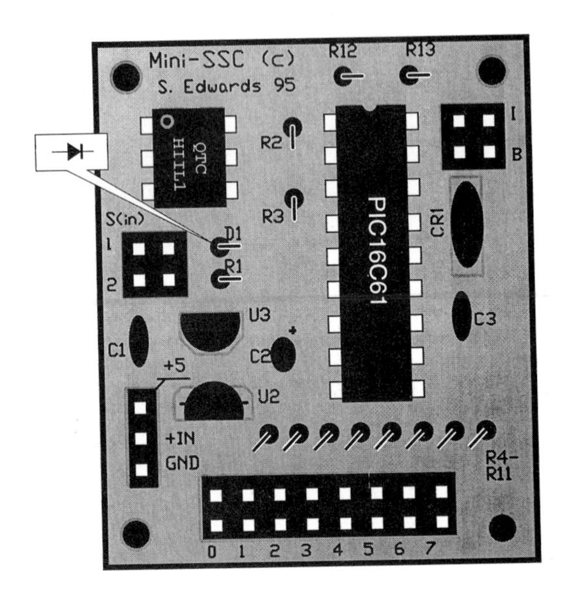

U 1 QTC H 1 1 Ll Optoisolator (dot at upper left)
U2 LP2950 voltage regulator (flat side as shown)
U3 MN1381 or TC44VC4303 reset circuit (flat side as shown)
U4 PIC1 6C61 microcontroller (in 18-pin socket; notch at top)
Rl 1.8k (brown-gray-red) ⅛W resistor
R2 10k (brown-black-orange) ⅛W resistor
R3–Rl 1 220Ω (red-red-brown) ⅛W resistor
Rl 2, Rl 3 100k (brown-black-yellow) ⅛W resistor
Cl, C3 0.1µF monolithic or ceramic capacitor
C2 1µF tantalum capacitor (longer + lead in hole marked +)
D1 1 N4148 diode (striped end upward, body on left)
CR1 3-terminal 8MHz ceramic resonator (marked 8.000)
Header stakes – mount the 2×2, 2×8, and 1×3 header strips as shown
9V clip – socket connects to 1×3 header; red to +IN and black to GND
Shunts – shorting jumpers provided for baud rate (B) and address/ID (1);

Using the Mini SSC(Serial Servo Controller)

The Mini SSC is a module that controls eight servos according to instructions received over a 2400- or 9600-baud serial connection. The Mini SSC is serially addressable, so up to 32 units can share one serial line to control 256 servos.

The controller chip supplied with the Mini SSC provides 90 degrees of positioning range with 0.36-degree resolution. An extended-range version of the chip (up to 180-degree range, 0.72-degree resolution) is available from Scott Edwards Electronics.

PC-specific hookup instructions appear later, but PC users should at least skim the Stamp writeup below in order to get familiar with the Mini SSC.

Configuring the Mini SSC

The default configuration is 2400-baud communication and a serial address (ID) of 0 (zero). The configuration header is at the upper-right corner of the Mini SSC circuit board. Installing a jumper on the posts marked B sets the unit for 9600-baud communication; a jumper at 1 changes the ID to 1 (one). The ID number sets the range of servo addresses according to the formula (ID × 8) + servo. For instance, if the ID is 1 (jumper installed), and you want to address the servo connected to output 3, you would send 11 [(1 × 8) + 3] as the servo number. If your system expands beyond two Mini SSCs, you may order additional units with different IDs.

Connecting the Mini SSC

The BASIC Stamp or other serial device connects to the posts marked S(in) 1 and 2 located on the left edge of the circuit board as shown at right. This connection assumes that the Stamp is set for "inverted" serial data as described in the programming section below, and will also work with other inverted data sources, such as a PC serial port.

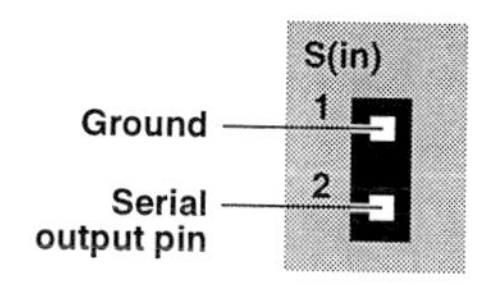

The diagram below shows how to connect servos to the Mini SSC. Most servos require 4.8 to 6 Vdc from a source capable of delivering peak currents of several amperes per servo. Four-packs of Nicad or alkaline C or D cells are perfect. The Mini SSC can be powered by its own 9V battery, the Stamp's battery, or any supply that can consistently deliver 6 to 15 volts DC. If you use the Stamp's battery, make sure to

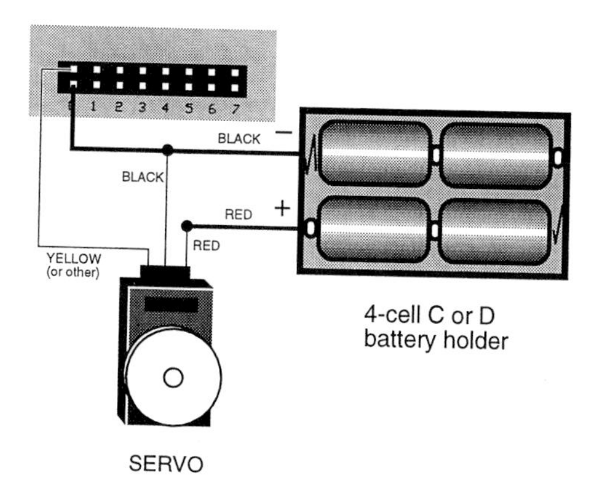

connect ground to both the power ground (marked gnd) and pin 1 of the S(in) header.

Note that it's best not to use the same power supply for the servos and Mini SSC. Under load, the servos may draw down the supply voltage. This would cause the Mini SSC to reset, losing servo position data.

Servos come with several different connector styles. The simplest way to make them compatible with the Mini SSC is to remove the existing connector and replace it with header sockets that fit the Mini SSC's 0.025" square posts. See the Hints section for more information.

Programming the Mini SSC

To command a servo to a new position requires sending three bytes at the appropriate serial rate (2400 or 9600 baud, N81). These bytes consist of:

byte 1: 255
byte 2: servo (0-254)
byte3: position (0-254)

Note that these must be sent as individual byte values, not as text representations of numbers as you might type at a terminal. Sending numbers as byte values in PBASIC simply requires that you omit any text-formatting functions (# for the BS1; dec, hex, ?, etc. for the BS2). In other BASICs, use the chr$ function to convert numbers to bytes; see the PC-specific section. Here's a line of BS1 PBASIC that sends servo 4 to position 50:

```
Serout 0,N2400,(255,4,50)     ' Servo 4 to position 50
```

The line above assumes that Stamp pin 0 is connected to S(in) 2 as shown on the previous page. Note that the Mini SSC's serial protocol requires the byte 255 to be sent as a marker indicating the start of a servo instruction. Next comes the servo number, followed by the position value (0 through 254).

The servo number and position value may, of course, be determined by variables:

```
Serout 0,N2400,(255,b2,b3)
```

That line will send the servo whose number is stored in the byte variable b2 to the position stored in byte variable b3. Using variables, you can use the Stamp's math, logic, table, and looping operators to determine which servos to send to what positions. For example, here's a pair of For/Next loops that cycle all eight servos back and forth:

```
Again:                  'Positions 0 to 254.
  for b3 = 0 to 254     'All 8 servos.
    for b2 = 0 to 7     'Send servo b2 to position b3.
    Serout O,N2400,(255,b2,b3)
    next b2
  next b3
Goto Again              'Endless loop.
```

If you run this example, try changing the first for statement by adding different step values, like so:

```
for b3 = 0 to 254 step 10        'Positions 0 to 254.
```

The servos will move through the position range much more rapidly than before, in choppy steps. Keep this in mind as you write your own programs for the Mini SSC you can trade off smoothness and speed to achieve the exact results you need.

Hints on using the Mini SSC

- You can conveniently connect servos and other devices to the Mini SSC's header posts (and the posts on the Stamp and lots of other electronic devices) using crimp-on sockets, as shown at right. The sockets are available from Jameco (phone: 1-800-831-4242 or 1-415-592-8097; fax: 1-415592-2503) as part number 100765. A tool, part number 99442, makes the crimping job easy. Jameco also carries plastic housings that align the sockets at standard 0. 1" intervals, such as part number 10081 1. An excellent alternative is to cover the individual header sockets with pieces of heat-shrink tubing.

- Futaba J connectors used on many servos already have sockets installed, but they must be removed from their plastic housing. To do this, just pry up the fingers on the side of the housing and slide the sockets out.
- When it is first powered up, the Mini SSC positions all servos to the center of their travel, the equivalent of sending each servo a position value of 127. If the starting positions of the servos are critical in your application, make sure that your program initializes all servos to their correct starting positions as soon as possible after startup. In some cases the starting positions of the servos are really critical (e.g., to prevent damage to a mechanism). In such cases, you should configure the mechanical linkages so that 127 is a safe starting position. If that's not possible, you may want to use a switch or relay to control power to the servos. Turn on servo power after your program initializes the Mini SSC to appropriate starting positions.
- The Mini SSC reads the baud-rate (B) and ID (I) configuration headers only when it is first powered up. If you change the jumper settings while the Mini SSC is on, the changes won't take effect until the power is turned off and back on.
- Up to nine Mini SSCs may be connected in parallel to a single Stamp pin. If your appli-

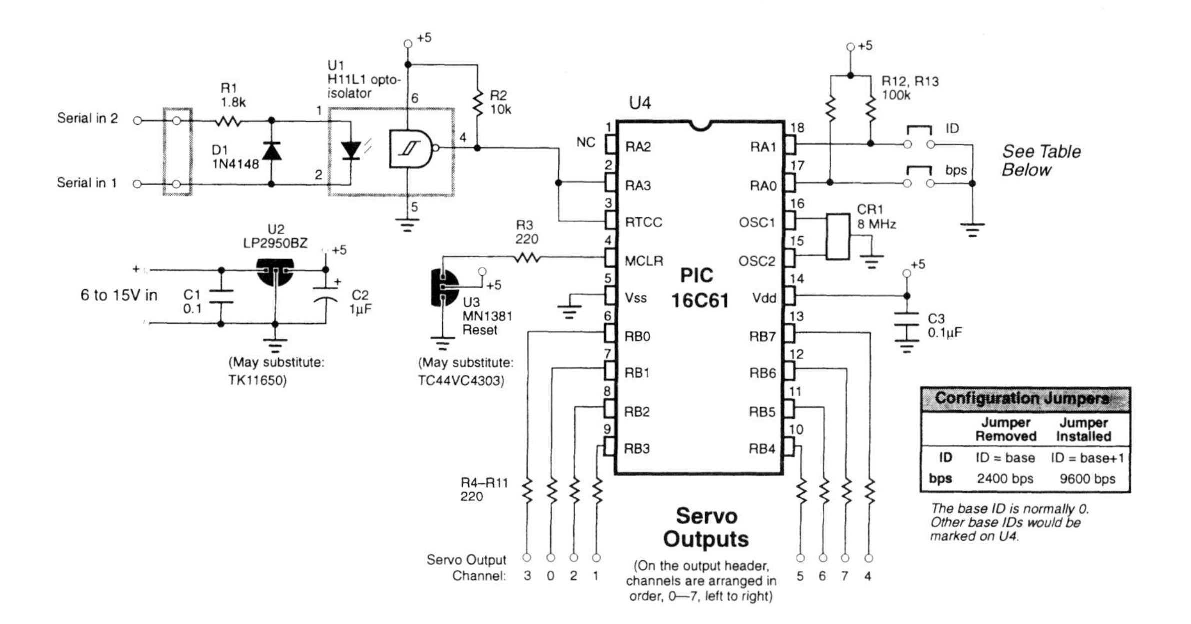

	Jumper Removed	Jumper Installed
ID	ID = base	ID = base+1
bps	2400 bps	9600 bps

cation requires driving more controllers, either use a separate Stamp I/0 pin for each group of nine controllers, or add a buffer capable of driving at least 2 mA per connected Mini SSC.

- With multiple Mini SSCS, IDs can be set so that the servo numbers are sequential. For example, the servos of a Mini SSC with ID 0 are numbered 0 through 7; the servos of ID 1 are numbered 8 through 15. Mini SSC PICs with base IDs of 2 through 30 may be obtained from the manufacturer (address on cover) or by special order through the dealer from whom you purchased this unit.
- The Mini SSC printed circuit board features a top-layer ground plane and plated through hole construction. As a result, the mounting holes at the four corners of the board are grounded. *Any wiring that should not short to ground shouldn't contact metal screws used in these mounting holes either.*
- Terminal software generally cannot send instructions to the Mini SSC. The reason is that terminals send numeric values as strings of text. For example, when you type "255" on the screen, it is sent as three bytes; the ASCII character codes for the symbols "2", "5", and "5". The Mini SSC expects a single byte with all its bits set to 1; a byte value of 255. Some terminal pro-grams can send these values, but only through a combination of keys or a special menu.

PC-*Specific Instructions*

Two Mini SSCs may be connected in parallel to the output of a PC serial (com) port. A simple program (listing 2) is all that's required to command the servos. If your application requires driving more controllers, either use a separate port for each pair of controllers, or add a buffer capable of driving at least 2 mA per connected Mini SSC. The Mini SSC is also compatible with the RS-422 signaling protocol. Connect TD+ to S(in) 1 and TD- to S(in) 2.

Listing Ia. BASIC Stamp I (BS I) Demonstration Program

```
' Program: LEGS.BAS
' This program demonstrates servo control using the Mini SSC.
' It commands six servos through a simplified, insectile walking sequence.
' The servo identifiers and positions are stored in a pair of tables in the routine Servo_value.

SYMBOL   steps = b0                        ' Current place in step sequence.
SYMBOL   servo = b3                        ' Servo being addressed.
SYMBOL   position = b4                     ' Servo position value.
SYMBOL   temp  b5                          ' Temporary variable used in table lookup.
SYMBOL   delay w5                          ' Delay between leg movements; controls speed.

let delay = 1000                           ' 1 second between steps.

again:
  for steps = 0 to 13
    gosub servo_value                      ' Get the servo no. and position value.
    serout 0,n2400,(255,servo,position)    ' Send to the SSC.
     if bito = 0 then skip-delay           ' Delay after every 2nd xmission.
    pause delay
skip-delay:
  next steps
goto again                                 ' Endless loop.

' Look up the servo number and position value. Since the same data is sent to two different servos,
' the position table is half the length of the servo table. Looking up the correct position entry requires
' dividing the step number by 2.

Servo-value:
  lookup steps,(1,4,0,2,1,4,0,2,3,5,1,4,3,5),servo
  let temp = steps/2
  lookup temp,(80,200,170,50,50,80,200),position
return
```

Listing Ib. BASIC Stamp I I (BS2) Demonstration Program

```
' Program: LEGS.BS2
' This program demonstrates servo control using the mini SSC.
' It commands six servos through a simplified, insectile walking sequence. The servo identifiers
' and positions are stored in a pair of tables in the routine servo-value.

steps    var  byte            ' Current place in step sequence.
oddStep  var  steps.lowbit    ' Least-significant bit of step no.
servo    var  byte            ' Servo being addressed.
position var  byte            ' Servo position value.
temp     var  byte            ' Temporary variable used in table lookup.
delay    var  word            ' Delay between leg movements; controls speed.
n96n     con  $4054           ' Baudmode for 9600 bps.
n24n     con  $418d           ' Baudmode for 2400 bps.
delay =  1000                 ' 1 second between steps.

again:
  for steps = 0 to 13
    gosub servo-value                     ' Get servo no. and position value.
    serout 0,n24n,[255,servo,position]    ' Send to SSC at 2400 baud.
    if oddstep = 0 then skip-delay        ' Delay every second xmission.
    pause delay
skip-delay:
  next
goto again                                ' Endless loop.

' Look up the servo number and position value. Since the same data is sent to two different servos,
' the position table is half the length of the servo table. Looking up the correct position entry requires
' dividing the step number by 2.

Servo_value:
  lookup steps,[1,4,0,2,1,4,0,2,3,5,1,4,3,51,servo
  temp = steps/2
  lookup temp,[80,200,170,50,50,80,200],position
return
```

Connecting the Mini SSC to a PC

The diagram below shows how to connect the serial output of PC COM ports to the Mini SSC. The diagrams include additional connections that loop back the port's handshaking lines. The Mini SSC doesn't use these connections, and some software requires handshaking in order to work properly (The example QBASIC program in listing 2 disables handshaking when it opens the com port, so the loopback connections aren't required.)

Note: The additional connections shown above are loopbacks for the handshaking lines.

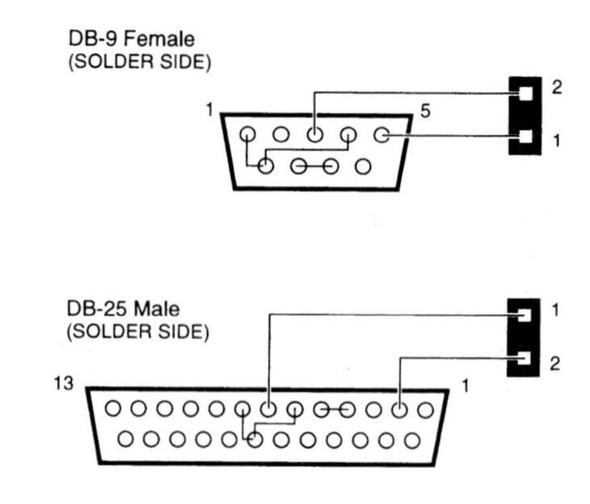

These deactivate hardware handshaking required by some software.

Listing 2. QBASIC (PC) *Demonstration Program*

```
DEFINT A–Z

Sync.byte = 255

'  The line below assumes that the B jumper is installed for 9600-baud operation, and that the
'  Mini SSC is connected to COM1.

OPEN    "coml:9600,N,8,1,CDO,CSO,DSO,OPO" FOR OUTPUT AS #1
CLS
PRINT   "                    MINI SERIAL SERVO CONTROLLER
PRINT   :  PRINT
PRINT   "At the prompt, type the servo number (0 to 7), a comma,
PRINT   "and a position value (0 to 254)."
PRINT   "Press <CNTL> - <Break> to end."
Again:
   LOCATE 8, 1
   PRINT    "     1.
   LOCATE 8, 1
   INPUT    "Servo,position>", Servo, Position
'  Perform some basic error trapping
   IF Servo > 7 THEN Servo = 7
   IF Servo < 0 THEN Servo = 0
   IF Position > 254 THEN Position = 254
   IF Position < 0 THEN Position = 0
   PRINT #1, CHR$(Sync.byte); CHR$(Servo); CHR$(Position);
GOTO Again
```

APPENDIX FOUR

Information on software diskettes

All the the program listings in this book are available on diskette. These diskettes allow you to read the information from diskette and import it directly into the programs that you are writing without having to re-type the existing software.

- Two diskettes are provided.
- One disk has information in Apple Macintosh format. 1.4 Mb diskette.
- The other disk has information in IBM-PC format. 1.4 Mb diskette.
- No other formats are available.
- Printouts of latest program listings on paper as hard copy.
- Any errors reported to date.

All information on the diskettes is in the form of text files that can be read by any program that will accept text as data.

Even after the publication of this book I intend to continue to work on additional software. This software will be included on the diskettes along with complete documentation for the software. There will be other information on the diskettes including an explanatory text file if that is necessary.

The charge for the diskettes is $20.00 (in USA) or £13.00 sterling (or international money order for $20.00) These prices will be held firm to the end of 2000. The price includes air mail shipping for overseas orders and first class mail in the USA.

Send order and payment for diskettes to

H. S. Sandhu
705 West Kirby
Champaign, IL 61820 USA

APPENDIX FIVE

Drawings and construction notes

These drawings are not exactly the same as were used to build the robot in the photographs. I have incorporated some minor changes that will improve the performance of the robot.

The inch drawings relate to the metric drawings at 24mm to the inch. The actual conversion is 25.4mm per inch but 24mm makes a good conversion on a woodworking project like this. This converts to 3mm to an even ⅛ inch. Both metric and imperial drawings are provided.

Dimensions around the actual servos have been omitted on purpose. The openings shown for the servos have to be made to match the servos that you have. Do not start fabrication until you have your servos in hand!

Incorporate two switches in the electrical circuit to control the power to the motors and to the logic of the controller. See photographs.

During fabrication and assembly, keep in mind that the legs are mirror images of each other.

The soles of the feet should be made larger to start with to create a more stable robot and then reduced in size to be more aesthetically pleasing when you become more skilled at controlling the robot.

All construction uses 3mm (⅛in.) 5 ply aircraft grade plywood.

You should not build the body of the robot until you have your controller in hand. The member to support the controller can then be designed to accommodate the controller and built into the design in a suitable way. The controller needs to be as low in the body as possible to reach all servo wires.

The intention in Figure App 5.5 is to provide adequate bracing for the four members that will support the bearings for the two legs. The servos have to be installed and secured before they are boxed in. Put a dowel through all four bearing members before gluing to make sure that everything lines up perfectly.

Make the battery box to the battery to ensure a snug fit.

The servos I used have an overall dimension of 1.96cm×4.04cm×3.58cm (0.77in.×1.59in.×1.41in.). See Appendix 6 for information on sources of servos.

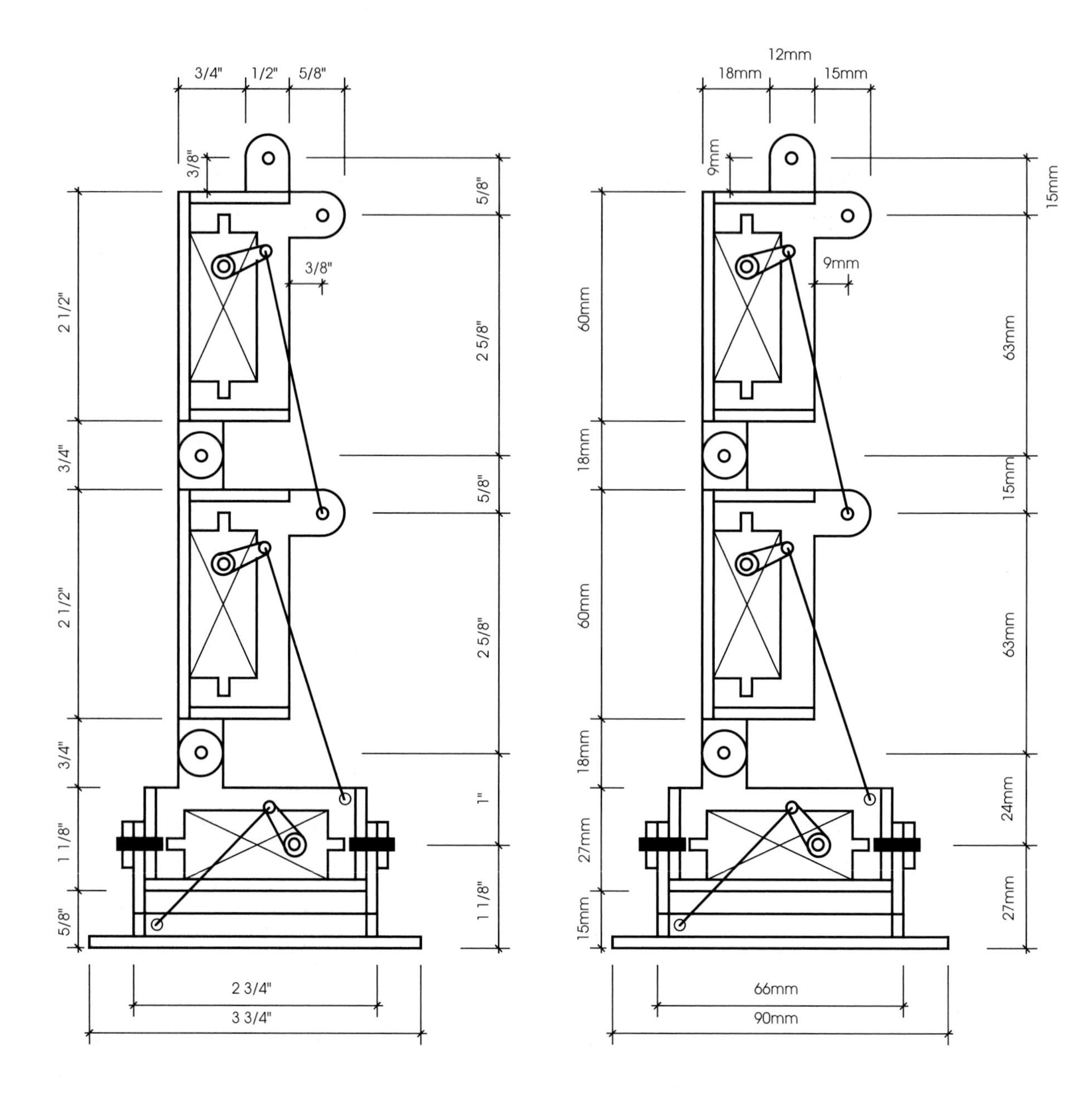

Figure App 5.1 Side elevation of legs (the right leg is shown here). Servos are shown as a schematic representation.

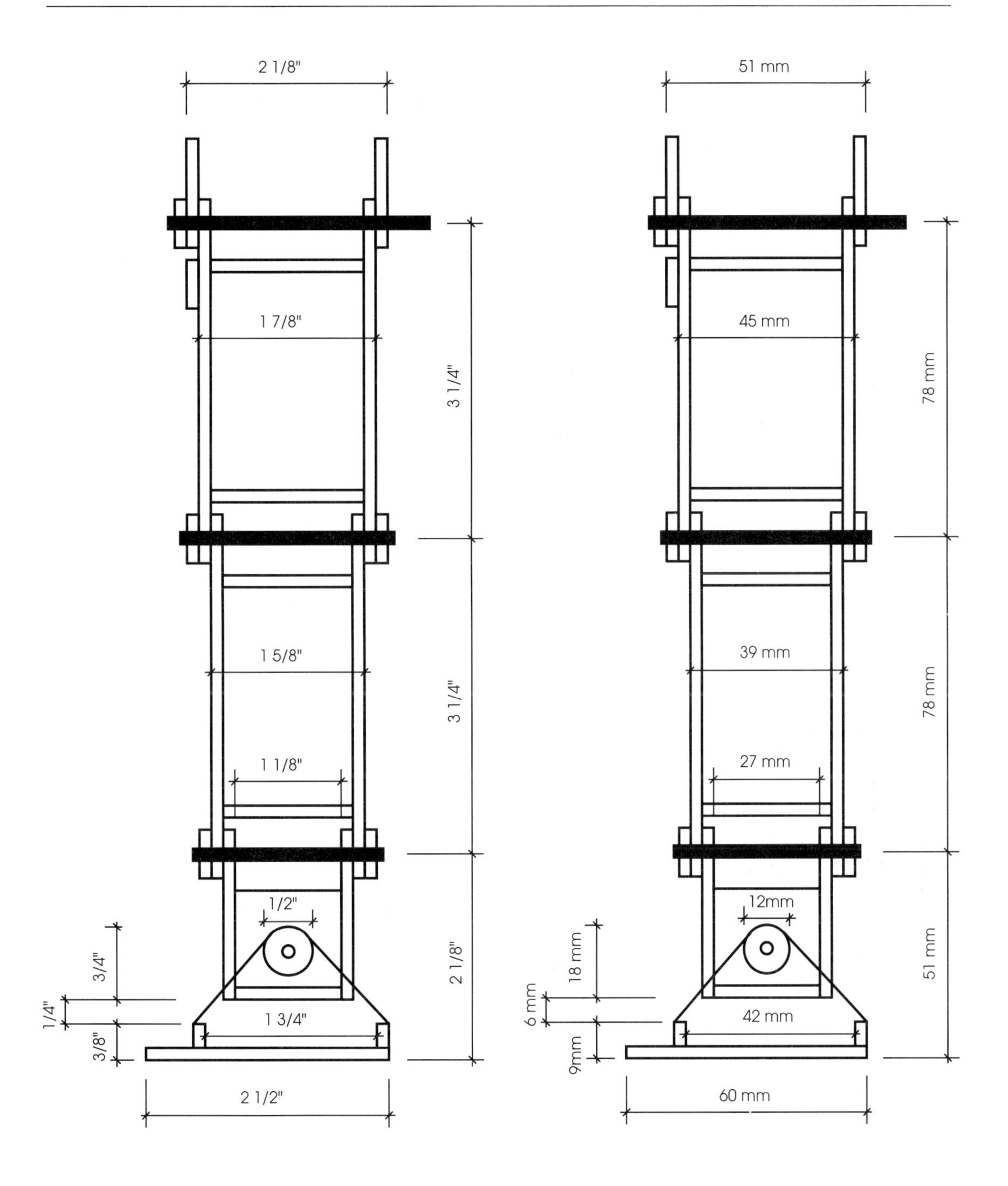

Figure App 5.2 Front elevation of legs (the right leg is shown here).

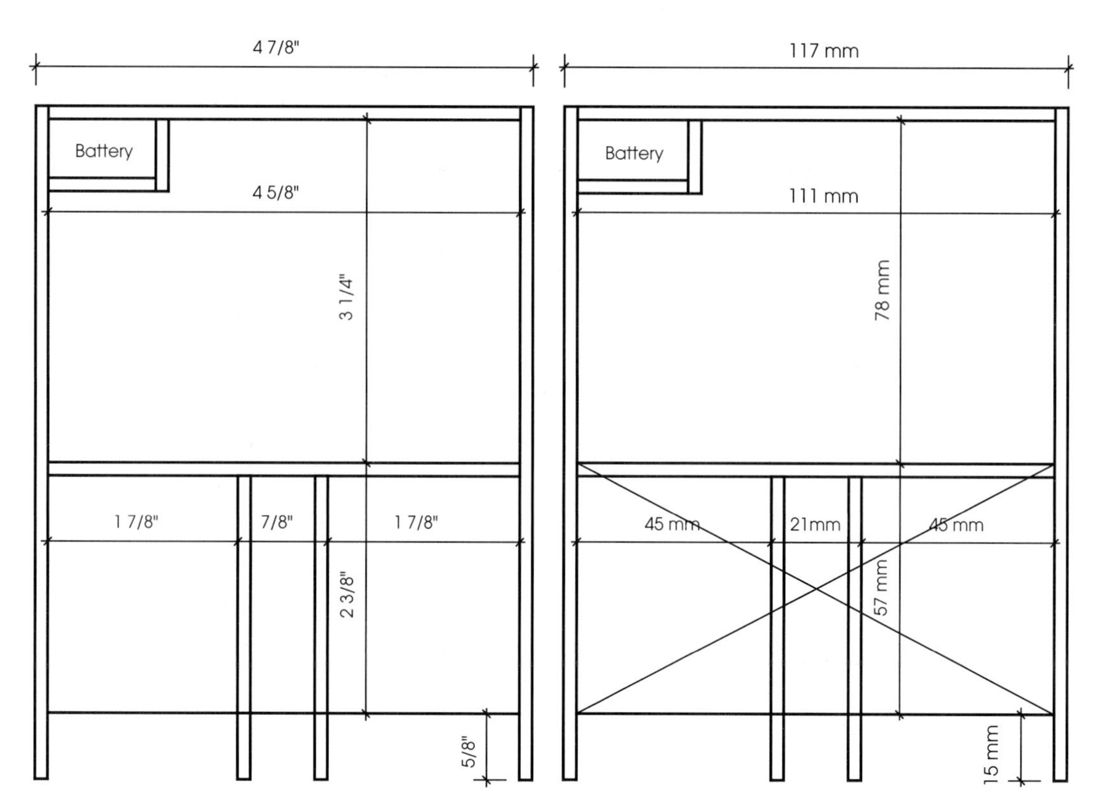

Figure App 5.3 Front elevation of body.

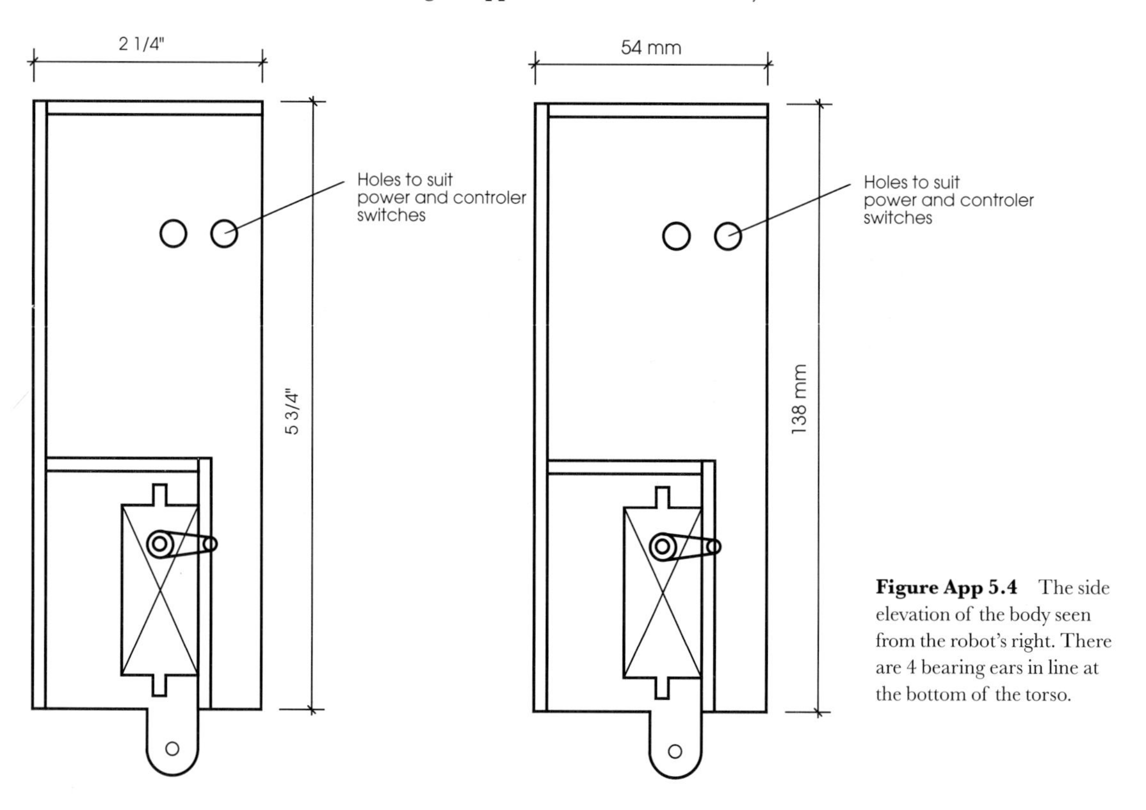

Figure App 5.4 The side elevation of the body seen from the robot's right. There are 4 bearing ears in line at the bottom of the torso.

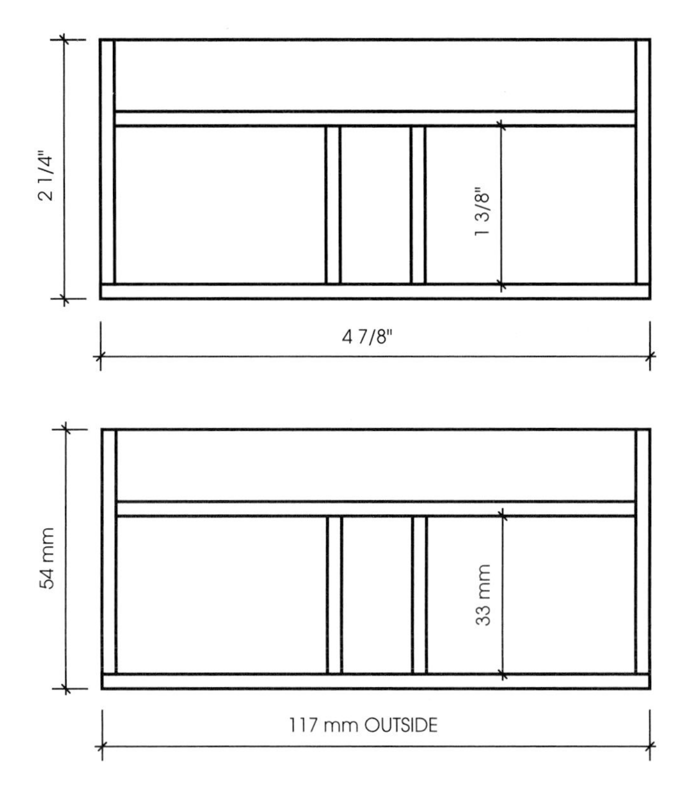

Figure App 5.5 Bottom elevation showing all 4 bearing members and structural cap.

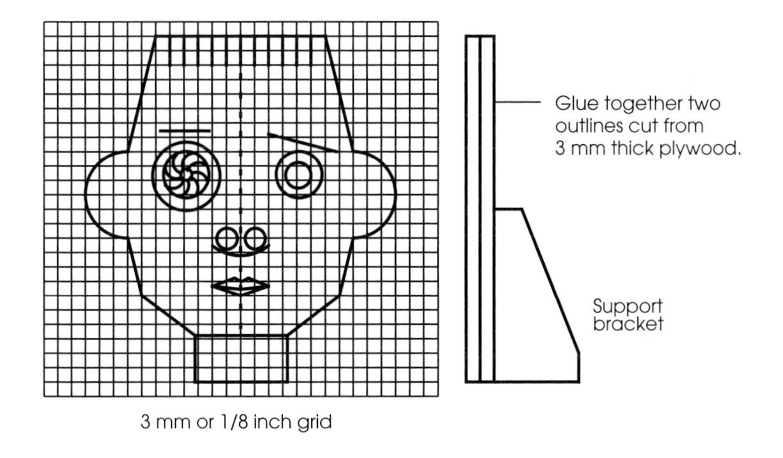

Figure App 5.6 Head dimensions. Use this to lay out the head.

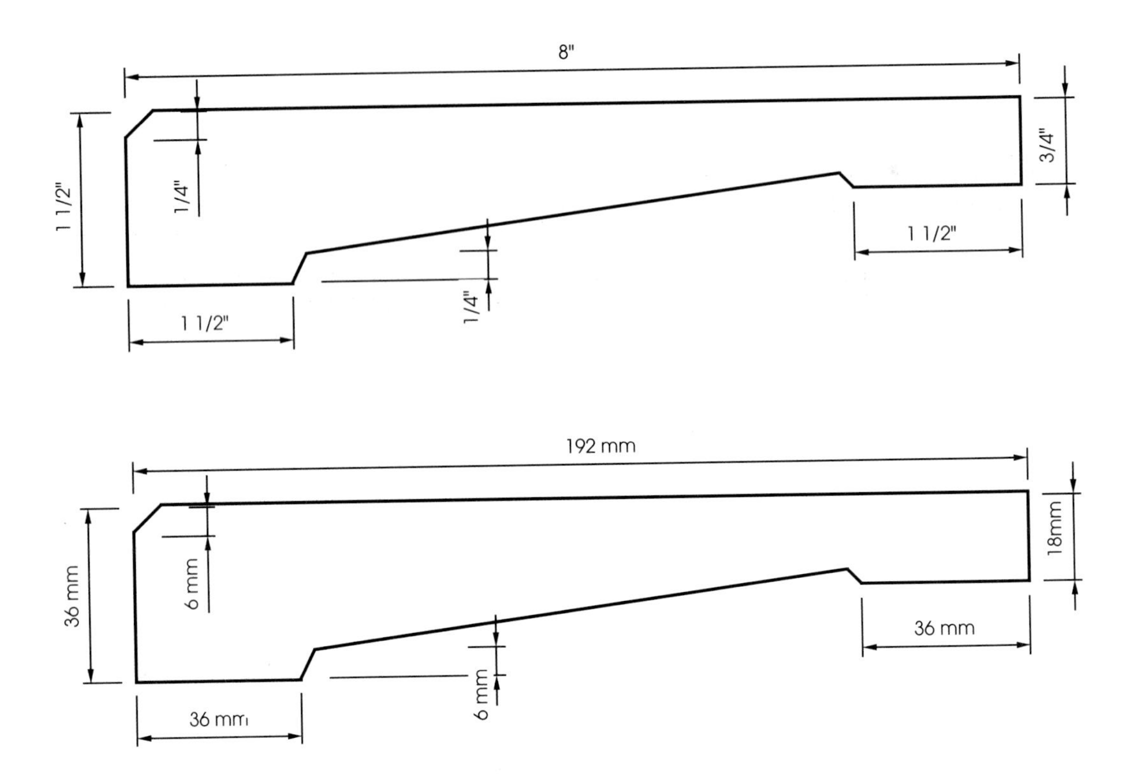

Figure App 5.7 Arm dimensions.

APPENDIX SIX

Component supplier information

The companies listed are not the only suppliers of these items. Please check your hobby magazines for names of alternative suppliers.

Model aircraft servos

USA and overseas

Tower Hobbies
PO Box 9078
Champaign
IL 61826-9076, USA

Tel: 217-398-3636 or 800-637-6050
Order fax: 800-637-7303

Tower is a very large mail order house specializing in radio controlled model aircraft supplies. (Very comprehensive 300-page catalogue). They accept Mastercard and Visa.

Part number for servos used
TS-33 Series
ZM7967 for Futaba J connector

3000 Standard servo

Size	1.96cm × 4.04cm × 3.58cm (0.77in. × 1.59in. × 1.41in.)
Torque	42 inch oz
Weight	1.5 oz
Speed	0.22 sec for 60 degrees
Reference:	1997 catalogue pages 185A, 193.

Tower does not have a European distributor but does ship overseas. Shipping overseas is of course expensive but at least the service is available to those who have no other source for servos.

Multiplex Modelltechnik GmbH
Neuer Weg 15
Niefern-Oschelbronn 1
D-7532 Germany

Graupner
Postfach 1242
D7312 Kircheim Teck, Germany

Robbe GmbH Modellsport
Postfach 1108
6264 Grebenheim, Germany

In the UK

Irvine Engines/OS Products
2 Brunswick Ind. Park
Brunswick Way
New Southgate
London N11 1JL

MacGregor Industries Ltd
Canal Estate
Langley
Berks SK3 6EQ

Ripmax Models plc
241 Green Street
Enfield
Middlesex EN3 7SJ

Amerang Ltd
Commerce Way
Lancing
W. Sussex BN15 8TE

J Perkins Distribution Ltd
90–96 Greenwich High Road
London SE10 8JE

Fleet Control Systems
47 Fleet Road
Fleet
Hants. GU13 8PJ

Micron
24 Brendon Way
Long Eaton
Notts. NG10 4JS

Servo controllers

In the USA

Scott Edwards

Scott Edwards Electronics
PO Box 160
Sierra Vista
AZ 85636-0160
USA

Tel: 520-459-4802
Fax: 520-459-0623
e-mail: 72037.2612@compuserve.com

Order 8-axis servo controller and an adapter board for Futaba J servo connectors and the power lines. Specify whether you want 90 degree or 180 degree travel on your servos.

They will accept Visa, Mastercard and American Express. No other forms of payment are acceptable from outside the USA. All shipments to outside the USA are via Federal Express. No exceptions.

The controller is also available in kit form for those who feel they are qualified to do the assembling and soldering. There is a considerable saving if you buy the kit.

Please contact Scott Edwards Electronics direct for latest information and prices.

In the UK

The same Scott Edwards controllers are available from Milford Instruments, the UK distributor for Scott Edwards Electronics. Their address is:

Milford Instruments
Milford House
120 High Street
South Milford
Leeds LL25 5AQ

Tel: 019-7768-3665

Please contact Milford Instruments directly for latest information and prices.